Visualization, Modeling, and Graphics for Engineering Design

Lieu/Sorby

CENGAGE
Learning

Australia • Brazil • Japan • Korea • Mexico • Singapore • Spain • United Kingdom • United States

CENGAGE
Learning™

Visualization, Modeling, and Graphics for Engineering Design

Lieu/Sorby

Executive Editors:
Maureen Staudt
Michael Stranz

Senior Project Development Manager:
Linda DeStefano

Marketing Specialist:
Sara Mercurio
Lindsay Shapiro

Senior Production / Manufacturing Manager:
Donna M. Brown

PreMedia Supervisor:
Joel Brennecke

Rights & Permissions Specialist:
Kalina Hintz
Todd Osborne

Cover Image:
Getty Images*

For product information and technology assistance, contact us at
Cengage Learning Customer & Sales Support, 1-800-354-9706

For permission to use material from this text or product, submit all requests online at **cengage.com/permissions**
Further permissions questions can be emailed to
permissionrequest@cengage.com

ISBN-13: 978-1-111-05693-3

ISBN-10: 1-111-05693-5

Cengage Learning
5191 Natorp Boulevard
Mason, Ohio 45040
USA

Cengage Learning is a leading provider of customized learning solutions with office locations around the globe, including Singapore, the United Kingdom, Australia, Mexico, Brazil, and Japan. Locate your local office at:
international.cengage.com/region

Cengage Learning products are represented in Canada by Nelson Education, Ltd.

For your lifelong learning solutions, visit **www.cengage.com/custom**

Visit our corporate website at **www.cengage.com**

Printed in the United States of America

Custom Contents

Sketching

2.01

introduction

Sketching is one of the primary modes of communication in the initial stages of the design process. Sketching also is a means to creative thinking. It has been shown that your mind works more creatively when your hand is sketching as you are engaged in thinking about a problem.

This chapter focuses on one of the fundamental skills required of engineers and technologists—freehand sketching. The importance of sketching in the initial phases of the design process is presented, as are some techniques to help you create sketches that correctly convey your design ideas. The definition of 3-D coordinate systems and the way they are portrayed on a 2-D sheet of paper will be covered, along with the difference between right-handed and left-handed coordinate systems. The chapter will investigate how to create simple pictorial sketches. Finally, the advanced sketching techniques of shading and cartooning will be presented with a framework for creating sketches of complex objects. You will begin to explore these topics in this chapter and will further refine your sketching abilities as you progress through your graphics course.

2.02 Sketching in the Engineering Design Process

As you may remember from Chapter 1, engineers communicate with one another primarily through graphical means. Those graphical communications take several forms, ranging from precise, complex drawings to simple sketches on the back of an envelope. Most of this text is focused on complex drawings; however, this chapter focuses on simple sketches.

Technically speaking, a sketch is any drawing made without the use of drawing instruments such as triangles and T squares. Some computer graphics packages allow you to create sketches; however, you will probably be more creative (and thus more effective) if you stick to hand sketching, particularly in the initial stages of the design process. In fact, carefully constructed, exact drawings often serve as a hindrance to creativity when they are employed in the initial stages of the design process. Typically, all you need for sketching are a pencil, paper, an eraser, and your imagination.

Your initial sketches may be based on rough ideas. But as you refine your ideas, you will want to refine your sketches, including details that you left out of the originals. For example, suppose you were remodeling the bathroom in your house. Figure 2.01 shows two sketches that define the layout of the bathroom, with details added as ideas evolve. Once you have completed the layout to your satisfaction, you can create an official engineering drawing showing exact dimensions and features that you can give to the contractor who will perform the remodeling work for you.

When engineers sit down to brainstorm solutions to problems, before long, one of them usually takes out a sheet of paper and sketches an idea on it. The others in the

FIGURE 2.01. Sketches for a bathroom remodel.

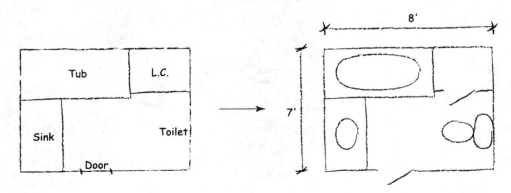

discussion may add to the original sketch, or they may create sketches of their own. The paper-and-pencil sketches then become media for the effective exchange of ideas. Although few "rules" regulate the creation of sketches, you should follow some general guidelines to ensure clarity.

2.03 Sketching Lines

Most of your sketches will involve basic shapes made from lines and circles. Although you are not expected to make perfect sketches, a few simple techniques will enable you to create understandable sketches.

When drawing **lines**, the key is to make them as straight as possible. If you are right-handed, you should sketch your vertical lines from top to bottom and your horizontal lines from left to right. If you are sketching an angled line, choose a direction that matches the general inclination of the line—for angled lines that are mostly vertical, sketch them from top to bottom; for angled lines that are mostly horizontal, sketch them from left to right. If you are left-handed, you should sketch your vertical lines from top to bottom, but your horizontal lines from right to left. For angled lines, left-handed people should sketch from either right to left or top to bottom, again depending on the inclination of the line. To keep your lines straight, focus on the endpoint as you sketch. The best practices for sketching straight lines are illustrated in Figure 2.02.

FIGURE 2.02. Techniques for sketching straight lines.

For right-handed people:

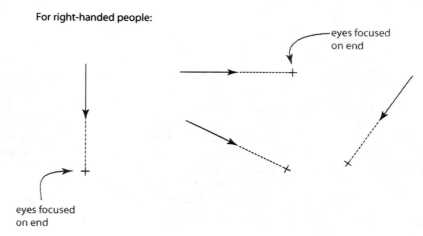

For left-handed people:

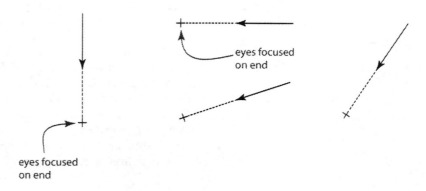

FIGURE 2.03. Rotating the paper to draw an angled line.

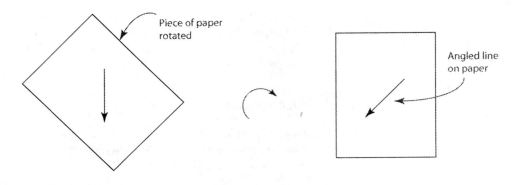

Piece of paper rotated

Angled line on paper

FIGURE 2.04. Sketching long lines in segments.

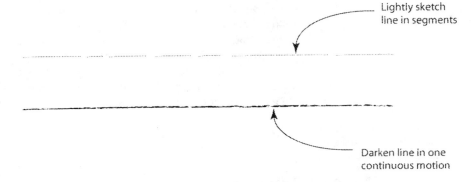

Lightly sketch line in segments

Darken line in one continuous motion

You also can try rotating the paper on the desk to suit your preferences. For example, if you find that drawing vertical lines is easiest for you and you are confronted with an angled line to sketch, rotate the paper on the desk so you can sketch a "vertical" line. Or you can rotate the paper 90 degrees to sketch a horizontal line. Figure 2.03 illustrates rotation of the paper to create an angled line.

One last point to consider when sketching lines is that you initially may have to create "long" lines as a series of connected segments. Then you can sketch over the segments in a continuous motion to make sure the line appears to be one entity and not several joined end to end. Using segments to define long lines is illustrated in Figure 2.04.

2.04 Sketching Curved Entities

Arcs and **circles** are other types of geometric entities you often will be required to sketch. When sketching arcs and circles, use lightly sketched square **bounding boxes** to define the limits of the curved entities and then construct the curved entities as tangent to the edges of the bounding box. For example, to sketch a circle, you first lightly sketch a square (with straight lines). Note that the length of the sides of the bounding box is equal to the diameter of the circle you are attempting to sketch. At the centers of each edge of the box, you can make a short **tick mark** to establish the point of tangency for the circle, then draw the four arcs that make up the circle. Initially, you may find it easier to sketch one arc at a time to complete the circle; but as you gain experience, you may be able to sketch the entire circle all at once. Figure 2.05 shows the procedure used to sketch a circle by creating a bounding box first.

One problem you may have when using a bounding box to sketch a circle occurs when the radius of the circle is relatively large. In that case, the arcs you create may be too flat or too curved, as shown in Figure 2.06. To avoid this type of error, you might try marking the radius at points halfway between the tick marks included on the bounding box. Using simple geometry, when you draw a line between the center of the circle and the corner of the bounding box, the radius is about two-thirds of the distance (technically, the radius is 0.707, but that number is close enough to two-thirds for your purposes). Then you can include some additional tick marks around the circle to guide your sketching and to improve the appearance of your circles. This technique is illustrated in Figure 2.07.

Sketching an arc follows the same general procedure as sketching a circle, except that your curved entity is only a portion of a circle. Sketching an **ellipse** follows the same general rules as sketching a circle, except that your bounding box is a rectangle and not a square. Sketching arcs and ellipses is illustrated in Figure 2.08.

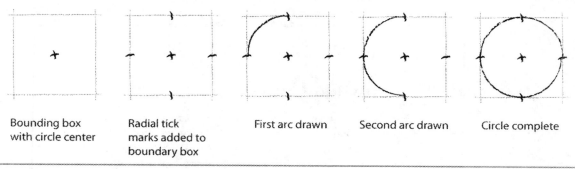

| Bounding box with circle center | Radial tick marks added to boundary box | First arc drawn | Second arc drawn | Circle complete |

FIGURE 2.05. Sketching a circle using a bounding box.

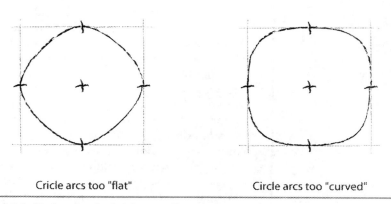

Cricle arcs too "flat"   Circle arcs too "curved"

FIGURE 2.06. Circles sketched either too flat or too curved.

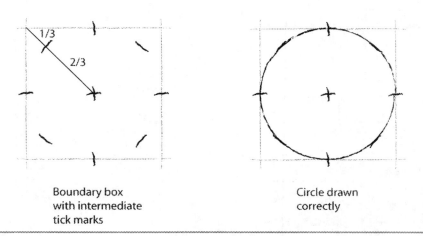

Boundary box with intermediate tick marks   Circle drawn correctly

FIGURE 2.07. Using intermediate radial tick marks for large circles.

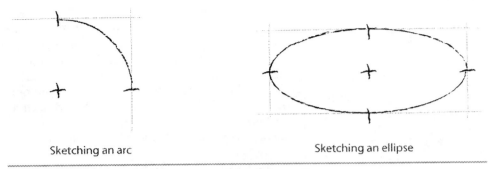

Sketching an arc   Sketching an ellipse

FIGURE 2.08. Using boundary boxes to sketch arcs and ellipses.

2.05 Construction Lines

Similar to the way you used bounding boxes to create circles and ellipses, other construction lines help with your sketching. Using construction lines, you outline the shape of the object you are trying to sketch. Then you fill in the details of the sketch using the construction lines as a guide. Figure 2.09 shows the front view of an object you need to sketch. To create the sketch, you lightly draw the construction lines that outline the main body of the object and then create the construction lines that define the prominent features of it. One rule of thumb is that construction lines should be drawn so lightly on the page that when it is held at arm's length, the lines are nearly impossible to see. The creation of the relevant construction lines is illustrated in Figure 2.10.

Using construction lines as a guide, you can fill in the details of the front view of the object until it is complete. The final result is shown in Figure 2.11.

Another way you can use construction lines is to locate the center of a square or rectangle. Recall from your geometry class that the diagonals of a box (either a rectangle or a square) intersect at its center. After you create construction lines for the edges of the box, you sketch the two diagonals that intersect at the center. Once you find the center of the box, you can use it to create a new centered box of smaller dimensions—a kind of concentric box. Locating the center of a box and creating construction lines for a newly centered box within the original box are illustrated in Figure 2.12.

Once you have created your centered box within a box, you can sketch a circle using the smaller box as a bounding box, resulting in a circle that is centered within the larger box as shown in Figure 2.13. Or you can use these techniques to create a square with four holes located in the corners of the box as illustrated in Figure 2.14.

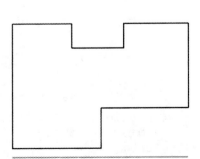

FIGURE 2.09. The front view of an object to sketch.

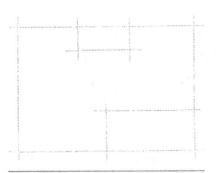

FIGURE 2.10. Construction lines used to create a sketch.

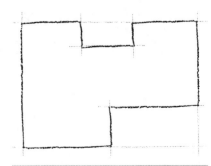

FIGURE 2.11. Completed sketch using construction lines as a guide.

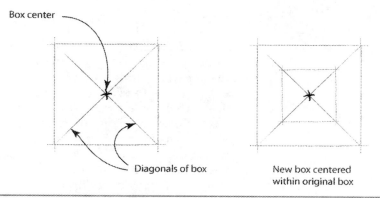

FIGURE 2.12. Creating concentric bounding boxes.

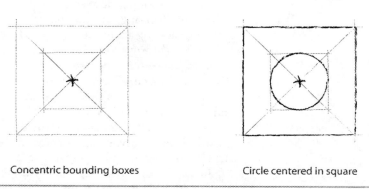

Concentric bounding boxes

Circle centered in square

FIGURE 2.13. Sketching a circle in a box.

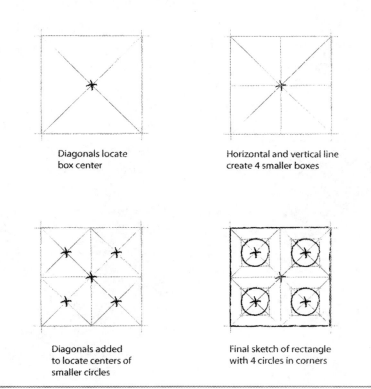

Diagonals locate
box center

Horizontal and vertical line
create 4 smaller boxes

Diagonals added
to locate centers of
smaller circles

Final sketch of rectangle
with 4 circles in corners

FIGURE 2.14. Using diagonal construction lines to locate centers.

2.06 Coordinate Systems

When sketching, you often have to portray 3-D objects on a flat 2-D sheet of paper. As is usually the case with graphical communication, a few conventions have evolved over time for representing 3-D space on a 2-D sheet of paper. One convention, called the **3-D coordinate system**, is that space can be represented by three mutually perpendicular coordinate axes, typically the x-, y-, and z-axes. To visualize those three axes, look at the bottom corner of the room. Notice the lines that are formed by the intersection of each of the two walls with the floor and the line that is formed where the two walls intersect. You can think of these lines of intersection as the x-, y-, and z-coordinate axes. You can define all locations in the room with respect to this corner, just as all points in 3-D space can be defined from an origin where the three axes intersect.

You are probably familiar with the concept of the three coordinate axes from your math classes. In Figure 2.15, a set of coordinate axes, notice the positive and negative directions for each of the axes. Typically, arrows at the ends of the axes denote the positive direction along the axes.

For engineering, the axes usually define a right-handed coordinate system. Since most engineering analysis techniques are defined by a right-handed system, you should learn what this means and how to recognize such a system when you see it. A **right-handed system** means that if you point the fingers of your right hand down the positive x-axis and curl them in the direction of the positive y-axis, your thumb will point in the direction of the positive z-axis, as illustrated in Figure 2.16. This procedure is sometimes referred to as the **right-hand rule**.

Another way to think about the right-hand rule is to point your thumb down the positive x-axis and your index finger down the positive y-axis; your middle finger will then automatically point down the positive z-axis. This technique is illustrated in Figure 2.17. Either method for illustrating the right-hand rule results in the same set of coordinate axes; choose the method that is easiest for you to use.

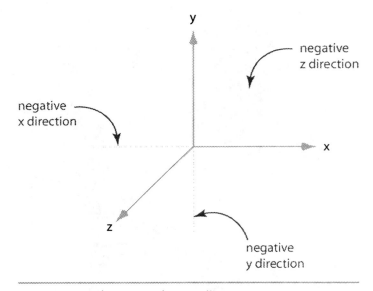

FIGURE 2.15. The x-, y-, and z- coordinate axes.

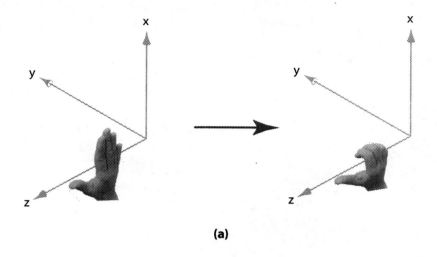

(a)

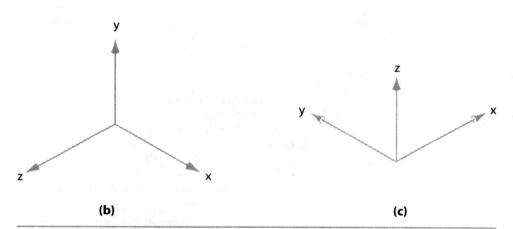

(b)

(c)

FIGURE 2.16. Curling the fingers to check for a right-handed coordinate system in (a) and alternative presentations of right-handed coordinate systems in (b) and (c).

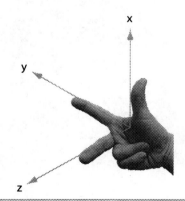

FIGURE 2.17. An alternative method to check for a right-handed coordinate system.

FIGURE 2.18. The result of
using the left hand to test for a
right-handed coordinate system.

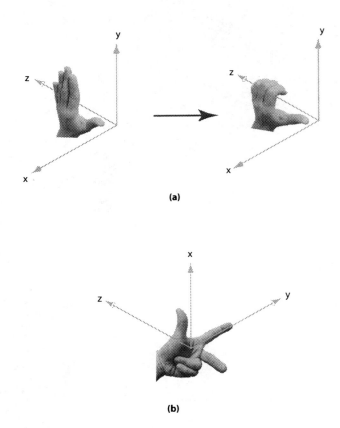

(a)

(b)

Notice that if you try either technique with your left hand, your thumb (or middle finger) will point down the negative z-axis, as illustrated in Figure 2.18.

A **left-handed system** is defined similarly to a right-handed system, except that you use your left hand to show the positive directions of the coordinate axes. Left-handed systems are typically used in engineering applications that are geologically based—positive z is defined as going down into the earth. Figure 2.19 illustrates left-handed coordinate systems. (Use the left-hand rule to verify that these are left-handed coordinate systems.)

The question remains about how to represent 3-D space on a 2-D sheet of paper when sketching. The answer is that the three coordinate axes are typically represented as oblique or isometric, depending on the preferences of the person making the sketch. You are probably most familiar with oblique representation of the coordinate axes, which seems to be the preferred method of many individuals. With this method, two axes are sketched perpendicular to each other and the third is drawn at an angle, usually 45 degrees to both axes. The angle of the inclined line does not have to be 45 degrees, but

FIGURE 2.19. Left-handed coordinate systems.

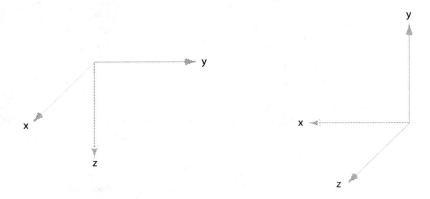

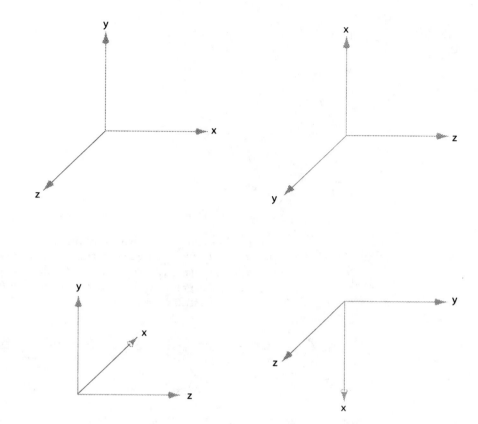

it is usually sketched that way. Your math teachers probably sketched the three coordinate axes that way in their classes. Figure 2.20 shows multiple sets of coordinate axes drawn as oblique axes. Notice that all of the coordinate systems are right-handed systems. (Verify this for yourself by using the right-hand rule.)

Another way of portraying the 3-D coordinate axes on a 2-D sheet of paper is through isometric representation. With this method, the axes are projected onto the paper as if you were looking down the diagonal of a cube. When you do this, the axes appear to be 120 degrees apart, as shown in Figure 2.21. In fact, the term *isometric* comes from the Greek *iso* (meaning "the same") and *metric* (meaning "measure"). Notice that for **isometric axes** representations, the right-hand rule still applies.

Isometric axes also can be sketched with one of the axes extending in the "opposite" direction. This results in angles other than 120 degrees, depending on the orientation of the axes with respect to the paper, as shown in Figure 2.22.

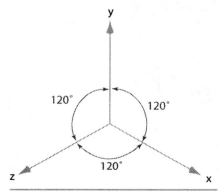

FIGURE 2.21. An isometric representation of a right-handed coordinate system.

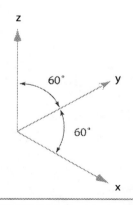

FIGURE 2.22. An isometric representation of axes with angles less than 120 degrees.

FIGURE 2.23. Isometric grid and dot paper.

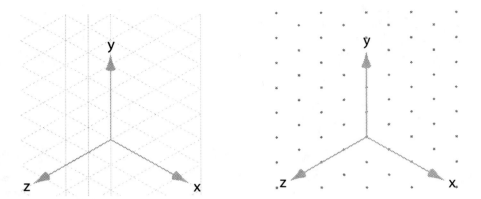

Grid or dot paper can help you make isometric sketches. With **isometric dot paper**, the dots are oriented such that when you sketch lines through the dots, you end up with standard 120 degree axes. With grid paper, the lines are already drawn at an angle of 120 degrees with respect to one another. Isometric grid paper and isometric dot paper are illustrated in Figure 2.23.

2.07 Isometric Sketches of Simple Objects

Creating isometric drawings and sketches of complex objects will be covered in more detail in a later chapter; however, this section serves as an introduction to the topic for simple objects. Mastering the techniques used to create isometric sketches of simple objects may help as you branch out to tackle increasingly complex objects. Figure 2.24 shows how **isometric grid paper** is used to sketch a $3 \times 3 \times 3$ block. Notice that there is more than one orientation from which the block can be sketched on the same sheet of grid paper. Ultimately, the orientation you choose depends on your needs or preferences.

Coded plans can be used to define simple objects that are constructed entirely out of blocks. The numerical values in the coded plan represent the height of the stack of blocks at that location. The object then "grows" up from the plan according to the numbers specified. Figure 2.25 shows a coded plan on isometric grid paper and the object that results from it.

The object shown in Figure 2.25 clearly outlines all of the blocks used to create it. When isometric sketches of an object are made, however, standard practice dictates that lines appear only where two surfaces intersect—lines between blocks on the same surface are not shown. Figure 2.26 shows the object from Figure 2.25 after the unwanted lines have been removed. Notice that the only lines on the sketch are those formed from the intersection of two surfaces. Also notice that object edges hidden from view on the back side are not shown in the sketch. Not showing hidden edges on an **isometric pictorial** also is standard practice in technical sketching.

FIGURE 2.24. Using isometric grid paper to sketch a block.

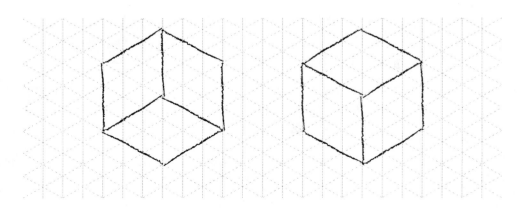

Sometimes when you are creating an isometric sketch of a simple object, part of one surface is obscured by one of the more prominent features of the object. When creating the sketch, make sure you show only the visible part of the surface in question, as illustrated in Figure 2.27.

Figure 2.28 shows several coded plans and the corresponding isometric sketches. Look at each isometric sketch carefully to verify that it matches the defining coded plan: those lines are shown only at the edges between surfaces (not to define each block), that no hidden edges are shown, and that only the visible portions of partially obscured surfaces are shown.

FIGURE 2.25. A coded plan and the resulting object.

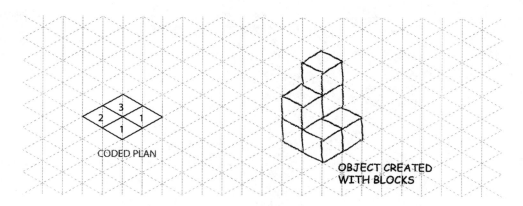

CODED PLAN

OBJECT CREATED WITH BLOCKS

FIGURE 2.26. A properly drawn isometric sketch of the object from the coded plan.

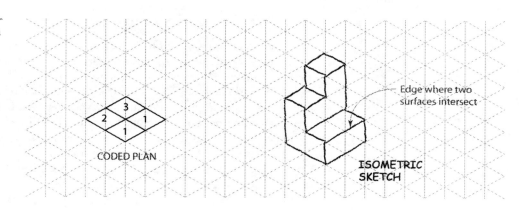

CODED PLAN

Edge where two surfaces intersect

ISOMETRIC SKETCH

FIGURE 2.27. The partially obscured surface on an isometric sketch.

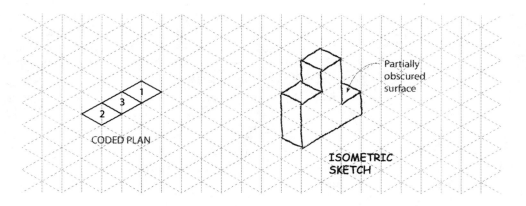

CODED PLAN

Partially obscured surface

ISOMETRIC SKETCH

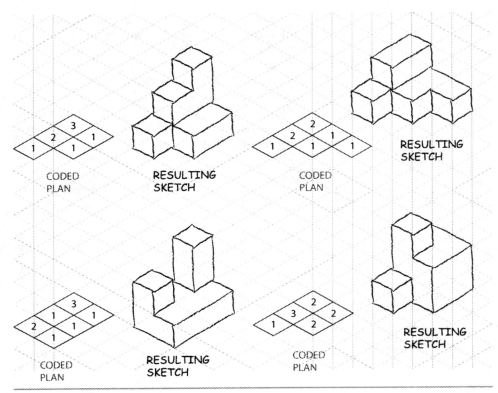

FIGURE 2.28. Four coded plans and the resulting isometric sketches.

2.07.01 Circles in Isometric Sketches

Look back at the 3 × 3 × 3 block shown in Figure 2.24. In reality, you know that all of the surfaces of the block are 3 × 3 squares; yet in the isometric sketch, each surface is shown as a parallelogram. The distortion of planar surfaces is one disadvantage of creating isometric sketches. The isometric portrayal of circles and arcs is particularly difficult. Circles appear as ellipses in isometric sketches; however, you will not be able to create a rectangular bounding box to sketch the ellipse in isometric as described earlier in this chapter. To create an ellipse that represents a circle in an isometric sketch, you first create a square bounding box as before; however, the bounding box will appear as a parallelogram in the isometric sketch. To create your bounding box, locate the center of the circle first. From the center, locate the four radial points. The direction you move on the grid corresponds to the lines that define the surface. If you are sketching the circle on a rectangular surface, look at the sides of the rectangle as they appear in isometric and move that same direction on the grid. Figure 2.29 shows a 4 × 4 × 4 cube with a circle center and four radial points located on one of the sides.

Once you have located the center of the circle and the four radial points, the next step is to create the bounding box through the radial points. The edges of the bounding box should correspond to the lines that define this particular surface. The edges will be parallel to the edges of the parallelogram that define the surface if that surface is square or rectangular. Figure 2.30 shows the cube with the circle center and the bounding box located on its side.

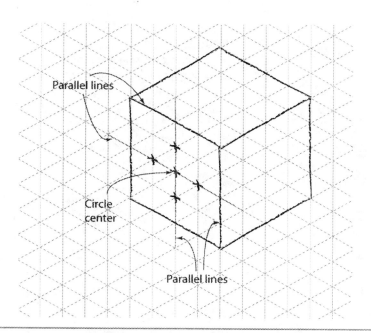

FIGURE 2.29. A cube with a circle center and radial points located.

Four arcs that go through the radial points define the ellipse, just like an ellipse drawn in a regular rectangular bounding box. The difference is that for the isometric ellipse, the arcs are of varying curvatures—two long arcs and two short arcs in this case. The arcs are tangent to the bounding box at the radial points, as before. It is usually

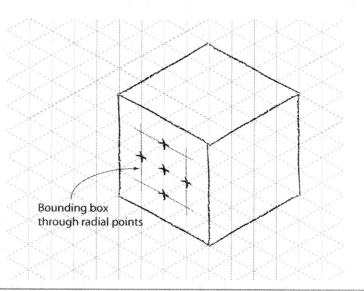

FIGURE 2.30. A cube with the circle center and bounding box on the side.

best if you start by sketching the long arcs, and then add the short arcs to complete the ellipse. Sketching the arcs that form the ellipse is illustrated in Figure 2.31.

Creating ellipses that represent circles on the other faces of the cube is accomplished in a similar manner, as illustrated in Figure 2.32 and Figure 2.33.

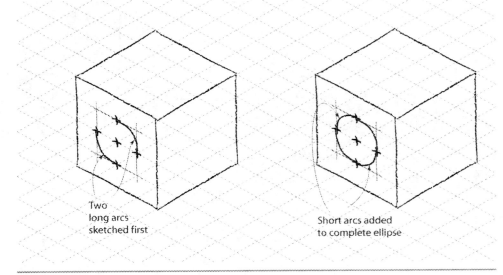

FIGURE 2.31. Sketching arcs to form an ellipse.

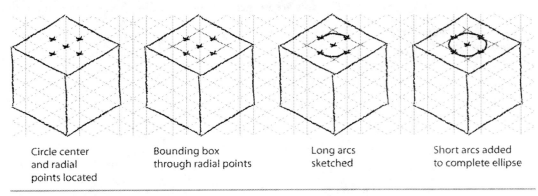

Circle center and radial points located

Bounding box through radial points

Long arcs sketched

Short arcs added to complete ellipse

FIGURE 2.32. Sketching an ellipse on the top surface of a cube.

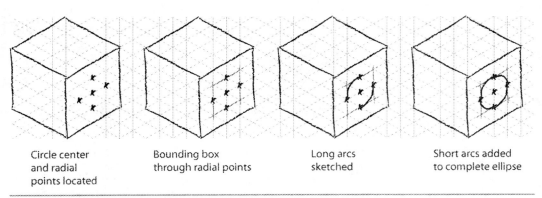

Circle center and radial points located

Bounding box through radial points

Long arcs sketched

Short arcs added to complete ellipse

FIGURE 2.33. Sketching an ellipse on the side face of a cube.

2.07.02 Circular Holes in Isometric Sketches

One of the most common occurrences that produces a circular feature in an isometric sketch is a hole in the object. You will learn more about circular holes and object features in a later chapter, but a short introduction follows here. A circular hole usually extends all the way through an object. In an isometric pictorial, a portion of the "back" edge of a circular hole is often visible through the hole and should be included in your sketch. As a rule of thumb, the back edge of a hole is partially visible when the object is relatively thin or the hole is relatively large; when the object is thick or the diameter of the hole is small, the back edge of the hole is not visible. Figure 2.34 shows two blocks with circular holes going through them. Notice in the "thin" block that you can see a portion of the back edge of the hole; in the thicker block, though, the back edge is not visible.

To determine whether a part of the back edge of a hole is visible in an isometric sketch, you first need to locate the center of the back hole. To locate the back center, start from the center of the hole on the front surface and move in a direction perpendicular to the front surface toward the back of the object a distance equal to the object's dimension in that direction. Figure 2.35 shows the location of the center of the two back circles for the objects in Figure 2.34.

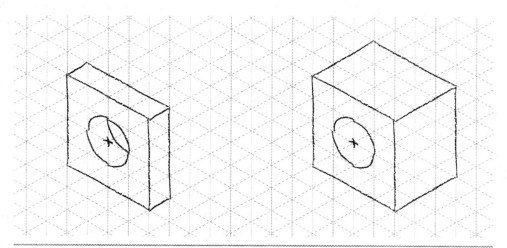

FIGURE 2.34. Blocks with circular holes in them.

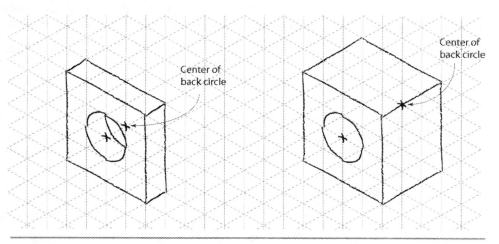

FIGURE 2.35. Centers of back circles located.

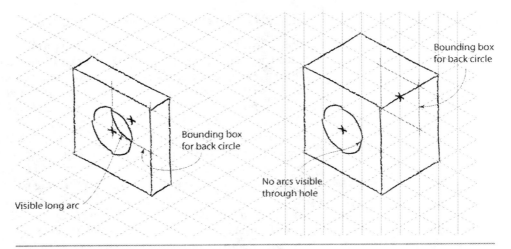

FIGURE 2.36. Determining visibility of back circles.

Starting from the back center point, lightly sketch the radial points and the bounding box for the back circle similar to the way you did for the front circle. Then add the long arc that is visible through the hole. (Note that only *one* of the long arcs is typically visible through the hole.) Add segments of the short arcs as needed to complete the visible portion of the back edge of the hole. Conversely, if after you sketch the back bounding box you notice that no portion of the ellipse will be visible on the sketch, do not include any arcs within the hole on the sketch and erase any lines associated with the bounding box. Figure 2.36 illustrates the inclusion and noninclusion of segments of the back edges of holes for the objects in Figure 2.34 and Figure 2.35.

2.08   Oblique Pictorials

Oblique pictorials are another type of sketch you can create to show a 3-D object. Oblique pictorials are usually preferred for freehand sketching because a specialized grid is not required. With oblique pictorials, as with **oblique axes**, the three dimensions of the object are shown with the height and width of the object in the plane of the paper and the third dimension (the depth) receding off at an angle from the others. Although the angle is usually 45 degrees, it can be any value.

The advantage that oblique pictorials have over isometric pictorials is that when one face of the object is placed in the plane of the paper, the object will appear in its true shape and size in that plane—it will be undistorted. This means that squares remain squares, rectangles remain rectangles, and circles remain circles. Figure 2.37 shows two pictorial representations of simple objects—one in isometric and one in

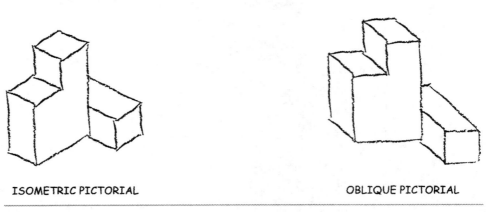

ISOMETRIC PICTORIAL   OBLIQUE PICTORIAL

FIGURE 2.37. A comparison of isometric and oblique pictorials.

oblique. Notice that the rules established for isometric pictorial sketches also hold true for oblique pictorial sketches—you do not show the hidden back edges, you show lines only where two surfaces intersect to form an edge, and you show only the visible parts of partially obstructed surfaces.

When making oblique sketches, the length of the **receding dimension** is not too important. In fact, oblique pictorials typically look better when the true length of the receding dimension is not shown. When the true length of an object's receding dimension is sketched, the object often appears distorted and unrealistic. Figure 2.38a shows the true length of a cube's receding dimension (use a ruler to make sure), and Figure 2.38b shows the same cube with the receding dimension drawn at about one-half to three-fourths its true length. Notice that the sketch in Figure 2.38a appears distorted—it does not look very much like a cube—whereas the sketch in Figure 2.38b looks like a cube.

Other conventions pertain to the way the receding dimension is portrayed in an oblique sketch; you will learn about them in a later chapter. For now, you will concentrate on trying to make a sketch that looks proportionally correct.

When creating oblique pictorials, you can choose to have the receding dimension going back and to the left or back and to the right. The direction you choose should be the one that produces the fewest obstructed surfaces in the resulting sketch. Figure 2.39 shows two possible sketches of the same object—one with the receding dimension to the left and one with the receding dimension to the right. Notice that the first sketch (Figure 2.39a) is preferable since none of the surfaces are obscured as they are with the second sketch (Figure 2.39b).

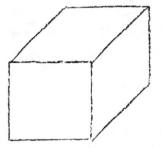

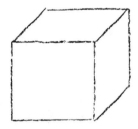

(a) Receding dimension drawn true length.

(b) Receding dimension drawn less than true length.

FIGURE 2.38. Oblique pictorials of a cube.

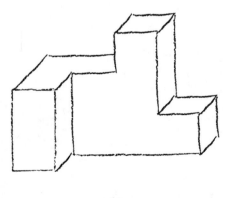

(a)

(b)

FIGURE 2.39. Two possible orientations for an oblique pictorial.

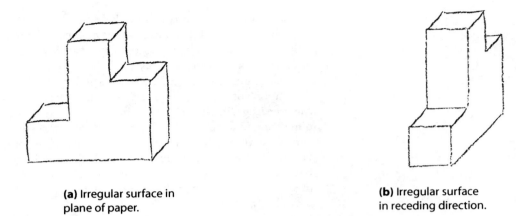

(a) Irregular surface in plane of paper.

(b) Irregular surface in receding direction.

FIGURE 2.40. Two possible orientations for an oblique pictorial.

When creating an oblique pictorial, you should put the most irregular surface in the plane of the paper. This is particularly true about any surface that has a circular feature on it. Figure 2.40 shows two different oblique pictorials of the same object. In the first sketch (Figure 2.40a), the most irregular surface is placed in the plane of the paper as it should be; in the second sketch (Figure 2.40b), the irregular surface is shown in the receding dimension. Notice that the first sketch shows the features of the object more clearly than the second sketch does.

2.08.01 Circular Holes in Oblique Pictorial Sketches

When circular holes appear in an oblique pictorial sketch, as with isometric sketches, you show the partial edges of the back circle where they are visible through the hole. Once again, partial circles are visible when the object is relatively thin or when the hole has a relatively large diameter; otherwise, partial edges are not shown. Figure 2.41 shows two oblique sketches—one in which a portion of the back edge of the hole is visible and the other in which it is not.

The procedure you use to determine whether a portion of the back circle edge is visible and, if so, which portion is visible follows the procedure outlined for isometric sketches. You start by locating the center of the back edge of the hole and marking off the four radial points. You then lightly sketch the bounding box that defines the circle. Finally, as needed, you sketch the visible portions of arcs within the circular hole. Figure 2.42 shows the procedure used to sketch the visible back edges of a circular hole in an oblique pictorial.

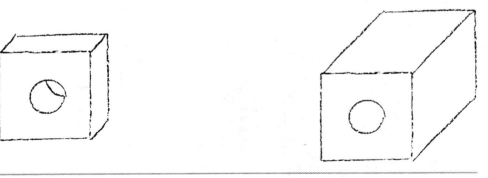

FIGURE 2.41. Oblique pictorials with circular holes in objects.

FIGURE 2.42. Determining visible back arcs in a hole.

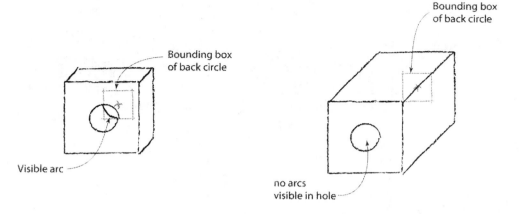

2.09 Shading and Other Special Effects

One thing you can do to improve the quality of your pictorial sketches is to include **shading** on selected surfaces to make them stand out from other surfaces or to provide clarity for the viewer. Figure 2.43 shows an isometric sketch with all of the top surfaces shaded. Notice that the shading better defines the object for the viewer. When including shading on a pictorial sketch, try not to overdo the shading. Too much shading can be confusing or irritating to the viewer—two things you should avoid in effective graphical communication.

Another common use of shading is to show curvature of a surface. For example, the visible portion of a hole's curved surface might be shaded in a pictorial sketch. A curved surface on an exterior corner also might be shaded to highlight its curvature. Figure 2.44 shows a pictorial sketch of a simple object with curved surfaces that are shaded.

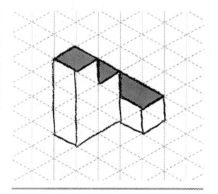

FIGURE 2.43. An object with the top surface shaded.

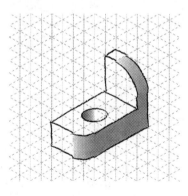

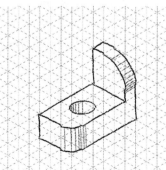

FIGURE 2.44. A simple object with two possible types of progressive shading used to emphasize the curvature of surfaces.

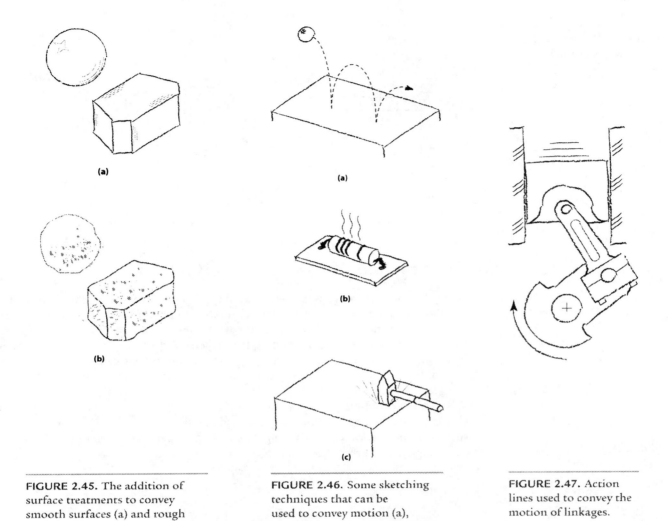

(a)

(b)

(a)

(b)

(c)

FIGURE 2.45. The addition of surface treatments to convey smooth surfaces (a) and rough surfaces (b).

FIGURE 2.46. Some sketching techniques that can be used to convey motion (a), temperature (b), and sound (c).

FIGURE 2.47. Action lines used to convey the motion of linkages.

Other sketching techniques can be used to convey features such as smooth or rough surfaces. Figure 2.45 shows different types of surface treatments that are possible for sketched objects.

You are probably familiar with techniques used in cartoons to convey ideas such as motion, temperature, and sound. Figure 2.46 shows typical cartooning lines that convey concepts not easily incorporated in a static sketch. Many of these same markings can be used in technical sketches. For example, Figure 2.47 uses action lines to convey motion for the sketch of linkages.

2.10 Sketching Complex Objects

As you refine your sketching skills, you will be able to tackle increasingly complex objects. Figures 2.48, 2.49, and 2.50 show pictorial sketches of small electronic devices. These sketches were not made to any particular scale, but were constructed so the object features appear proportionally correct with respect to one another. Notice the use of shading to enhance object appearance and to make the objects look

FIGURE 2.48. A sketch of a cell telephone.

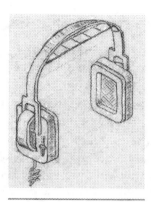

FIGURE 2.49. A sketch of a set of headphones.

FIGURE 2.50. A sketch of a camera.

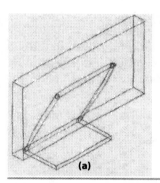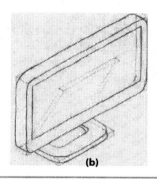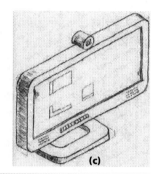

FIGURE 2.51. A sketch of a computer monitor using the method of "foundation (a), frame (b), finish (c)."

more realistic. Being able to sketch relatively complicated objects such as these will improve your ability to communicate with colleagues throughout your career. To develop this important skill, you should practice often. Do not be afraid to make mistakes—just keep trying until you get the results you want.

One way to tackle sketching a complex object is to think about it in the same way that a house is constructed—namely, "foundation, frame, finish." Using this method, you start with the "foundation" of the sketch, which usually consists of multiple guidelines and construction lines. When creating the sketch foundation, think about outlining the volume taken up by the entire object. You next "frame" the object by darkening some of the construction lines to define the basic shape of the object and its features. Once the basic frame is complete, you "finish" the sketch by adding necessary details and special features such as shading, especially on curved surfaces. Figure 2.51 shows a sketch of a flat panel computer monitor by the "foundation, frame, finish" method. Several of the exercises at the end of this chapter ask you to use this technique to develop your skills in sketching complex objects.

2.11 Strategies for Simple Pictorial Sketches

In this chapter, you learned two different ways to construct pictorial views of objects. This section outlines strategies for each type.

2.11.01 Simple Isometric Sketches

When creating an isometric pictorial from a coded plan, remember that the object "grows" up from the base according to the specified heights. You should start your sketch by drawing the visible *V* at the base of the object, as shown in Figure 2.52. You can determine the length of each side of the *V* from the coded plan. For the object defined by the coded plan in Figure 2.52, the left leg of the *V* is 2 units long and the right leg is 3 units long. The remaining bottom edges of the coded plans are hidden from view in the sketch and, therefore, are not included in the first drawing stages.

After you have created the base *V*, sketch the corner of the object at the correct height of the apex. Note that this corner will be the edge that is closest to you, the viewer. For the object shown in Figure 2.52, the height of this corner is 2 units as defined by the coded plan. The start of the isometric sketch including this corner is shown in Figure 2.53.

Starting at the "top" of this corner, move back and to the left the number of squares that are at this same height. If a change in object height is specified in the coded plan, move up or down (as shown in the coded plan) where the change occurs. When you reach the back corner, draw a vertical line back to the tip of the *V* you first sketched. This procedure is illustrated in Figure 2.54.

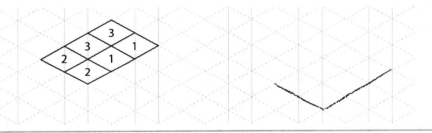

FIGURE 2.52. A coded plan with the *V* for the isometric sketch drawn.

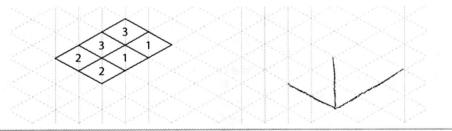

FIGURE 2.53. An isometric sketch with the nearest corner included.

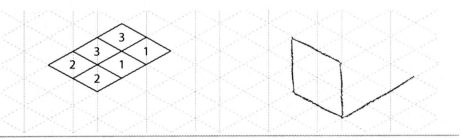

FIGURE 2.54. An isometric sketch with the first side of the surface drawn.

Follow the same procedure for the surface going off to the right from the apex of the *V*, as shown in Figure 2.55.

Complete the sketch by drawing the missing top and side surfaces of the object as shown in Figure 2.56. When adding these final features, make sure you do not include lines on surfaces—only *between* surfaces. Also, include only the visible portions of surfaces that are partially obscured.

Some of the objects you sketch may not form a simple *V* at a point nearest the viewer; instead, they will have a jagged edge along the bottom. You can use a similar procedure to sketch these objects, again starting at the bottom and outlining the shape of the object from the coded plan, as shown in Figure 2.57.

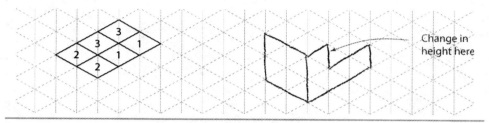

FIGURE 2.55. An isometric sketch with two side surfaces drawn.

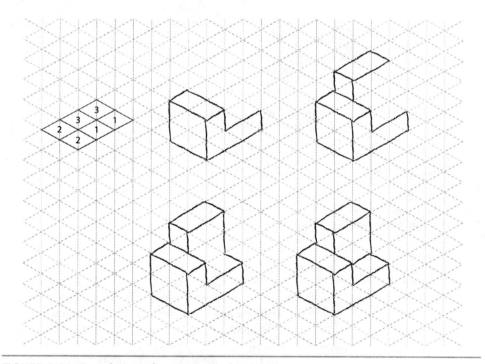

FIGURE 2.56. Completion of an isometric sketch.

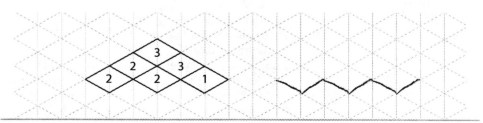

FIGURE 2.57. A jagged *V* from a coded plan.

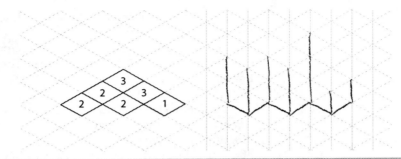

FIGURE 2.58. Heights at each corner included.

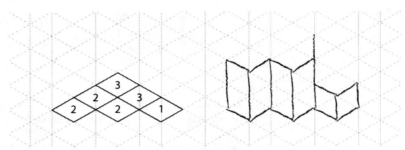

FIGURE 2.59. Side surfaces sketched.

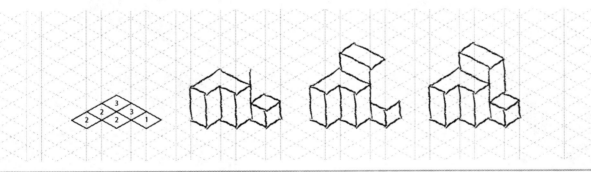

FIGURE 2.60. A completed isometric sketch.

Then you can sketch the lines that represent the height at each corner, similar to the way you sketched the height from the apex of the single *V* (see Figure 2.58). Complete the sketch by including the side and top surfaces of the object as illustrated in Figure 2.59 and Figure 2.60. For the object shown in the example, note that the final step involves erasing a portion of one of the first lines drawn (the corner at a height of 3). You need to remove part of this line so a line does not appear on the jagged side of the object.

2.11.02 Oblique Sketches

To begin your oblique sketch, you need to determine which surface on the object is closest to the viewer. Figure 2.61 shows an isometric sketch of an object with an arrow denoting the direction of the desired oblique pictorial. For this object and viewing direction, the surface labeled *A* is the one closest to the viewer in the oblique pictorial sketch.

Sketch the closest surface (in this case, surface A) in its true shape and size and decide whether you want the third dimension on the object receding back and to the left or back and to the right. Draw the visible edges receding back from each corner of

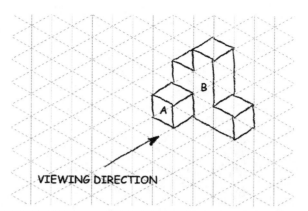

FIGURE 2.61. An isometric pictorial of an object and a viewing direction for an oblique sketch.

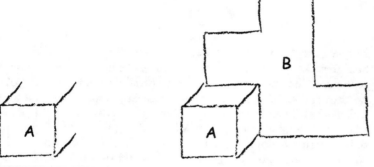

FIGURE 2.62. Surface A with receding dimensions sketched.

FIGURE 2.63. Surface B included in pictorial.

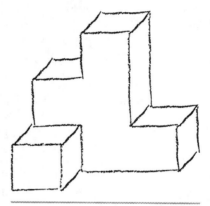

FIGURE 2.64. A completed oblique pictorial sketch.

the surface. Note that at least one corner on the surface will not have a receding line extending back from it—the receding edge will not be visible in the sketch. Figure 2.62 shows surface A with the receding edges sketched in place.

Now sketch the next surface that is parallel to the plane of the paper. For the object shown in Figure 2.63, the next closest surface is the one labeled *B*. Notice that by sketching this surface, you are connecting the endpoints of the lines drawn receding from the corners of the initial surface and, thus, are defining the side and top surfaces of the object in the pictorial. Figure 2.63 shows the result from including surface B in the oblique pictorial sketch.

Repeat these steps as often as necessary until the pictorial sketch is finished. Note that the final step is to include the back edges of the object (connecting the ends of the last set of receding lines drawn) to complete the sketch as shown in Figure 2.64.

CAUTION

When creating isometric pictorials of simple objects, remember the general rules presented earlier in this chapter—that lines are included only at the intersection between surfaces, that no hidden lines are shown, and that only the visible portion of partially obscured surfaces are sketched. One common error novices are prone to make is to include extra lines on a single surface of an object, especially when there are several changes in the object's height. Figure 2.65a shows an improper isometric pictorial sketch. Notice the extra lines included on the sketch. Figure 2.65b shows the sketch after it has been cleaned up to remove the unnecessary lines.

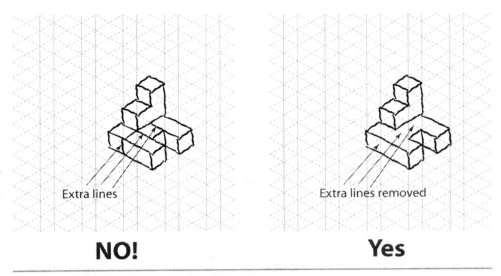

Extra lines

Extra lines removed

NO!

Yes

FIGURE 2.65. Isometric pictorials with and without extra lines.

Students make other common mistakes when sketching holes in isometric pictorials. One of those mistakes involves including the "back" edges of holes, even when they are not visible. Figure 2.66 shows an isometric pictorial with a hole in the object that goes all the way through. An arc representing the back edge of the hole is shown improperly in the visible part of the hole. Including the arc implies that the hole does not go all the way through the object, but stops part-way back. (Such holes are referred to as blind holes.) To avoid confusion in your isometric pictorial sketches, show only the back edge if it is visible—do not include a back edge every time you sketch an object with a hole.

Sometimes students use grid points improperly to mark off the bounding box for an isometric circular hole. Those novices fail to remember that in order to set the radial points, they need to move in the directions of the edges of the face of the object. Consider a simple box in which you want to include a circular hole emanating from the top surface. Figure 2.67a shows the four radial points incorrectly located from the center of the circle, and Figure 2.67b shows the resulting incorrect hole. Figure 2.68a shows the radial points located properly, and Figure 2.68b shows the resulting correct circular hole.

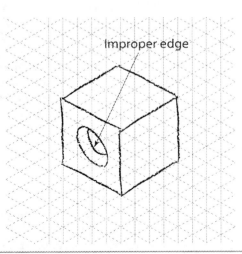

Improper edge

FIGURE 2.66. An isometric pictorial improperly showing the back edge of a hole.

One final error that students commonly make involves the creation of oblique pictorials. Novices sometimes forget to put the most complicated surface in the plane of the paper and show it in the receding direction instead. Figure 2.69a shows an oblique pictorial with a complex surface in the receding dimension, and Figure 2.69b shows the same object with the complex surface in the plane of the paper. Observe how the object is more understandable when you are viewing the complex surface "straight on." Also note that putting the complex surface in the plane of the paper actually makes your job easier; it is far easier to sketch the complex surface in its true size and shape than it is to sketch it as a distorted receding surface.

FIGURE 2.67. Improperly locating radial points on an isometric pictorial.

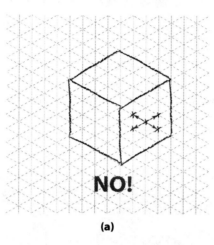

(a)

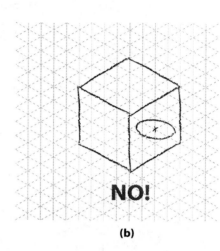

(b)

FIGURE 2.68. Properly locating radial points on an isometric pictorial.

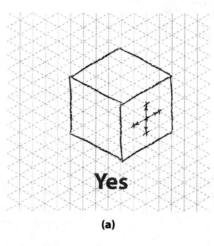

(a)

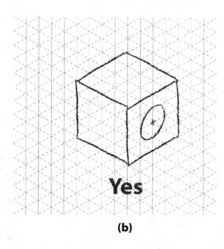

(b)

FIGURE 2.69. Oblique pictorials showing improper and proper placement of a complex surface.

NO!

Yes

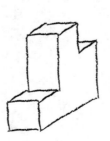

(a)

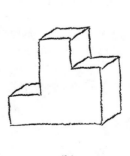

(b)

2.12 Chapter Summary

In this chapter, you learned about technical sketching and about some techniques to help you master this important form of communication. Specifically, you:

- Learned about the importance of sketching for engineering professionals and the link between creativity and freehand sketching.
- Developed techniques for successfully sketching basic shapes such as lines, arcs, circles, and ellipses.
- Learned about the right-hand rule and the way it is used to define 3-D coordinate systems in space. The axes can be portrayed on paper in either isometric or oblique format.
- Discovered how to make basic isometric sketches of objects from coded plans and about some of the rules that govern the creation of these sketches. You also learned about creating ellipses in isometric to represent circular holes in objects.
- Developed techniques for creating oblique pictorials. You also learned that for this type of pictorial, you should not show the receding dimension of the object true to size in order to avoid a distorted image.

2.13 glossary of key terms

arc: A curved entity that represents a portion of a circle.

bounding box: A square box used to sketch circles or ellipses.

circle: A closed curved figure where all points on it are equidistant from its center point.

construction line: A faint line used in sketching to align items and define shapes.

ellipse: A closed curve figure where the sum of the distance between any point on the figure and its two foci is constant.

isometric axes: A set of three coordinate axes that are portrayed on the paper at 120 degrees relative to one another.

isometric dot paper: Paper used for sketching purposes that includes dots located along lines that meet at 120 degrees.

isometric grid paper: Paper used for sketching purposes that includes grid lines at 120 degrees relative to one another.

isometric pictorial: A sketch of an object that shows its three dimensions where isometric axes were used as the basis for defining the edges of the object.

left-handed system: Any 3-D coordinate system that is defined by the left-hand rule.

line: Shortest distance between two points.

oblique axes: A set of three coordinate axes that are portrayed on the paper as two perpendicular lines, with the third axis meeting them at an angle, typically 45 degrees.

oblique pictorial: A sketch of an object that shows one face in the plane of the paper and the third dimension receding off at an angle relative to the face.

receding dimension: The portion of the object that appears to go back from the plane of the paper in an oblique pictorial.

right-hand rule: Used to define a 3-D coordinate system whereby by pointing the fingers of the right hand down the x-axis and curling them in the direction of the y-axis, the thumb will point down the z-axis.

right-handed system: Any 3-D coordinate system that is defined by the right-hand-rule.

shading: Marks added to surfaces and features of a sketch to highlight 3-D effects.

3-D coordinate system: A set of three mutually perpendicular axes used to define 3-D space.

tick mark: A short dash used in sketching to locate points on the paper.

2.14 questions for review

1. What is the role of sketching in engineering design? In creativity?
2. Describe which procedure you should use to sketch straight lines. (Are you right- or left-handed?)
3. How do circles appear on an isometric pictorial? On an oblique pictorial?
4. What is a bounding box?
5. How are construction lines used in sketching?
6. Why is it important to know the right-hand rule?

2.15 problems

1. For each of the coordinate axes shown below, indicate whether they are isometric or oblique and whether they represent right-handed or left-handed systems.

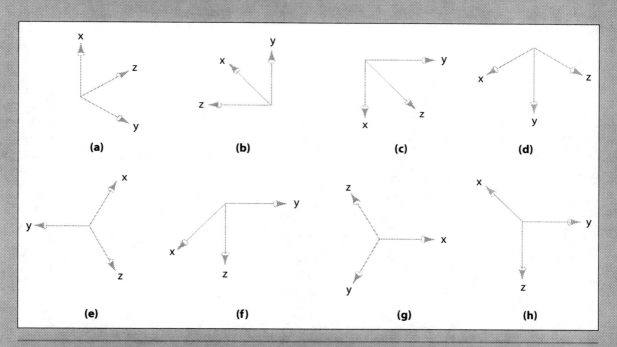

FIGURE P2.1.

2.15 problems (continued)

2. Label the third axis in each of the following figures to define a right-handed system.

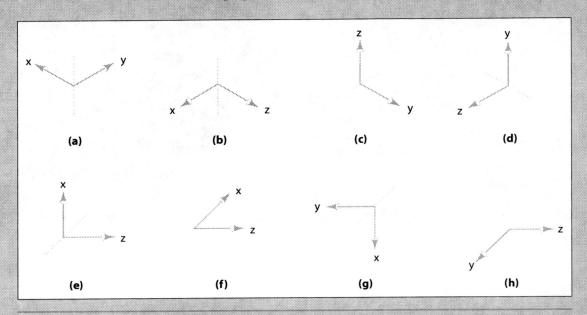

FIGURE P2.2.

2.15 problems (continued)

3. Create isometric sketches from the coded plans shown below.

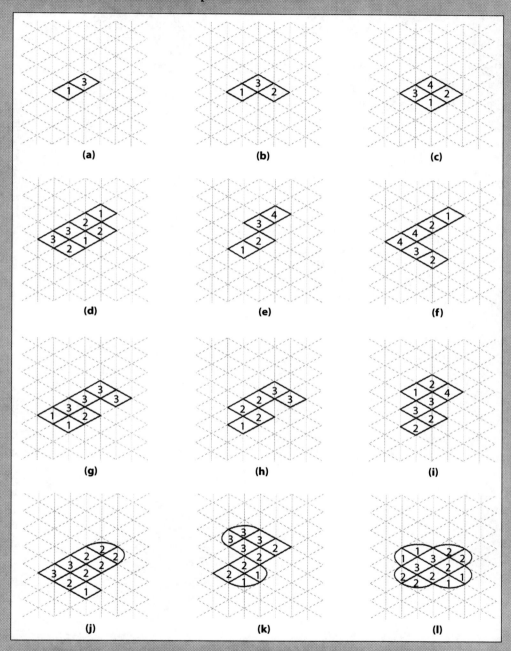

FIGURE P2.3.

4. Sketch a 6 × 6 × 2 block in isometric. On the 6 × 6 side, sketch a hole of diameter 4, making sure you include back edges of the hole as appropriate. Also create an oblique pictorial of the block.

5. Sketch a 6 × 6 × 2 block in isometric. On the 6 × 6 side, sketch a hole of diameter 2, making sure you include back edges of the hole as appropriate. Also create an oblique pictorial of the block.

2.15 problems (continued)

6. Sketch a 6 × 6 × 4 block in isometric. On the 6 × 6 side, sketch a hole of diameter 2, making sure you include back edges of the hole as appropriate. Also create an oblique pictorial of the block.

7. From the isometric pictorials and viewing directions defined in the following sketches, create oblique pictorial sketches that look proportionally correct.

8. Use the "foundation, frame, finish" method to create sketches of the following:

   a. stapler   c. coffee mug   e. calculator
   b. speedboat   d. bicycle   f. laptop computer

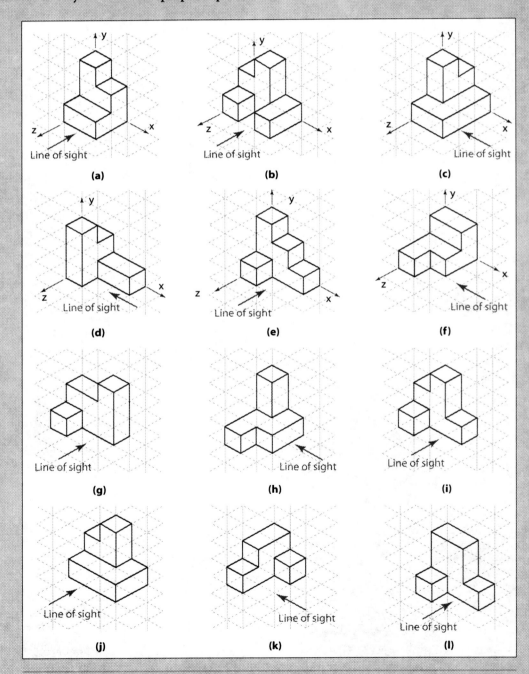

FIGURE P2.4.

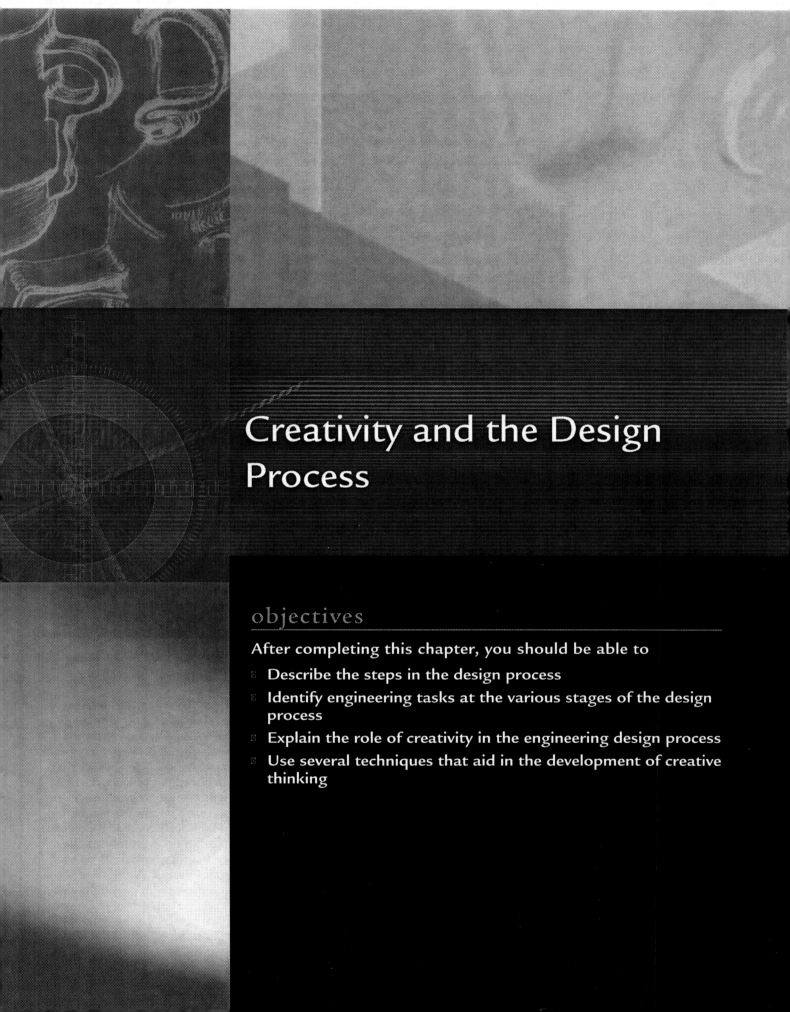

Creativity and the Design Process

objectives

After completing this chapter, you should be able to

- Describe the steps in the design process
- Identify engineering tasks at the various stages of the design process
- Explain the role of creativity in the engineering design process
- Use several techniques that aid in the development of creative thinking

5.01

introduction

What distinguishes engineers from scientists is that engineers design and create solutions to the many technical problems of the world, whereas scientists study problems and report their findings in literature. For example, environmental scientists studied Earth's atmosphere several years ago and found that, as a society, the world is creating too many air pollutants—especially from automobile emissions. Certain engineers acted on the results of those studies and designed cars that were more fuel-efficient and that produced less pollution. Other engineers worked on changing the composition of fuel so that fewer pollutants were produced during combustion. Engineers are now working on solar-powered and electrically powered vehicles and on hydrogen fuel cells to further reduce the quantity of air pollutants emitted into the atmosphere. Other engineers are working on ways to use biofuels for cars.

Engineering is a design-oriented profession. Engineers design devices or systems and figure out how to mass-produce them, how to package them, and how to ship them to their intended destination. As an engineer, the type of device or system you design may depend on your discipline, but the design procedure you use will be essentially the same regardless of the industry in which you work.

As described in a previous chapter, engineers function in many capacities in business enterprises. Some engineers are involved in manufacturing, some in marketing, some in management, and some in testing. However, design is the central function of engineers. Typically, as you move through an engineering career, you will be responsible for different aspects of the enterprise at different times; but at some point, you will probably play a primary role in the design of new products. At other times, you may oversee the design of new products as a supervisor of a team of engineers. You also may be responsible for making sure the entire enterprise—including designers, manufacturers, and marketers—is running smoothly and the various team members are communicating with one another and working together to achieve the optimal end product. Because design is such a central portion of the engineering endeavor, you need to understand the design process thoroughly. The remainder of this chapter describes the **engineering design** process and the role creativity plays in the process.

5.02 What Is Design?

Design is a goal-oriented, problem-solving activity that typically takes many iterations—teams rarely come up with the "optimal" design the first time around. As an example, think of the minivan. When Chrysler developed the first minivan, it was considered a revolutionary concept in design and other car manufacturers quickly developed competing models. With each model, improvements were made to the original design such that the minivans of today are much improved compared to the initial product. The key activity in the design process is the development and testing of a descriptive model of the finished product before the product is finally manufactured or constructed. In the case of a manufactured product, the descriptive model usually includes solid 3-D computer models, engineering sketches and drawings, and possibly rapid prototypes. For a civil engineering project, the descriptive model includes drawings, specifications, and sometimes a scale model made of wood or plastic. Three-dimensional CAD models also are becoming more prevalent in the civil/construction industry. Engineering design includes a systematic approach to product definition, conceptualization, development, testing, documentation, and production/construction. Design is usually accomplished in a group environment with many people contributing ideas and skills to complete the finished design. Hence, creativity and interpersonal skills are important attributes of the design engineer.

When designing a device or a system, the engineer must keep certain factors in mind. These factors are usually related to the function and cost of the resulting system. For **sustainable design**, life cycle analysis and environmental impact are especially important factors. In most cases, engineers must make a number of choices during the design process. For example, consider the automobile. Engineers may choose from metals, composites, or plastics for the materials that make up the car's body. Each type of material has advantages and disadvantages. Although steel is strong and ductile, it is prone to corrosion (rust) and is relatively heavy, reducing the fuel efficiency of the car, which, in turn, leads to increased pollution. Composites are strong and can absorb a great deal of energy during crashes, but can be brittle and may be more expensive than steel. Plastics are readily formed in almost any shape and are resistant to corrosion, but are relatively weak, making safety a significant concern. Although plastics are widely used in car bumper systems, they typically are not used in the car's body. These are just a few of the factors that engineers must consider as they design an automobile body.

Engineers make choices by weighing the often competing factors associated with function, cost, and environmental impact. A car could be built that causes virtually no pollution and that is perfectly safe; however, the average person may not be able to afford it. So engineers make trade-offs between cost, safety, and environmental impact and design a car that is reasonably safe, is relatively inexpensive, and has minimal emissions.

Design is an aspect in virtually every discipline of engineering; however, chemical engineers typically view design differently than do mechanical engineers. For a chemical engineer, design includes determining the correct chemicals/materials to combine in the correct quantities and in the correct order to achieve the desired final product. Chemical engineers determine when to stir the mixture, heat it, or cool it. Electrical engineers may design computer chips or wiring for a building or the antenna system for a car or a satellite receiver. Civil engineers, like most chemical engineers, typically design one-off systems with features and/or specifications that are unique to a single application or location. They may design a single bridge or roadway, or a water distribution system or sewage system. Because civil and chemical engineering designs usually are not mass-produced, it is often impossible to create a **prototype** for testing before construction begins. Imagine the cost of building a "practice" bridge for every bridge that a civil engineering team designs and constructs.

Mechanical engineers typically design products that will be mass-produced for consumer use—cars, bicycles, washing machines, etc. Therefore, prototyping is an important part of the design process for mechanical engineers. Prototypes are the initial design concepts that are often created so that further design analysis can be performed before machines are retooled to produce, say, 10 million copies of a product. The process of creating and testing prototypes often saves a company money because engineers can work out the kinks or discover flaws early in the design stage. In the past, the design process included the production of several prototypes for testing and analysis. Today much of the testing can be accomplished using computer software tools, greatly reducing the need for prototypes. However, most manufacturing companies still produce at least one prototype before going into the production of a new product. The foundation for many computer-based testing and analyses in the design process is a 3-D solid model, which is a focal topic of this text.

Although modifications exist in the design process for engineers of different disciplines, there are similarities too. Almost all designs require drawings, sketches, models, and analysis (calculations). The remainder of this chapter will focus on design in a manufacturing arena—the type of design most familiar to mechanical engineers. This type of design results in products that are mass-produced. Where appropriate, variations to the design process for one-off designs (as in civil and chemical engineering) will be described.

5.02.01 Computers in Design

Computers have been used in engineering design for several decades. In the early years, computers were used primarily for their number-crunching capabilities. In other words, computers were employed to perform the tedious calculations involved in engineering design. Over the years, the role of computers in the design process changed significantly. Graphical computer workstations evolved and with them the ability of engineers to see their designs before building them. Engineers also can do much of the testing of design iterations on-screen, eliminating the need for numerous prototypes. Numerical methods such as **finite element analysis (FEA)**, modal analysis, and thermal analysis have enabled engineers to design systems in a fraction of the time that traditional design methods require. Modern design software often is easily incorporated into the manufacturing process, enabling the designer to establish cutting tool paths on-screen for the efficient manufacture of computer-generated models. Even other manufacturing capabilities, such as rapid prototyping, in which physical prototypes can be created within a matter of hours rather than days, have been a direct result of computer-aided design capabilities.

Today **computer-aided design (CAD)** is an efficient design method. The basis for CAD is the construction of a graphical 3-D model on the computer. This model can then be tested by any of the available numerical methods. Design modifications can be accomplished on-screen and the modified 3-D models tested again. When the engineer is satisfied that the design will meet or exceed all of the design criteria, a 2-D drawing can be created using the 3-D model as its basis. From this drawing, a physical prototype can be created and tested by traditional means to ensure compliance with the design criteria. Then the drawing is usually handed over to the manufacturing division for mass production. Alternatively, when a **computer-aided manufacturing (CAM)** system is available, the part or parts are produced directly from the 3-D computer models.

5.02.02 Classification of Engineering Designers

Engineering design is a broad concept with many integrated stages, competing alternatives, and diverse requirements for success. As such, many design teams in industry have specialty engineers who are responsible for certain aspects of the design process. Most design projects have a team leader, or **chief designer**, who oversees the work of the individual team members. In the early stages of the process for mass-produced designs, **industrial designers** lend their creative skills to develop the product concept and style. For civil engineering projects, **architects** may be employed for their creative talents in **conceptual design**. Specialists in CAD, **CAD designers**, develop the computer geometry for the new design. **Design analysts**, specialists in FEA and other software tools, check the new design for stress and load distribution, fluid flow, heat transfer, and a host of other simulated mechanical properties. **Model builders** are engineers who make physical mock-ups of the design using modern rapid prototyping and CAM equipment. **Detail designers** complete the final design requirements by making engineering drawings and other forms of **design documentation**. Before you begin reading about the **design process**, you should consider the role that creativity plays in the process.

5.03   Creativity in Design

Creativity is an important feature of the design process. Often engineers get hung up on the "rules" and "constraints" of design and forget to think creatively. Historically, there is a strong link between engineering and art. One of the earliest recognized engineers is Leonardo da Vinci. In fact, some people say that da Vinci was an engineer who sometimes sold a painting so he could make a living. If you examine the sketches and drawings of da Vinci, you will see that he was interested in the development of products

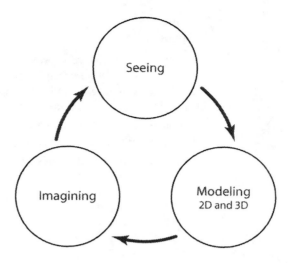

FIGURE 5.01. Visual thinking model.

to help improve people's lives, including some of the first recorded conceptual designs of airplanes and helicopters. Creativity is at the heart of innovation, and it can be enhanced with both individual and group activities. Some of the more common activities used to facilitate creative thinking are described subsequently. However, psychologists have found that the brain works most creatively when the hands are engaged in completing a mindless task. You probably have experienced occasions when you try to remember something but cannot, then find that the thought pops into your head when you begin another task. So to free your mind for creative thoughts, it may be best to take a break and wash the dishes, do some yard work, lift weights, or do laundry. Performing any of these mindless tasks will help free your mind for creative thoughts.

5.03.01 Visual Thinking

Visual thinking is the process of expanding one's creative ideas using visual cues and feedback. The visual cues can take the form of sketches or computer models; however, in the *initial* stages of design, sketching is often viewed as a necessary ingredient for creative thought. Visual thinking can be thought of as a circular feedback loop, as illustrated in Figure 5.01. The visual thinking process can start at any place in the feedback loop; but for the sake of simplicity, start with the step labeled "Imagining." You first imagine an idea for a new design or product and then sketch the idea in some graphical mode (2-D sketch, 3-D sketch, or computer image). Seeing the idea adds to your understanding of it, which can be extrapolated more deeply. You get a better mental image with a visual cue, which allows you to take the preliminary idea and refine it, sketch it again, etc. You can continue the process until you have a well-defined sketch or idea of the product for formal analysis and design.

5.03.02 Brainstorming

Brainstorming is the most common form of group ideation and concept generation and is a process used for generating as many ideas as possible. Brainstorming is typically done as early in the design process as possible (i.e., before you start solving the problem, before breaking the project into tasks, and before deciding who will do each task). Once individuals begin to focus on specific tasks, it may be too late to consider alternatives. Too often, teams will tackle a problem by taking the first idea presented and pursuing that idea without considering any alternatives. Teams also can use brainstorming to generate a list of the tasks that need to be done before the project can be completed. Five simple steps define a brainstorming session:

Step 1: Assemble your project team and make sure you allow ample time for the session. Diversity in the group will enhance the quality and breadth of the ideas generated. Select a group leader to run the session and select a group recorder to take notes.

Step 2: Define the idea of the design project to be discussed. Write down the idea and make sure everyone in the group understands it.

Step 3: Discuss the rules about brainstorming and make sure everyone in the group agrees to abide by them. If necessary, keep the rules on display as a reminder to members who may stray. Rules for brainstorming are intended to help the team generate more ideas. Comments about an idea, whether positive or negative, can stifle the brainstorming process. Although the following rules are simple, you may find them difficult to follow:

1. Everyone participates.
2. Every idea is recorded.
3. Judgment is suspended—there is no such thing as a bad idea.
4. No criticism is permitted.
5. No commentary is permitted.
6. No one dominates the process.

Step 4: Start the brainstorming session by asking everyone in the group to offer an idea. If possible, the recorder writes down all responses so everyone can see them. Alternatively, each member of the team can keep a list of his own ideas. These lists will prevent ideas from being lost and will help restart the process if there is a pause in the flow of ideas.

Step 5: At the end of the session, spend time going through all of the ideas. Combine, categorize, and eliminate the ideas to narrow the list. Once team members are sure that all possible ideas have been included, the team should discuss the advantages and disadvantages of each idea. After talking about the pros and cons, each member should rank the best three ideas on the list. The team should keep the ideas with the highest rank and decide as a group which approach to use.

Instead of conducting the entire brainstorming session by the process outlined previously, you may consider using the following steps for a brainstorming session:

1. Individually spend ten minutes writing down ideas for tackling the assigned project.
2. Combine the individual lists onto a flip-chart, blackboard, or whiteboard. Team members may ask questions to clarify an idea, but no other comments are allowed during this process.
3. Continue brainstorming as a group until all ideas have been exhausted.

5.03.03 Brainwriting (6-3-5 Method)

Brainwriting is an alternative to brainstorming. In brainwriting, each member of the group focuses on sketching his ideas rather than verbalizing them. With brainwriting, you typically start with a team of six people. Each person sketches three ideas on a sheet of paper, leaving ample room for additional graphics and annotations. The idea sketches are then passed around the table so fellow members can add their own comments and ideas, as shown in Figure 5.02. Usually the idea sketches are passed around the group five times. The expectation is that by the fifth time around, a favorable design idea will have emerged. Brainwriting also is called the *6-3-5 method* (six people, three ideas each, five times around the table).

FIGURE 5.02. Brainwriting.

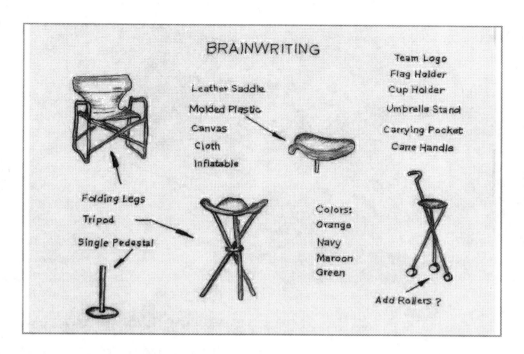

5.03.04 Morphological Charts

Morphology refers to the study of form and structure. A **morphological chart** can be used to generate ideas about a new design concept. The chart has a leading column that lists the various desirable functions of the proposed design. Along each row, various options for each function are listed, as shown in Figure 5.03. You can use brainstorming techniques to list as many options as possible for each function. The group then reviews and decides on a priority pathway through the options to address each desired function.

5.03.05 Concept Mapping

Concept mapping is a technique used to network various ideas together, as shown in Figure 5.04. During idea generation, the main design concept is placed in the center of the map with the various options linked outward in a brainstorming-like session. Each option then serves as a node for other choices. In that manner, the team can explore a big picture of all ideas and see a strong visual image of the connectivity of the different ideas.

FIGURE 5.03. A morphological chart.

MORPHOLOGICAL CHART					
Function	**Options**				
Seat Style	Saddle	Molded Dish	Strap	Inflatable	
Seat Materials	Leather	Plastic	Canvas	Rubber	Cloth
Number of Legs	One	Three	Four		
Leg Material	Wood	Aluminum	Plastic	Wrought Iron	
Leg Assembly	Pin	Hinge	Force Fit	Folding	
Accessories	Cup Holder	Beverage Cooler	Umbrella Holder	Flag Post	
Aesthetic Offerings	Team Logo	Choice of Colors			
Carrying Style	Carrying Handle	Handle Like Cane	Strap On Back	Roller Wheels	

FIGURE 5.04. A concept map.

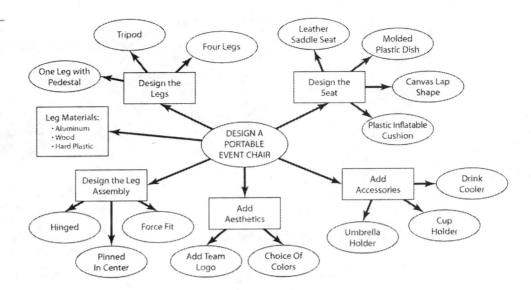

5.04 The Engineering Design Process

Design is a multistep process. However, there is considerable disagreement on exactly how many steps are involved in the process. Figure 5.05 shows one example of the sequence of steps in the design process. The design team often starts with stage 1 (Identify) and continues to stage 7 (Produce) and then begins again. Often the process does not proceed sequentially from stage 1 to stage 7; the design team might discover a serious problem in stage 4 (Analyze) and then return to stage 2 (Conceptualize) before moving on to stage 5 (Prototype).

Textbooks and writings on the design process include many different versions of and names for the stages in the design process. The stages presented previously are just one way to look at the design process; therefore, you should not think of them as the definitive word on the subject. However, the stages described in the remainder of this chapter are related to the graphical tools you will study in this textbook. For this reason, they have been adopted here. Knowing the number of stages and the labels for each stage is not nearly as important as understanding the overall process.

FIGURE 5.05. An engineering design process.

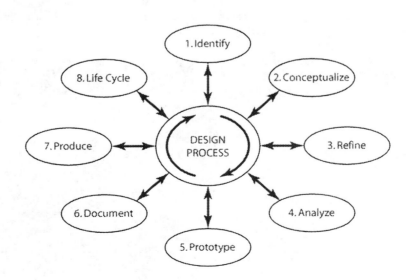

5.04.01 Stage 1: Problem Identification

Good design practice starts with a clearly defined need for a new product or system. Alternatively, a revised, improved design for an existing product may be required. A market survey may demonstrate that the new product or system is useful, has market appeal, is producible with today's technology, and will make a profit for the company supporting the design effort. Sometimes a new design idea is simply an alternate solution to a problem answered by an existing competing product. Indeed, many of today's highly successful products are the evolutionary result of free market enterprise. In the civil engineering world, a design project is typically the result of a client requesting a specific structure or system. For example, a governmental agency such as a county may request that a civil engineering firm design a new water distribution system to serve the needs of the county's residents. In this case, the client may have already defined the problem.

In the **problem identification** stage, the design engineer must address questions and answers from the customer's/client's perspective and from the engineer's perspective. For example, Table 5.01 shows two different perspectives for a new urban bicycle design.

When a product is designed, one of the design considerations is how long will it be used before it is no longer effective, which is called the **life cycle** of the product. Some products are designed for replacement on a regular basis. Thus, environmental considerations and disposal of a product must be considered throughout the design process. In the design process called **green engineering**, environmental concerns are considered throughout the process, not just at the end, because an engineer's choices in the problem definition stage often influence the overall environmental impact and life cycle of the product. Once the functional requirements have been identified, the design team can start the design process by generating some concepts.

5.04.02 Stage 2: Concept Generation

Concept generation is the most creative phase of the design process. You learned about some methods for creative thinking and concept generation earlier in this chapter. Typically, concept generation starts with brainstorming, brainwriting, or a similar team meeting where ideas are tossed around and discussed. Criticism is usually limited

TABLE 5.01. Functional Requirements for a New Urban Bicycle.

CUSTOMER'S PERSPECTIVE	ENGINEER'S PERSPECTIVE
MODERATE STREET SPEED	SUSTAINABLE SPEED OF XX MPH MAXIMUM SPEED OF YY MPH
COMPACT SIZE	DIMENSIONS NOT TO EXCEED A X B X C
SAFE	STRUCTURAL STRENGTH CONTROLLABILITY BRAKING CAPABILITY TIRE PUNCTURE RESISTANCE
COMFORTABLE	ERGONOMICS OF SEAT EFFICIENCY OF POWER TRAIN POSITION(S) OF HANDLEBAR
ATTRACTIVE	CHOICES OF PAINT COLOR LIGHTS AND REFLECTORS
AFFORDABLE	SELECTION OF MATERIALS MANUFACTURING PROCESS NUMBER OF PARTS SALES VOLUME

FIGURE 5.06. Concept sketches.

in the concept generation stage, since maximizing the number of good ideas is desirable. At the end of the concept generation stage, the team should have selected a few main ideas that it will focus on for future refinement and analysis. Sketching is an integral way to develop concepts for a new design. Figure 5.06 shows some examples of concept sketches.

5.04.03 Stage 3: Concept Selection and Refinement

Once a few quality concepts have been identified, the design team must converge on one or two final concepts to further explore in the design process. A common technique for selecting the final concept(s) is to use a **weighted decision table**, as shown in Figure 5.07. With a weighted decision table, all of the common attributes and desirable features of each concept are list in the first column. A weighting factor for each feature/attribute is then established (e.g., using a scale of 0 to 10). The various design options are listed in subsequent columns in a parallel fashion to the listed features/attributes. The team then conscientiously scores each option for every feature/attribute, each time applying the weighting factor to the score, as illustrated in Figure 5.07. Adding all of the scores for individual attributes yields a final "bottom-line" number that can be used to select the highest-ranked option.

Sometimes the initial concepts may need to be refined before a final decision can be made. Refinement will likely include the development of 3-D computer models for defining geometry not accurately expressed in the concept sketches. For example, as shown in Figure 5.08, different computer models of a new product can assist the members of the design team in visualizing the specific model that has the marketing appeal they are seeking and in making the final decision.

FEATURE ATTRIBUTE		WEIGHT 0-10	DESIGN 1 OPEN BOTTOM SCORE 0-10	TOTAL S*W	DESIGN 2 THUMB GRIP SCORE 0-10	TOTAL S*W	DESIGN 3 DOUBLE LOOP SCORE 0-10	TOTAL S*W	DESIGN 4 SINGLE LOOP W/FINGER SUPPORT SCORE 0-10	TOTAL S*W
AESTHETICS										
	Color	5	3	15	3	15	3	15	3	15
	Form	8	7	56	7	56	7	56	7	56
ERGONOMICS										
	Grip ability	8	7	56	6	48	2	16	9	72
	Drinking Ease	6	3	18	5	30	4	24	8	48
FUNCTIONALITY										
	Adapts to Hand	8	5	40	7	56	2	16	8	56
STABILITY										
	Base size	6	7	42	9	54	3	18	9	54
	Height	8	7	56	8	64	3	24	8	64
MANUFACTURABILITY										
	Injection Molding	5	3	15	3	15	3	15	3	15
	Slip Molding	5	3	15	3	15	3	15	3	15
			Weighted Total	313	Weighted Total	353	Weighted Total	199	Weighted Total	395

FIGURE 5.07. A weighted decision table for concept selection.

FIGURE 5.08. Computer models for concept selection.

FIGURE 5.09. Object mass properties.

MASS PROPERTIES REPORT (Concept 4)

Mass Properties of ergonomic cup (Material – ABS Plastic)

Output coordinate System: -- default --

Density = 0.037 pounds per cubic inch

Mass = 0.948 pounds

Volume = 25.722 cubic inches

Surface area = 134.693 inches^2

Center of mass: (inches)
$$X = 0.071$$
$$Y = 1.648$$
$$Z = 0.000$$

Principal axes of inertia and principal moments of inertia: (pounds * square inches)
Taken at the center of mass.

$$Ix = (0.033, 0.999, 0.000) \quad Px = 2.401$$
$$Iy = (-0.999, 0.033, 0.000) \quad Py = 3.770$$
$$Iz = (0.000, 0.000, 1.000) \quad Pz = 3.921$$

Moments of inertia: (pounds * square inches)
Taken at the center of mass and aligned with the output coordinate system.

Lxx = 3.768	Lxy = 0.046	Lxz = -0.000
Lyx = 0.046	Lyy = 2.402	Lyz = -0.000
Lzx = -0.000	Lzy = -0.000	Lzz = 3.921

Moments of inertia: (pounds * square inches)
Taken at the output coordinate system.

Ixx = 6.341	Ixy = 0.157	Ixz = -0.000
Iyx = 0.157	Iyy = 2.407	Iyz = -0.000
Izx = -0.000	Izy = -0.000	Izz = 6.498

5.04.04 Stage 4: Design Evaluation and Analysis

In this stage, the selected concept is further analyzed by any number of numerical methods. Before the advent of CAD and analysis tools, this stage of the design process involved building and testing physical models. Now the building and testing can be done on the computer, saving companies a great deal of time and money. The tests are conducted to determine mechanical properties of objects or systems and their performance during simulated conditions.

One of the simpler types of analysis that can be performed with a computer model is the computation of the object's mechanical properties, such as mass, center of gravity, and moment of inertia. All of these properties may not be meaningful to you right now; however, they are key quantities used in performing most types of static and dynamic analyses. A **mass properties analysis** report, shown in Figure 5.09, is a useful document for evaluating and presenting the static mechanical conditions of the design.

Further analysis of the design might include an FEA of stress contours and deformation. Heat transfer and aerodynamic flow also can be simulated using modern computational software (Figure 5.10). These numerical methods will be discussed in more detail in a later chapter and are themselves topics of entire texts.

FIGURE 5.10. A numerical analysis model.

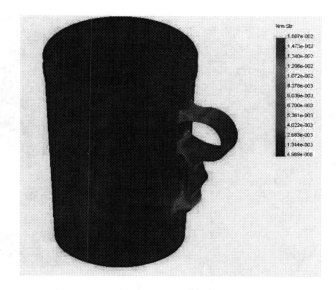

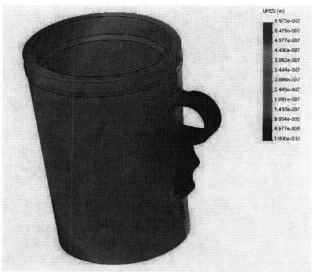

5.04.05 Stage 5: Physical Prototyping

Most designers and clients would like to see a physical model of the design—they want to look at it, hold it in their hand, and show it to other interested parties. Several different types of physical models can be developed during this stage of the design process. Engineers can have the shop people build a *scale model*, an actual *true-size model*, or just a simple *mock-up concept model* that shows the general physical appearance of the design.

In recent years, modern technology has accelerated the production of prototype models in the design process. CAM systems can take data from a 3-D solid model and cut the pattern using computer numerical control (CNC) machines. Figure 5.11 shows a part that was created through CNC machining. CNC machining will be covered in more detail in a later chapter of this text.

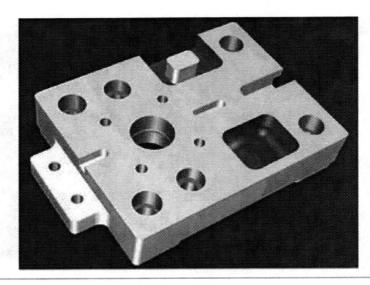

FIGURE 5.11. A part created through CNC machining.

Today rapid prototyping systems can perform some of the same functions of traditional machining tools, except that they require far less time (hence, the term *rapid*) and fewer resources than traditional methods. Some of the modern rapid prototyping methods include stereolithography (SLA), Selective Laser Sintering (SLS), Laminated Object Manufacturing (LOM), Fused Deposition Modeling (FDM), Solid Ground Curing (SGC), and inkjet printing techniques. Most recently, 3-D printers have become affordable prototyping alternatives for the office environment. Reasonable 3-D models can be printed using 3-D printers, as shown in Figure 5.12.

5.04.06 Stage 6: Design Documentation

There are many forms of design documentation, but the most common form is a finished detailed drawing, as shown in Figure 5.13. A detailed drawing shows the information needed to manufacture the final part. A good portion of the rest of this text discusses detailed engineering drawings. You will learn how to create drawings and how

FIGURE 5.12. Models created with a 3-D printer.

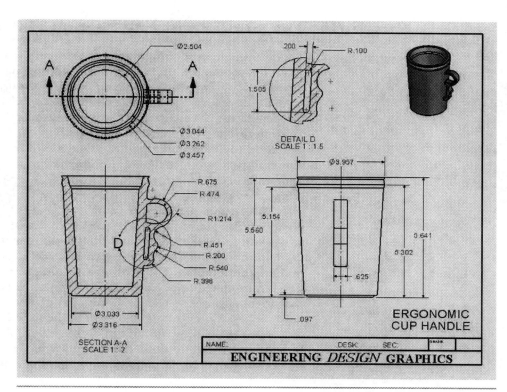

FIGURE 5.13. A detailed design drawing.

to interpret them correctly. You will learn about dimensioning and tolerancing for annotation of the drawing. You will learn about conventions developed over the years that provide everyone with the same understanding of what is on the drawing. You also will learn how drawings are created from 3-D computer models of parts and systems.

5.04.07 Stage 7: Production

Once the design documentation is complete, it is time to begin the production stage. For a civil engineering design, production is called the construction stage; for mechanical engineering, production is the manufacturing stage. Many engineers claim that the design process ends with the documentation stage. However, the way the product is designed may impact its production and distribution processes later on. For mechanical engineering projects in this stage, the goal is usually (but not always) to produce the product in large quantities, to meet performance standards, and to keep manufacturing costs low. Many different methods for manufacturing parts have been developed and are widely used, including machining, casting, rolling, and sheet metal cutting processes. These methods will be covered in more detail in a later chapter.

For civil engineering projects, because no prototypes have been built, design modifications are common in the production stage. Contractors may find, for example, that ductwork does not fit within the space provided on the drawings, or they may find that piping needs to be rerouted around an obstruction. For this reason, in civil engineering projects, it is important to continue to document the design by making notations on the drawings where changes are made. These drawings are called **as-built drawings**, and they reflect the way the project was actually constructed—not just the way it was designed. As-built drawings are an important part of the design process because if piping is rerouted through a building, for example, someone will need to know exactly where the plumbing is in case leaks or other problems arise.

5.05 The Concurrent Engineering Design Process

The new paradigm of **concurrent engineering** is sometimes referred to as "design for manufacturability." In traditional engineering, the part being designed progresses through each stage, moving from one team to the next. At each new stage, the team takes the design from the previous team and applies its own expertise. The first time the manufacturing engineer sees the part for production is when the design and analysis teams finish their work. With concurrent engineering, designers, analysts, and manufacturing engineers work together from the initial stages of the design process. In this way, each person can apply his own expertise to the problem at hand *from the start*. Thus, early in the design process, the manufacturing engineer might say, "If you made this minor modification to the part geometry, we would save $100,000 in retooling costs." The design change in question could be easily implemented during the initial phases of the process; whereas, without concurrent engineering, the change (and related cost savings) might be impossible in the final stage.

Modern computer workstations have enabled concurrent engineering to become a reality in the workplace. With local area networks, wide area networks, and the Internet, data can be moved from one desktop to another almost effortlessly. Members of the concurrent engineering team who work in different countries can share design ideas nearly as easily as engineers who work in the same building. Using the principles of concurrent engineering, manufacturers can save thousands, even millions, of dollars. In addition, computer-aided concurrent engineering design is more efficient and results are often of higher quality compared with designs produced in the past.

5.06 Patents

Patents are a way to protect the intellectual property of a new design. In the United States, a patent generally gives the inventor sole claim to intellectual property rights for twenty years. Application for a patent is made to the director of the United States Patent and Trademark Office and typically includes three components:

1. A written document made up of a specification (description and claims) and an oath or a declaration.
2. A patent drawing (Figure 5.14) in those cases in which a drawing is necessary.
3. Filing, search, and examination fees.

Frequently, inventors hire a lawyer to do the legal work and to make sure the idea has not already been patented. In some cases, the individual inventor conducts a patent search using a for-hire Internet site.

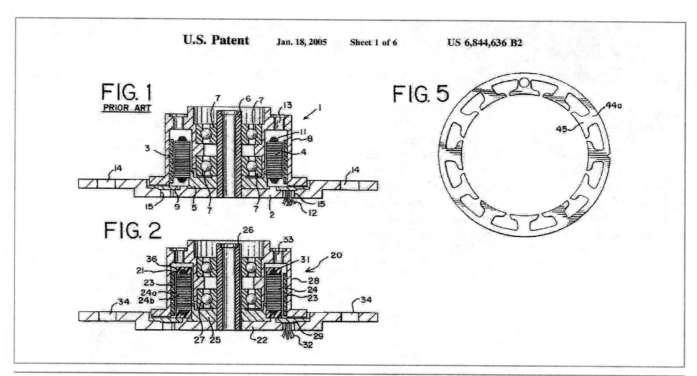

FIGURE 5.14. A patent drawing.

5.07   Chapter Summary

In this chapter, you learned that design is an iterative process and that the process has several stages; however, there is no general agreement about the exact number of stages. You learned that engineers must weigh competing factors such as cost, function, and environmental impact when making design decisions. You learned about design in the information age and ways computers are used throughout the process, greatly reducing costs. You learned about the importance of creativity in engineering design and about several techniques you can use, either as an individual or as part of a team, to foster creative thinking. Finally, you learned about concurrent engineering, which is enabled by computer technologies and can be used to reduce product costs and improve product quality.

Hoyt USA was founded in 1931 by sportsman and bow maker Earl Hoyt. The company is located in Salt Lake City, Utah, where it has both engineering and fabrication facilities. Hoyt USA has a long-standing reputation as a high-quality maker of bows for sports, recreation, and competition. In 1972, the company revolutionized competition archery when it introduced its first metal-handled collapsible recurve bow at the 1972 Olympic games. Given only to the U.S. team, the metal-handle design offered significant advantages over other bows, which were mostly made of wood at that time. A metal handle was relatively immune to the effects of changing temperature, humidity, and time, which affected the geometry, stiffness, and vibration properties of the bow. These variations made it difficult to use a wooden bow to land arrows shot after shot in the same place on a target. In addition, lighter arrows produce higher stresses in a wooden bow, sometimes causing the bow to break. By contrast, the strength of the handle's metal enabled an archer to use lighter arrows, which reached more distant targets in shorter times. Soon after Hoyt USA introduced the metal-handled bow, other bow manufacturers followed suit.

In the early 1990s, Hoyt USA wanted to improve the design of its metal bow handle to improve its share of the target archery equipment market. This market was very competitive, with a typical recurve bow lasting only three or four years before it needed to be replaced. In the development of a new design, Hoyt USA had to consider several things. For product performance, the main considerations were strength, weight, and vibration. A new product had to be stronger than previous ones. Super-light carbon arrows, light composite bow limbs, and synthetic strings produced increasing levels of stress in bows, to the point where even metal handles were breaking. But additional strength could not be gained at the expense of weight. Many archers already complained about the excessive weight of metal-handled bows. Any new product also needed to be less flexible and have less vibration than existing bows. Target archers considered excessive flexibility, noise, and vibration to be undesirable characteristics.

The new product needed to be developed with analysis and production in mind. Detailed stress analysis was necessary to ensure that there would be no breakage problems, as had been the case with other products. Also, the new product had to be designed so it could be easily produced in state-of-the-art fabrication facilities consisting mostly of computer-controlled four-axis milling machines, which Hoyt USA was expanding at the time.

A conventional metal-handled recurve target bow.

The new concept that Hoyt USA developed was a structural support member located behind the grip of the bow handle. The support member was designed with an outward bend so it would not touch the arm of the user. Touching the bow at any location except the grip was a violation of the rules in target archery. The new design allowed the forces in the bow handle to be more widely distributed, resulting in reduced stresses without a significant increase in weight.

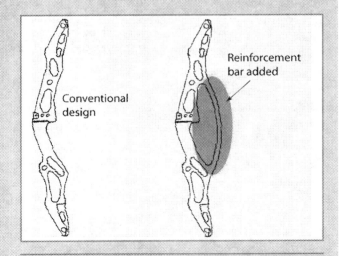

Concept sketches showing the addition of a structural reinforcement bar to a conventional bow handle to reduce its flexibility and vibration.

Conceptual sketches for the new design were developed first. The sketches enabled Hoyt USA engineers to communicate ideas among themselves, as well as to engineers outside their group, managers, production specialists, and potential customers. About twenty design variations were examined on the drawing board, after which three or four were selected for further development. A solid model was built using a computer, because the model could be used for stress analysis with finite element methods and because the model could be exported directly to the fabrication machines on Hoyt USA's production floor.

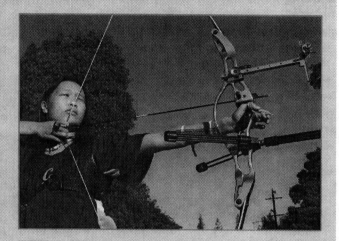

The production version of the structurally reinforced handle.

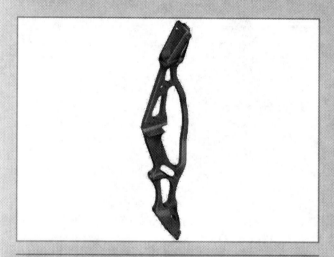

A solid model of the new design used for analysis and fabrication.

After final selection and refinement of the design as a result of the stress analyses and field testing, Hoyt USA began full production of the new product less than one year after the concept was first discussed. To protect the innovative design from being copied by competitors, Hoyt USA applied for and was granted a U.S. patent. Patents also were secured in foreign countries. The design concept was trademarked TEC for "Total Engineering Concept." Because of the relatively radical appearance of the product (and the rather conservative nature of archers), at first, the product was slowly and cautiously adopted by the market. But after a few years (and some outstanding performances at the Olympics), TEC products by Hoyt USA were eagerly embraced by the market as a superior technology.

DISCUSSION QUESTIONS/ACTIVITIES

1. Explain the design process that the developers at Hoyt used to engineer the TEC bow.

2. Create a weighted decision table based on the questions and answers that might have been generated during the design process of the TEC bow.

3. In what ways were concurrent engineering techniques used throughout the development of the TEC bow?

5.08 glossary of key terms

architects: Professionals who complete conceptual designs for civil engineering projects.

as-built drawings: The marked-up drawings from a civil engineering project that show any modifications implemented in the field during construction.

brainstorming: The process of group creative thinking used to generate as many ideas as possible for consideration.

brainwriting: A process of group creative thinking where sketching is the primary mode of communication between team members.

CAD designers: Designers who create 3-D computer models for analysis and detailing.

chief designer: The individual who oversees other members of the design team and manages the overall project.

computer-aided design (CAD): The process by which computers are used to model and analyze designed products.

computer-aided manufacturing (CAM): The process by which parts are manufactured directly from 3-D computer models.

concept mapping: The creative process by which the central idea is placed in the middle of a page and related concepts radiate out from that central idea.

conceptual design: The initial idea for a design before analysis has been performed.

concurrent engineering: The process by which designers, analysts, and manufacturers work together from the start to design a product.

design analysts: Individuals who analyze design concepts by computer methods to determine their structural, thermal, or vibration characteristics.

design documentation: The set of drawings and specifications that illustrate and thoroughly describe a designed product.

design process: The multistep, iterative process by which products are conceived and produced.

detail designers: The individuals who create engineering drawings, complete with annotation, from 3-D computer models or from engineering sketches.

engineering design: The process by which many competing factors of a product are weighed to select the best alternative in terms of cost, sustainability, and function.

finite element analysis: A numerical method used to analyze a product in terms of it structural, thermal, and vibrational performance.

green engineering: The process by which environmental and life cycle considerations are examined from the outset in design.

industrial designers: The individuals who use their creative abilities to develop conceptual designs of potential products.

life cycle: The amount of time a product will be used before it is no longer effective.

mass properties analysis: A computer-generated document that gives the mechanical properties of a 3-D solid model.

model builders: Engineers who make physical mockups of designs using modern rapid prototyping and CAM equipment.

morphological chart: A chart used to generate ideas about the desirable qualities of a product and all of the possible options for achieving them.

patents: A formal way to protect intellectual property rights for a new product.

problem identification: The first stage in the design process where the need for a product or a product modification is clearly defined.

prototype: The initial creation of a product for testing and analysis before it is mass-produced.

sustainable design: A paradigm for making design decisions based on environmental considerations and life cycle analysis.

visual thinking: A method for creative thinking, usually through sketching, where visual feedback assists in the development of creative ideas.

weighted decision table: A matrix used to weigh design options to determine the best possible design characteristics.

5.09 questions for review

1. What are the main stages in the design process?
2. Why is creativity important in the engineering design process?
3. How does engineering design differ from the type of design artists perform?
4. What is meant by concurrent engineering?
5. How is a computer used in the modern-day design process?
6. What are some of the differences in design for a civil engineering project versus a mechanical engineering project?

5.10 design projects

The following sections will outline specifications for design projects. These projects were tested with students at the University of California at Berkeley over the years and are suitable for use in a first- or second-year design course at a university. The projects are designed for completion by a team of four or five students.

5.10.01 STANDARD PROJECT MATERIALS

Use the following standard list of materials, in addition to any special items listed in the specific design rules for the project, to construct the device assigned by your instructor. No other materials are permitted.

- Paper, 30# (maximum): 2 square meters maximum; 2 layers maximum
- Poster board, single-ply, medium weight: 1 square meter maximum
- Foam core modeling board, 3/16″ nominal thickness: 1 square meter maximum
- Twine, 60 lbs. (maximum) labeled breaking strength: 3 meter length maximum
- Wood dowel, 1/4″ nominal diameter: 1 meter length maximum
- Mailing tube, 2″ nominal diameter, medium-weight cardboard: 1 meter length maximum; no endcaps
- Rubber bands (sample to be supplied), #62 or #64: 10 maximum
- Elmer's Glue-All glue: 30 cc maximum
- Hot melt adhesive (polyolefin): 30 cc maximum
- Scotch brand transparent cellophane tape: 1 meter maximum

All of the materials can be purchased at local art supply or convenience stores. Equivalent material may be substituted only with the instructor's permission. Paints, markers, flags, and other decorative items not on the list may be used as long as they are purely decorative; for example, paint cannot be used as weight or ballast.

5.10.02 STANDARD PROJECT DELIVERABLES

The following list provides the standard deliverables for your project. Your instructor may assign additional deliverables and will let you know the due date for each deliverable. When you are organizing your team effort, you can use these deliverables as the milestones to produce a Gantt chart or critical path diagram to help you stay on track and complete the project on time.

Required Drawing Deliverables:

1. Conceptual sketches—alternative and final designs
2. Outline assembly drawings
   Multiview of assembled project
   Isometric or pictorial view of assembled project
   Cutaway views as required for clarity
   Sectional views as required for clarity
   Overall dimensions only
   Balloons to identify subassembly or part numbers and names
3. Detail drawings
   One multiview drawing per part (isometric or pictorial)
   All dimensions, datums, and tolerances
   Quantity
   Material
   Sectional views as required for clarity
   Isometric views as required for clarity

4. Exploded assembly drawings
   Blow-apart pictorial view of all assemblies
   Blow-apart pictorial view of all subassemblies
   Balloons to identify part numbers and part and
   subassembly names
   Subassemblies as required (highly recommended)
5. Bill of materials
   List of all parts by PN, showing name, quantity,
   and material
   List of all materials needed for assembly (e.g.,
   tape and glue)

Use millimeter dimensions and proper title blocks and borders for your engineering drawings. It is recommended that all drawings be cross-checked by different people. Alternate the functions of drafter, designer, and checker. The team leader must give final approval.

Final Demonstration and Oral Presentation:

Each team is expected to give an informative final presentation of its design, as well as a demonstration during the distance contest. Use descriptive graphics slides to complement the presentation. Keep the presentation short and direct.

Written Report:

In your written final report detailing the project results, describe the alternatives your team considered, describe which ones you selected, and explain why you selected them. Use drawings to illustrate key points in the design process. Include the results of your product testing and include a section on what you would have done differently.

DESIGN PROJECT #1: ESCAPE!

NASA is once again looking for a few good engineers. This time the agency is seeking conceptual ideas for an escape device that would allow launchpad crews and astronauts to leave the area quickly in case of a potentially explosive, toxic, or otherwise harmful situation. The device is to be remotely launched and should be designed to place personnel as far away from the launch point as possible. The device must land safely, leaving the personnel unharmed. However, for this project, you will demonstrate the concept of your device using a hard-boiled egg.

The Mission:

Your mission is to design and build a device that will launch a hard-boiled egg (USDA Grade A Large, which your team must provide) into the air and have it land as far from the launch point as possible. The device must land the egg totally intact (no cracks in the shell). The design, for example, may be composed of a mechanism for launching the egg and a device attached to the egg for lowering it slowly (like a parachute). You may surround the egg with a protective covering. However, the covering cannot penetrate the shell or be bonded to it. The function of your device will be graded on the distance from the point of launch relative to that of the other teams in the class. A stiff distance penalty will be assessed if the egg is damaged.

Design Rules:

The device must be constructed out of the standard project materials listed previously, in addition to *only* the following item: one hard-boiled egg (USDA Grade A Large).

Equivalent material may be substituted only with the permission of the instructor. Any design deemed by the instructor as unsafe will not be acceptable (e.g., no sharp flying objects, no explosive devices, and no raw or rotten eggs).

More Contest Rules:

- The device, including the launcher, must initially fit within a 1.0 m x 1.0 m x 1.0 m volume without external support, except for the triggering means.
- Once the egg has been launched, the device may expand to any size.
- The device must be freestanding and may not be taped, glued, or in any other way affixed to the ground.
- The device must be remotely triggered (e.g., by a string or rod). Team members (all parts of the body) must remain a minimum of 1 meter away from the device when the egg is launched.
- The device must be set up within 3 minutes; otherwise, a 3-meter distance penalty on the total distance will be assessed for every 10 seconds of overtime.
- Human power may be used to trigger the device, but not to impart motion to the egg. However, human power may be used to store energy (e.g., into the rubber bands) for any use.
- Distance is measured from the point the egg is completely clear of the launch structure (e.g., completely airborne with no attachment to the launch structure) to the point stops where any part of the device containing the egg touches a solid object connected to the ground.
- The egg must attain a distance of at least 3 meters from the launch position.
- The egg must survive the landing without cracking or sustaining any other visible signs of damage.
- Surviving eggs will be peeled and eaten by the team leader to ensure that they have not been altered in any way. If the team leader does not survive, the entire team will fail the project.
- The egg must be removed from its protective covering within 30 seconds.

5.10 design projects (continued)

- If the egg does not survive, the total distance will be recorded as zero.
- If the egg is damaged, it must be replaced in time for the next launch.
- The maximum distance from three trials will be recorded. A misfire will count as one trial.
- Spare parts are recommended and do not count in the materials inventory of the final assembly.

DESIGN PROJECT #2: FAST FOOD!

Food Service in the dormitories is experimenting with a new method of feeding students in the morning. Instead of going to the dining commons for breakfast, students will open a window before a prescribed time. Food Service will then deliver breakfast by launching it into the dorm room. That way, students do not need to wake up early just to get breakfast and can sleep late if they so choose. All students need to do is leave the window open in the evening to ensure that breakfast will be delivered in the morning. The dining service has asked your team to demonstrate a conceptual prototype of a device that will perform this function.

The Mission:

Your mission is to design and build a device that will launch a bagel with cream cheese into the air and have it land as far from the launch point as possible. The device must land the bagel totally intact and unsoiled. The design, for example, may be composed of a mechanism for launching the bagel and a box around the bagel to help protect it. However, the covering cannot pierce the bagel and cannot be bonded to it. The function of your device will be partially graded on the distance from the point of launch to the point of landing relative to that of the other teams in the class. A stiff distance penalty will be assessed if the bagel is damaged or soiled: you will have to eat it.

Design Rules:

The device must be constructed out of the standard project materials listed previously, in addition to *only* the following item: one plain bagel sliced horizontally and smeared with plain soft cream cheese to 1/4" average thickness. The bagel cannot be more than 24-hours old at the time of launch.

All of the materials (except the bagel with cream cheese) can be purchased at local art supply stores. Any design deemed by the instructor as unsafe will not be acceptable (e.g., no sharp flying objects, no explosive devices, and no spoiled food).

More Contest Rules:

- Once the bagel has been launched, the device may expand to any size.

- The device, including the launcher, must initially fit within a 1.0 m x 1.0 m x 1.0 m volume without external support, except for the triggering means.
- The device must be freestanding and may not be taped, glued, or in any other way affixed to the ground.
- The device must be remotely triggered (e.g., by a string or rod). Team members (all parts of the body) must remain a minimum of 1 meter away from the device when the bagel is launched.
- The device must be set up within 3 minutes; otherwise, a 3-meter distance penalty on the total distance will be assessed for every 10 seconds of overtime.
- Human power may be used to trigger the device, but not to impart motion to the bagel. However, human power may be used to store energy (e.g., into the rubber bands) for any use.
- Distance is measured from the point the bagel is completely clear of the launch structure (e.g., completely airborne with no attachment to the launch structure) to the point stops where any part of the device containing the bagel touches a solid object connected to the ground.
- The bagel must survive the landing without cracking, opening, soiling, or sustaining any other visible signs of damage.
- The surviving bagel with the longest distance will be eaten by the team leader to ensure that it has not been altered in any way. If the team leader does not survive, the entire team will fail the project.
- The bagel must be removed from its protective covering within 15 seconds.
- If the bagel does not survive, the total distance will be recorded as zero.
- If the bagel is damaged, it must be replaced in time for the next launch.
- The average of the three longest distances from as many launches as can be accomplished within a single 60-second period will be recorded. Thus, you should have multiple bagels and containers ready to launch. A misfire will be considered as zero distance.
- Spare parts are recommended and do not count in the materials inventory of the final assembly.

DESIGN PROJECT #3: REWARD!

Several problems are on the horizon for engineering graphics classes of the future. First, the classes are getting larger, requiring that lectures be held in larger rooms. This trend makes it difficult for the instructor to toss candy rewards to specific students in the class, because the instructor's throwing range is limited. Second, the course CD is apparently a flop in the market and customers from all over the country are returning their disks to the publisher. To solve both problems at the same time, someone recommended that candies be strapped to CDs and thrown together. The aerodynamic properties of the CD can be used to increase the range of the candy. This idea was immediately adopted, so here is your project.

The Mission:

Your mission is to design and build a device that will launch a Hershey's chocolate Nugget (with almonds) taped to a CD so it passes through an 8′ x 8′ target frame placed as far from the launch point as possible. The target frame will be placed such that the opening faces the launcher, with the bottom of the target frame on the ground. The launching field will be relatively flat. Each team will have 3 minutes to hit the target at least once. The target distance from the launcher will be specified by the team. The single longest distance at which the target is hit will be recorded for each team. If the target is not hit on any of the tries, the final recorded distance will be recorded as zero.

Design Rules:

The device must be constructed out of the standard project materials listed previously, in addition to *only* the following items:

- One genuine Hershey's chocolate Nugget (with almonds) at room temperature, still in the wrapper
- One standard 120 mm diameter optical CD

    Any design deemed by the instructor as unsafe will not be acceptable (e.g., no sharp flying objects, no explosive devices, and no spoiled food).

More Contest Rules:

- The device, including the launcher, must initially fit within a 1.0 m x 1.0 m x 1.0 m volume without external support, except for the triggering means.
- The device must be freestanding and may not be taped, glued, or in any other way affixed to the ground.
- The device must be remotely triggered (e.g., by a string or rod). Team members (all parts of the body) must remain a minimum of 1 meter away from the device when the Nugget is launched.
- When the launcher is armed and ready to be triggered, it must be entirely self-supporting and stable (e.g., it does not require any external support from team members).
- The device must be set up within 3 minutes; otherwise, a 1-meter distance penalty on the total distance will be assessed for every 10 seconds of overtime.
- Human power may be used to trigger the device, but not to impart motion to the Nugget. However, human power may be used to store energy (e.g., into the rubber bands) for any use.
- Distance is measured from the point the CD is completely clear of the launch structure (e.g., completely airborne with no attachment to the launch structure) to the 8′ x 8′ target frame.
- The Nugget with the longest distance will be eaten by the team leader to ensure that it has not been altered in any way. If the team leader does not survive, the entire team will fail the project.
- The single longest distance at which you hit the target from as many launches as can be accomplished within a single 3-minute period will be recorded. Thus, you should have multiple Nuggets on CDs ready to launch. A misfire will be considered as zero distance.
- Spare parts are recommended and do not count in the materials inventory of the final assembly.

DESIGN PROJECT #4: DEPLOY IT!

NASA is once again looking for a few good engineers. This time the agency is seeking conceptual ideas for the deployment of structures such as antennas and solar panels in spacecraft. The device is to be self-deploying and should be designed to extend as far from the base point as possible while still remaining connected to the base point. It is possible that deployment will occur in various environments—from gravity-free space to high gravity on planets and moons. However, you will demonstrate the concept for your device in earth gravity.

The Mission:

Your mission is to design and build a device that will deploy a structure to reach as far from the origin point as possible. The device must remain physically connected from the origin point to the point of furthest extension. Deployment must be automatic upon activation of a trigger mechanism, and the base structure is to be fixed to the ground. The design, for example, may be composed of a mechanism for extending a boom, cantilevered structure, or suspended structure from the origin point.

Design Rules:

The device must be constructed out of the standard project materials listed previously, in addition to *only* the following item: 4 meters of 3M #2090 Long-Mask masking tape, 2″ wide, to fix the base to the ground.

    Any design deemed by the instructor as unsafe will not be acceptable (e.g., no sharp flying objects and no explosive devices).

More Contest Rules:

- The device, without external support, must initially fit within a 1.0 m x 1.0 m base area on the ground, except for the triggering means.
- The device must initially be less than 0.5 m in height, except for the triggering means.
- Once triggered, the device must deploy automatically to its final state without further assistance and may expand to any size.
- The device must be remotely triggered (e.g., by a string or rod). The trigger may be used only to release energy from the system. The trigger cannot add energy to the system. Team members (all parts of the body) must remain a minimum of 1 meter away from the device when the device is deployed. The means of triggering must be contained on the allowable materials list but will not be counted in the final materials inventory.
- The device may be fixed to the ground only in the original base area, using only the 3M tape specified for this purpose.
- The device must be set up within 3 minutes; otherwise, a 0.1-meter distance penalty on the total distance will be assessed for every 10 seconds of overtime.
- Human power may be used to trigger the device, but not to impart motion to the structure. However, human power may be used during setup to store energy (e.g., into the rubber bands) for any use.
- Distance is measured from the forward-most point of the base prior to deployment to the forward-most connected point of the structure after deployment (in a predefined direction).
- Except within the original base area, no part of the structure may touch the ground in the final deployed position. Incidental (accidental) contact with the floor is permitted during deployment. However, prolonged contact (e.g., using the ground for support, using a wheeled carriage, or bouncing along the ground) is not permitted. No external structures (e.g., wall, ceiling, or pipes) can be used for guidance or support at any time.
- The maximum distance from three trials will be recorded. A misfire will count as one trial.
- Spare parts are recommended and do not count in the materials inventory of the final assembly.

DESIGN PROJECT #5: VERTICAL LIMIT

Your local fire department is looking for conceptual ideas for rescuing people in high-rise buildings. The firefighters have asked you to develop and build a test model for their review. The device is to be self-deploying and is to be designed to extend as high as possible while still remaining connected to the ground. The structure is to be freestanding in its original and deployed states.

The Mission:

Your mission is to design and build a device that will deploy from a prescribed initial size to a freestanding structure that reaches as high as possible. Deployment must be automatic upon activation of a trigger mechanism. The base structure is to be fixed to the ground. The design, for example, may be composed of a mechanism for extending a boom or truss structure.

Design Rules:

The device must be constructed out of the standard project materials listed previously, in addition to *only* the following item: 4 meters of duct tape, 2" wide, to fix the base to the ground.

Any design deemed by the instructor as unsafe will not be acceptable (e.g., no sharp flying objects and no explosive devices).

More Contest Rules:

- The device, without external support, must initially fit within a 1.0 m x 1.0 m base area on the ground, except for the triggering means.
- The device must initially be less than 0.5 m in height, except for the triggering means.
- Once triggered, the device must deploy automatically to its final state without further assistance and may expand to any size.
- The device must be remotely triggered (e.g., by a string or rod). The trigger may be used only to release energy from the system. The trigger cannot add energy to the system. Team members (all parts of the body) must remain a minimum of 1 meter away from the device when the device is deployed. The means of triggering must be contained on the allowable materials list but will not be counted in the final materials inventory.
- The device may be fixed to the ground only in the original base area, using only duct tape.
- The device must be set up within 3 minutes; otherwise, a 0.1-meter distance penalty on the total height will be assessed for every 10 seconds of overtime.
- Human power may be used to trigger the device, but not to impart motion to the structure. However, human power may be used during setup to store energy (e.g., into the rubber bands) for any use.
- Distance is measured from the ground to the highest point of the structure when it is fully deployed.
- No external structures (e.g., wall, ceiling, or pipes) can be used for guidance or support at any time.

- The maximum height from three trials will be recorded. The structure height must be maintained for the time it takes to measure the height (approximately 2 minutes). A misfire will count as one trial.
- Spare parts are recommended and do not count in the materials inventory of the final assembly.

DESIGN PROJECT #6: THERE 'N BACK

The problem of air pollution caused by automobiles has plagued cities worldwide for decades. Several solutions have been proposed over the years, including public mass transportation systems, electric vehicles, hybrid vehicles, low-emission fuels, human-powered vehicles, and solar- or wind-powered vehicles. None of these options have been very successful to date. Consequently, it is time to develop new concepts in powered vehicles. Recently, your instructor received an anonymous e-mail stating that energy in a vehicle might be stored in elastic elements. This idea was immediately adopted, and a study was commissioned to investigate the possibility of using a large number of surplus rubber bands to power a commuter vehicle.

The Mission:

Your mission is to design and build a small-scale concept vehicle that travels in a linear trajectory as far as possible and then automatically returns along the same trajectory. The device is to be powered by two rubber bands—either #62 or #64. On the day of testing, a travel line will be taped on the floor. Travel distances will be measured in the direction of the line only. Each team will have three launches of their vehicle. *The travel distance to be recorded will be the distance the vehicle travels backward along the trajectory line after the vehicle stops its forward travel.* The backward travel distance cannot exceed the forward travel distance. The single longest distance the vehicle travels backward in three attempts will be recorded for each team. If the vehicle has no forward or backward travel, the final distance will be recorded as zero.

Design Rules:

The device must be constructed out of the standard project materials listed previously (and *only* the materials listed).

Any design deemed by the instructor as unsafe will not be acceptable (e.g., no sharp flying objects, no explosive devices, and no burning or combustible materials).

More Contest Rules:

- The vehicle must be entirely self-contained (e.g., no external launching or guidance devices).
- The entire vehicle must initially fit within a 1.0 m x 1.0 m x 1.0 m volume without external support. After launching, the vehicle can expand to any size.
- The vehicle can be released by hand or remotely triggered. Any number of team members can be involved with the release. Once released, the vehicle cannot be touched.
- The device must be set up within 3 minutes for each launch; otherwise, a 0.5-meter distance penalty on the total distance will be assessed for every 10 seconds of overtime.
- The vehicle or a part of the vehicle must remain in contact with the ground at all times.
- Human power may be used to trigger the vehicle, but not to impart motion to the vehicle (i.e., no pushing or pulling the vehicle) However, human power may be used to store energy in the rubber bands for any use.
- Gravity cannot be used to produce motion (e.g., no launching from a ramp).
- Travel distance is measured in the direction parallel to the length of the path. If the vehicle hits the side wall of the hallway and stops, all vehicle motion is considered finished.
- The final recorded travel distance will be the distance from the closest point of forward travel (from the starting line) on the vehicle to the closest point of return travel (from the forward mark) on the vehicle.
- Objects expelled from the vehicle are still considered a part of the vehicle for measurement of travel distance.
- Spare parts are recommended and do not count in the materials inventory of the final assembly.

Pictorial Drawings

objectives

After completing this chapter, you should be able to

- Explain the importance of pictorial drawings as an aid in visualization

- Create an isometric drawing of an object composed of principal, inclined, and oblique surfaces

- Draw ellipses on the front, top, and right faces of the isometric to represent cylinders and holes

- Explain the difference between a cavalier and cabinet oblique drawing

- Create an oblique drawing given the orthographic drawing of an object

- Create a two-point perspective drawing given the orientation of the plan view and the location of the elevation view

12.01

introduction

A major problem in engineering graphics is the need to represent a 3-D object using a 2-D sheet of paper. Generally, this is done using orthographic views that show the top, front, and side views of the object as separate entities. Each view represents two dimensions of the object. The top view displays the width and depth dimensions, the front view shows the width and height dimensions, and the side view displays the width and height dimensions. Since each of these views represents only two dimensions, you have to move the views around in your mind's eye to figure out what the 3-D object looks like. Sometimes you will get it right, and sometimes you will get it wrong. A **pictorial** drawing or sketch can be effective in helping you visualize the 3-D shape. The pictorial shows all three dimensions (height, width, and depth) in a single view of the object. You already have been exposed to pictorials in previous chapters of this book, but in a rather informal way. Sketching pictorials helped you develop your visualization skills. The earlier chapters also used pictorials as a visualization aid for making formal multiview drawings. There are cases, however, when pictorial sketches are inappropriate for certain applications; for example, in formal engineering drawings and documents. In these cases, a more formal and more accurate method of creating pictorial drawings is needed.

Pictorials help you visualize, but they also are important when you attempt to assemble parts into mechanisms or need to purchase replacement parts for a tool. For example, when you purchase a lawn mower, the manufacturer will furnish a user's manual. In the user's manual, you are likely to find a series of pictorial drawings that show every lawn mower part with some identifying information. If you need to replace a part, you can use the pictorial to install the part. Pictorial drawings can be an effective way to ensure that a mechanism gets reassembled properly after a part is replaced.

Pictorial drawings are used mainly as visualization aids; they are not used as working drawings from which a part is produced. Historically, before the industrial revolution, craftsmen would sketch a design as a pictorial and use it to produce a product. If part of the design were to fail or break, they would have to custom-make another part in order for the product to be useful again. After the industrial revolution, products were manufactured using mass production and the concept of interchangeable parts came into being. With interchangeable parts, a detail drawing showing lines in true length and angles as true angles was necessary to guarantee that parts could be used interchangeably. Also, proper dimensions and tolerances were required to ensure that the parts would be interchangeable. Because a pictorial drawing shows all three dimensions on a 2-D sheet of paper, lines that define surfaces may not be true length and angles may not be true angles, as shown in Figure 12.01. The figure shows a pictorial representation of a cube. Note that the lines that define the cube are not shown in true length. Also, since a cube is composed of six surfaces that are squares, the angle of line AB and AC should be 90°; but it is not. For the object to be produced by mechanical processes, it is important that the shape be interpreted correctly. An effective way to do that is to use a multiview orthographic drawing (each view contains only two dimensions), which shows the true lengths of lines and the true angles. After the object is produced, the pictorial drawing can be used to compare the 3-D shape of the object with the actual object and the pictorial drawing will verify that the shape is correct.

There are many types and variations of pictorial drawings since they must serve different purposes. Some of the major types of pictorials are **axonometric** drawings, **oblique** drawings, and **perspective** drawings. An example of each is shown in Figure 12.02. The term *axonometric* is a broad category of pictorial drawings that includes **isometric, diametric,** and **trimetric** drawings. The term *axonometric* refers to the angle that the coordinate axes make with each other when the three dimensions are defined for the object. Figure 12.02 shows the coordinate axes relative to the type of pictorial drawing represented. An oblique drawing is a pictorial in which the irregular surface (often a circular cylinder) is drawn in the 2-D plane of the paper and the third dimension is drawn at some receding angle to this plane (Figure 12.02). A perspective drawing is one where the receding axis(es) converge at vanishing point(s) located on what is referred to as a horizon. When done correctly, a perspective drawing gives the impression that you are looking at a photograph. Each of these types of pictorial drawings will be discussed in detail later in this chapter.

Most of the following techniques for creating a pictorial drawing are traditional methods based on 2-D CAD and drafting techniques. These techniques can still be used when 3-D modeling tools are not available. For speed, efficiency, and accuracy, pictorial drawings are most easily created when they are extracted from 3-D models.

FIGURE 12.01. An isometric pictorial of a cube.

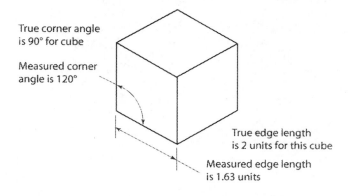

True corner angle is 90° for cube

Measured corner angle is 120°

True edge length is 2 units for this cube

Measured edge length is 1.63 units

FIGURE 12.02. Samples of pictorial drawing types of the same object.

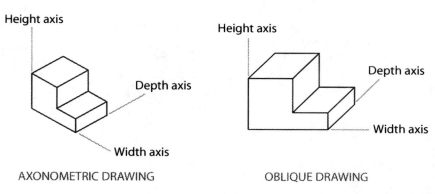

Height axis

Depth axis

Width axis

AXONOMETRIC DRAWING

Height axis

Depth axis

Width axis

OBLIQUE DRAWING

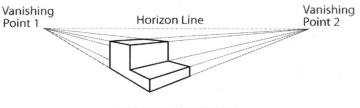

Vanishing Point 1

Horizon Line

Vanishing Point 2

PERSPECTIVE DRAWING

12.02 Axonometric Drawings

The word *axonometric* has its origin in Greek from the word *axon*, which means "axis," and the word *metric*, which means "measure." An axonometric drawing refers to three types of pictorial drawings: isometric, dimetric, and trimetric drawings that are created by measuring along three axes representing width, depth, and height. Isometric drawings are relatively easy to produce and usually can be done quickly. In an isometric drawing, the three dimensions of width, depth, and height are shown along the three isometric axes, as shown in Figure 12.03. When the dimensions of width, height, and depth are plotted in this fashion, the three normal surfaces (frontal, horizontal, and profile) of a rectangular solid object have equal angles between them (120°). In dimetric drawings, the three dimensions of width, depth, and height are shown along the three dimetric axes, as shown in Figure 12.04. When plotted correctly along these axes, two of the normal surfaces (frontal and profile) have equal angles between them, while the third normal surface (horizontal) has a different angle. In a trimetric drawing, the dimensions of width, height, and depth are plotted along axes so the normal surfaces of a rectangular solid (frontal, horizontal, and profile) have none of the three angles equal, as shown in Figure 12.05.

FIGURE 12.03. Three visible normal surfaces (frontal, horizontal, and profile) of a prism have equal angles between them (120°) in an isometric drawing.

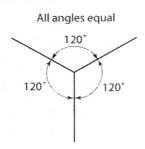
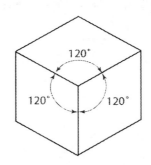

FIGURE 12.04. In a diametric drawing, two of the three visible normal surfaces (frontal and profile) of a prism have edges presented at equal angles, not equal to 120°.

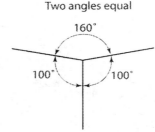
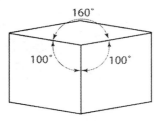

FIGURE 12.05. A trimetric drawing presents the three visible normal surfaces (frontal, horizontal, and profile) of a prism in a position where none of the angles between the surface edges is equal.

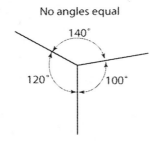
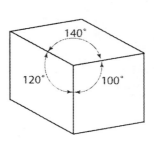

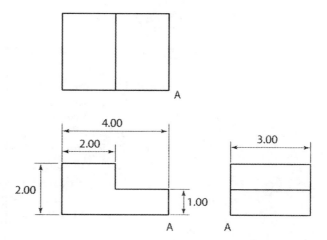

FIGURE 12.06. Orthographic
views of a step block.

The drawing of dimetric and trimetric pictorials takes a great deal of time because of the uncommon angles that are used. Therefore, the time it takes to complete this type of pictorial offsets any benefit there may be in producing it. Dimetric and trimetric pictorials are seldom used in engineering work; so they will not be discussed in detail. Instead, the chapter will focus on the easiest and most popular form of axonometric drawing, the isometric drawing.

12.02.01 Isometric Drawing

The best way to learn about formal isometric drawings is to study a simple example. Figure 12.06 shows the orthographic views of a step block. For this object, all of the surfaces are normal surfaces. This means that each surface is viewed in its true size and shape in one of the principal views and will appear as an edge view in the other principal views. A frontal surface appears in true size and shape in the frontal view, while a horizontal surface appears in true size and shape in the horizontal or top view. A profile surface appears in true size and shape in the right side or right profile view. Note that in the front view, you see the width and height dimensions; in the top view, you see the width and depth dimensions; and in the profile view, you see the depth and height dimensions. To draw the isometric pictorial of the step block, you must first set up the isometric axes that will define where to measure the width, height, and depth dimensions.

One way to define the isometric axes is shown in Figure 12.07. Two receding axes intersect at point A and are at 30 degrees to an imaginary horizontal line. The width dimensions will be plotted along the receding axis extending to the left of point A, and the depth dimensions will be plotted along the receding axis extending to the right of point A. The height dimension will be plotted along the vertical axis that extends upward from point A. When you look at the orthographic drawing in Figure 12.06, you see that the maximum width, depth, and height are 4 units, 3 units, and 2 units, respectively.

FIGURE 12.07. The
isometric axes.

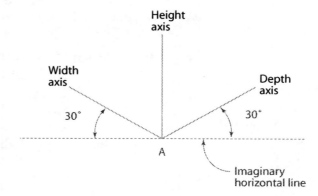

When beginning to draw the isometric, you want to frame the step block on the isometric axes and then take care of the details to finish the isometric. Match the following steps with the steps shown in Figure 12.08 to draw the isometric of the step block.

Step 1: On the isometric axis marked *Width*, measure the maximum width of the step block (4 units) from point A and label this measurement as point B. On the isometric axis marked *Depth*, measure the maximum depth of the step block (3 units) from point A and mark this measurement as point C. On the isometric axis marked *Height*, measure the maximum height of the step block (2 units) from point A and mark this measurement as point D.

Step 2: Draw vertical lines from points B and C. From point D, draw a line parallel with line AC that intersects with the vertical line from C. Label this point as E. In a similar manner, from point D, draw a line parallel with line AB that intersects with the vertical line from B. Label this point as F.

Step 3: Complete the "isometric reference prism" by drawing a line from E that is parallel with line DF. Then draw a line from F that is parallel with DE. The line from E and the line from F intersect at point G. The isometric reference prism contains the step block.

Step 4: Along line FD, measure the width of the upper surface (2 units) and label it point 1. From point 1, draw a line parallel with FG to line GE and label the point on GE as point 2. From point 1 and point 2, draw vertical lines downward parallel with BF.

Step 5: Along the vertical line AD, measure the height of the lower surface (1 inch) and label it on AD as point 3. From point 3, draw a line parallel with AC to line CE. Label the point where this line intersects CE as point 4.

Step 6: From point 3, draw a line parallel with AB that intersects the vertical line from point 1 and label it point 5. In a similar manner, draw a line from point 4 parallel with AB that intersects the vertical line from point 2 and label it point 6. Connect point 5 with point 6.

Step 7: Erase lines 1-D, D-3, 2-E, and E-4. The isometric drawing of the step block is complete. Darken all lines that define the step block.

The step block is relatively easy to draw because all of the lines that define it are called **isometric lines**. All of the lines defining the frontal surface are parallel or perpendicular, as are the lines defining the horizontal and profile surfaces. Isometric drawings can get rather complex when surfaces that need to be drawn are not defined as frontal, horizontal, or profile surfaces because the lines that form the surfaces are not parallel or perpendicular. Therefore, these lines are "nonisometric lines" and need to be plotted using their endpoints.

12.02.02 Inclined Surfaces

Figure 12.09 is an orthographic drawing showing a variation of the step block that has an inclined surface. The procedure to draw the isometric pictorial of this object is similar to drawing the step block in Figure 12.08 except that you have to account for the inclined surface. Use the following steps along with the steps in Figure 12.10.

Step 1: Follow the seven steps to draw the step block shown in Figure 12.08.

Step 2: From point 5, draw a vertical line downward that intersects AB at point 7.

Step 3: From point 7, draw a line to point C; and from point 5, draw a line to point 4. The inclined surface is defined by the points 5-4-C-7.

Step 4: Remove lines 5-3, 3-4, 7-A, and AC. These edges were used for construction only, and are not a part of the object. Darken all visible edges to complete the drawing.

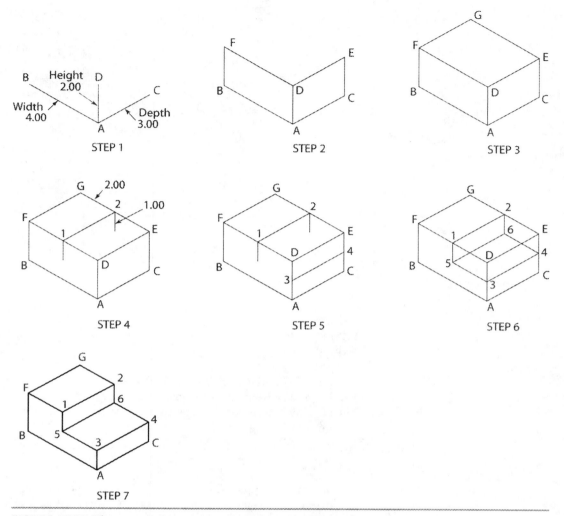

FIGURE 12.08. The steps to draw an isometric pictorial of the step block.

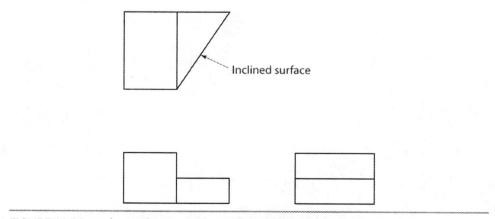

FIGURE 12.09. Orthographic views of a step block with an inclined surface.

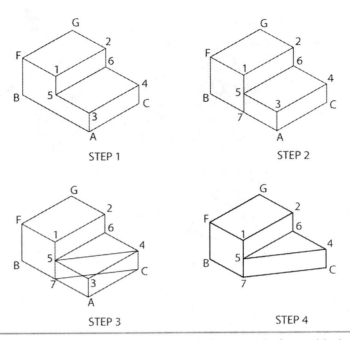

FIGURE 12.10. The step involved to create an isometric pictorial of a step block with an inclined surface.

Lines 5-4 and 7-C in Figure 12.10 are defined as nonisometric lines. They are not parallel to any isometric lines, which is why they are called nonisometric lines. They must be drawn by plotting the endpoints and then connecting them properly, as shown in Figure 12.10.

12.02.03 Oblique Surfaces

An even more complex example involving isometric drawings includes a drawing that has an oblique surface. An oblique surface is a surface that is neither parallel nor perpendicular to the frontal, horizontal, or profile projection plane; and the oblique surface will appear in all three views as its characteristic shape. That is, if the oblique surface is a triangle, it will be a triangle in all three views. It will not appear as an edge in any of the three views. Knowing this, it is reasonable to assume that an isometric drawing showing an oblique surface will show the surface in its characteristic shape. Figure 12.11 shows

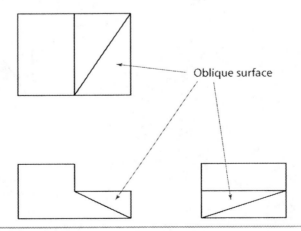

FIGURE 12.11. Orthographic views of a step block with an oblique surface.

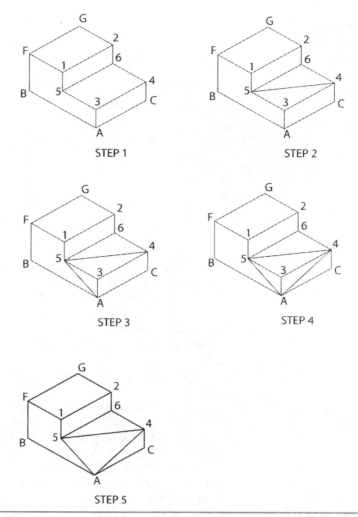

STEP 1   STEP 2

STEP 3   STEP 4

STEP 5

FIGURE 12.12. The steps involved to create an isometric pictorial of a step block with an oblique surface.

three orthographic views of a step block that includes an oblique surface. Use the following steps and the steps shown in Figure 12.12 to draw the isometric of the step block with the oblique surface.

Step 1:   Follow the seven steps to draw the step block shown in Figure 12.08.

Step 2:   Draw a line from point 5 to point 4.

Step 3:   Draw a line from point 5 to point A.

Step 4:   Draw a line from point 4 to point A.

Step 5:   Erase lines 4-3, 5-3, and 3-A to complete the isometric.

In Figure 12.12, the surface formed by 5-4-A is an oblique surface. The lines 5-4, 4-A, and 5-A are nonisometric lines. All of the remaining lines of the step block are isometric lines.

In an isometric drawing, orientation of the object depends on the placement of the axes, which locates the origin. In Figure 12.08, point A on the lower right-corner of the object was chosen as the location of the origin. From this point, you measured back along the left receding axis to lay off widths and you measured along the right receding axis to measure depth. Then you measured vertically to measure height. For all measurements, you assumed point A to be the origin, or the 0,0,0 point. Selection of the

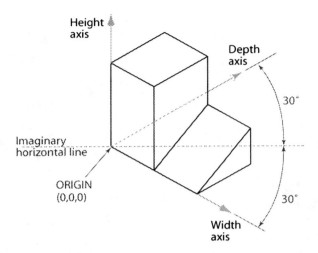

FIGURE 12.13. The origin used to locate an object using the lower-left corner.

origin (or point 0,0,0) in 3-D coordinates establishes the relative position of each point that makes up the object. The origin can be placed anywhere on the object, and the isometric can be drawn from this reference. For example, Figure 12.13 shows an origin that would be located at the lower-left corner of the object. The width, depth, and height measurements would be measured along the appropriate axes as shown in Figure 12.13. Notice that the width and depth axes are 30° from an imaginary horizontal line, as explained previously. No matter where the origin is located, all points that define the object can be plotted in 3-D space; then the points are connected to show the pictorial.

Refer back to Figure 12.6, the orthographic view of the step block. This set of views shows a front view, a top or horizontal view, and a right profile view. You also can orient the views for the step block to show a front view, a top or horizontal view, and a left profile view (Figure 12.14). Each of these orthographic arrangements allows for two different orientations of the pictorial. The pictorial can open to the right or it can open to the left. The term *open* refers to how the orthographic views are interpreted. When the orthographic drawing is oriented to show a front, top, and right-side view, the isometric pictorial opens to the right (Figure 12.15). When the orthographic drawing is oriented to show a front, top, and left-side view, the isometric pictorial opens to the left (Figure 12.15).

Orthographic views generally show all kinds of lines that define the object. Lines may be visible, or they may be hidden. Hidden lines are represented in orthographic views as dashed lines. In isometric pictorial views, hidden lines are generally not shown

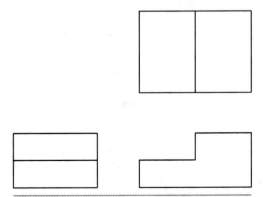

FIGURE 12.14. Orthographic views of the step block oriented as the front, top, and left profile views.

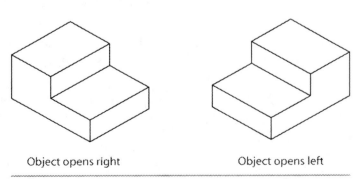

Object opens right　　　Object opens left

FIGURE 12.15. An isometric drawing has two primary positions for viewing. The object can be oriented so that it "opens" to the right or to the left.

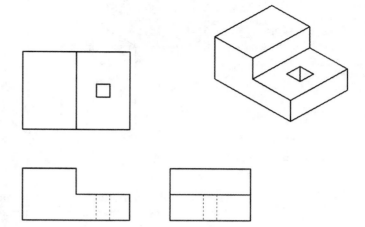

unless they are necessary for interpretation of the object. For example, Figure 12.16 shows an orthographic drawing of a step block on the left that has a square hole going all the way through it. In the orthographic views, hidden lines in the front view and in the right profile view define the hole. The isometric pictorial of this block is shown on the right. Notice that no hidden lines are shown. The square hole shown is assumed to go through the entire object. This is a correct representation of the step block in isometric. Figure 12.17 shows an orthographic drawing of a step block on the left that has a square hole that does not go all the way through. This is often referred to as a blind hole. As before, hidden lines are shown in the orthographic views; however, since the hole does not go all the way through the object, the isometric pictorial shown on the right must include hidden lines to define how deep the square hole goes into the step block. In this case, hidden lines are necessary to define the depth of the hole.

12.02.04 Cylindrical Surfaces

You have learned that 3-D objects can be composed of normal, inclined, and oblique surfaces, and you have learned how to represent each surface in an isometric pictorial. Another type of surface that is associated with 3-D objects is the cylindrical surface. The cylindrical surface may be positive (such as a post) or negative (such as a hole). When you are looking directly at a normal surface in an orthographic view, the cylinder is represented by a circle. Since the normal surfaces of an isometric pictorial are distorted and you are looking at all three dimensions on one sheet of paper, the cylinder is represented on an isometric drawing by an ellipse. The orientation of the ellipse is dependent upon whether it appears on the top face, the right face, or the left face. An

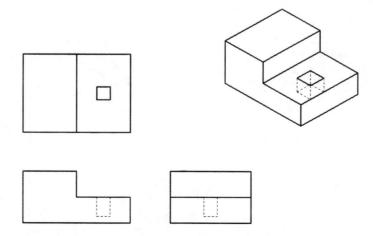

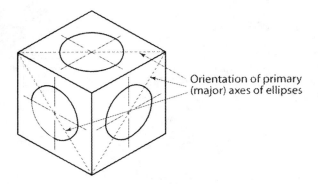

FIGURE 12.18. An isometric cube showing ellipses on each face. Note the orientation of the long (major) axis for the ellipse on each of the three normal faces.

Orientation of primary (major) axes of ellipses

isometric cube that has an ellipse on the right face, the left face, and the top face is shown in Figure 12.18. Note the orientation of the long axis for the ellipses on each of the three normal faces of the cube.

Figure 12.19 illustrates how to construct an ellipse on a horizontal (top) isometric surface. The first step is to establish the limits of the ellipse by drawing a limiting box, which appears as a parallelogram in the pictorial view. For normal surfaces on the object, the sides of the parallelogram are parallel to the isometric lines. The easiest way to create the ellipse is to use an ellipse template (when drawing is done by hand) and selecting the ellipse that is tangent to the sides of the limiting box. When a 2-D CAD tool is used, an ellipse is created by specifying its major and minor diameters in an ellipse creation tool; the ellipse is then rotated into the correct orientation.

The ellipse also can be constructed using the four-center method. The construction locates four centers that can be used for drawing four arcs (two large arcs and two small arcs) that approximate an ellipse. These arcs may be sketched or may be drawn with a compass. The following steps are shown in Figure 12.19.

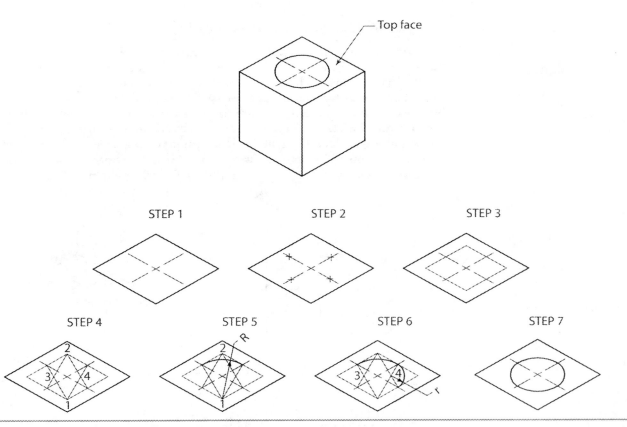

Top face

STEP 1   STEP 2   STEP 3

STEP 4   STEP 5   STEP 6   STEP 7

FIGURE 12.19. Drawing an ellipse on the top isometric surface using the traditional four-center method.

Step 1: Locate the center of the cylinder by showing the centerlines laid out parallel to the isometric sides.

Step 2: Measure along the centerlines the extreme points of the cylinder.

Step 3: Frame the limits of the ellipse that will represent the cylinder. The box should look like a diamond. (An isometric square is a diamond-shaped rhombus.)

Step 4: Note that the near point (point 1) and the far point (point 2) of the diamond are the first two points of the four centers. From these points, draw light construction lines across the diamond where the centerline intersects the box. You should have four light construction lines on the surface. Where these light construction lines cross is the location of point 3 and point 4 of the four centers.

Step 5: Assuming a long radius (R) as shown in the figure, draw arcs between the centerlines, using point 1 and point 2 as the center.

Step 6: Assuming a short radius (r) as shown in the figure, draw arcs between the centerlines, using point 3 and point 4 as the center.

Step 7: The ellipse is now complete.

The steps required to draw an ellipse on the right face are shown in Figure 12.20, and the steps required to draw an ellipse on the left face are shown in Figure 12.21. Essentially, they are the same as drawing the ellipse on the top face.

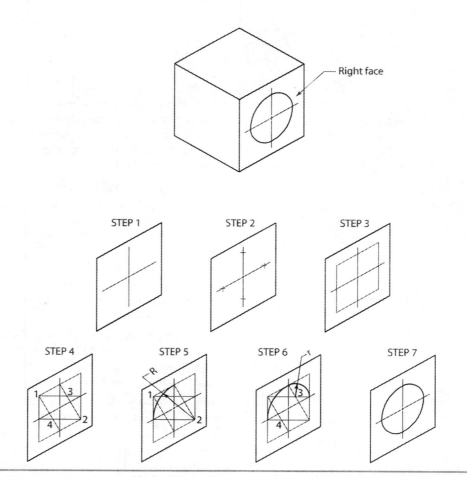

FIGURE 12.20. Drawing an ellipse on the right isometric surface using the traditional four-center method.

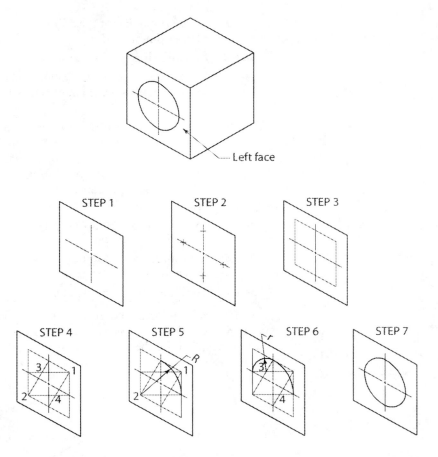

FIGURE 12.21. Drawing an ellipse on the left isometric surface using the traditional four-center method.

— Left face

STEP 1 STEP 2 STEP 3

STEP 4 STEP 5 STEP 6 STEP 7

Figure 12.22 shows the orthographic views of a step block that has one of the surfaces represented by a semicircle. When drawing the isometric pictorial of this object, you need to incorporate the steps involved in drawing an ellipse; but you are going to draw only half of it. Construct the isometric drawing of the step block shown in Figure 12.08. Figure 12.23 illustrates the steps required to draw the lower surface, which includes a semicircle.

Step 1: Locate the center of the radius (1.5 units) on surface 3-5-6-4. The center can be located by measuring 1.5 units from point 3 along line 3-4 and then measuring 1.5 units from point 3 along 3-5. When you are drawing isometric lines from these two points, the lines will intersect at the center location for the radius.

Step 2: Frame the ellipse by measuring along line 3-5 a distance of 3 units (you will have to extend line 3-5) and marking the point as X. Through X, draw a line parallel with line 3-4 until it intersects line 4-6, which has been extended, and mark this point as Y.

Step 3: From point 3, draw a light line to the midpoint of line 4-Y. From point 3, draw a light line to the midpoint of line X-Y. From point Y, draw a light line to the midpoint of line 3-4. Label this line Z where it intersects the line drawn in from point 3 to the midpoint of 4-Y.

Step 4: Construct a radius (length is the distance from Y to the midpoint of line 3-X) using point Y as the center point and drawing the arc from the midpoint of line 3-X to the midpoint of line 3-4. Construct another radius (length is the distance from Z to the midpoint of line 3-4) using point Z as the center point and drawing the arc from the midpoint of line 3-4 to the midpoint of line 4-Y. The partial ellipse is complete for the top surface.

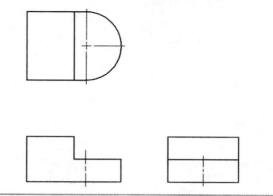

FIGURE 12.22. Orthographic views of a step block with a semicircular base.

Step 5: Repeat the previous steps on the lower surface to create two arcs that are "parallel" to the arcs drawn on the top surface.

Step 6: To complete the pictorial, draw a tangent between the upper and lower surface arcs, as shown in Figure 12.23.

12.02.05 Ellipses on Inclined Surfaces

Sometimes the need arises to draw an ellipse on an inclined surface that appears in an isometric drawing. To do this, you must project some points to ascertain the location of the ellipse on the inclined surface. This task is achieved by using the following steps with steps 1 and 2 shown in Figure 12.24, steps 3 and 4 shown in Figure 12.25, and steps 5 and 6 shown in Figure 12.26. Using these three illustrations, you will create a circular hole in the center of the inclined surface labeled as A-B-C-D.

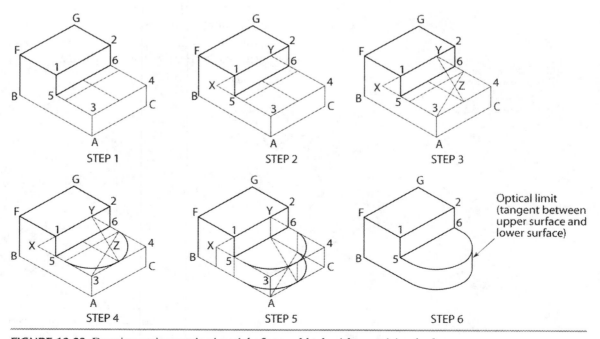

FIGURE 12.23. Drawing an isometric pictorial of a step block with a semicircular base.

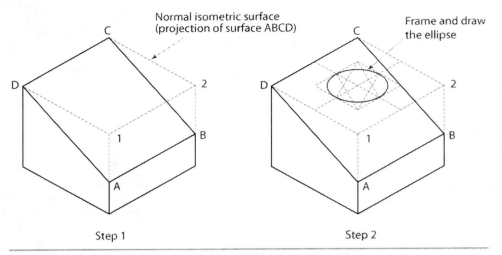

FIGURE 12.24. Steps 1 and 2 to create an isometric pictorial showing a vertical circular hole in an inclined surface.

Step 1: Create a normal isometric surface by locating point 1 using points B and A. Draw a light line from B along the isometric line shown. Draw a light line from A vertically until the line from B is intersected. This intersection is the location of point 1. Repeat step 1 using points C and D as your reference points and locate point 2. The rectangular surface shown as B-1-2-C represents a projection of the inclined surface B-A-D-C. You will use this projection to establish the cylindrical hole.

Step 2: In the center of the horizontal surface shown as B-1-1-C, locate the center-line for the cylindrical hole, which will be shown as an ellipse since this is an isometric surface. Frame the area that will contain the ellipse and draw the ellipse as shown in Figure 12.24.

Step 3: Locate several points on the ellipse that will be used to project to the inclined surface to locate the hole on the inclined surface. Project each point that you located on the ellipse to line C-2. Make sure these projections are parallel to lines BC and 1-2.

Step 4: Where the points projected in step 3 intersect line C-2, project them straight down (parallel to D-2) to line CD, which is on the inclined surface.

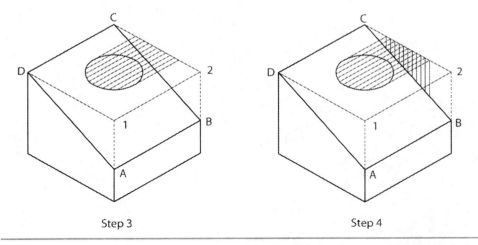

FIGURE 12.25. Steps 3 and 4 to create an isometric pictorial showing a vertical circular hole in an inclined surface.

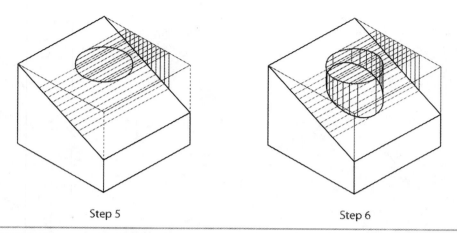

Step 5   Step 6

FIGURE 12.26. Steps 5 and 6 to create an isometric pictorial showing a vertical circular hole in an inclined surface.

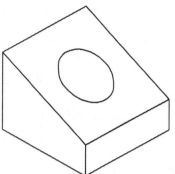

FIGURE 12.27. The finished construction of the vertical circular hole in an inclined surface.

Step 5: Where the points projected in step 4 intersect line CD, draw lines parallel to BC and AD on the inclined surface.

Step 6: From the points on the ellipse drawn on the normal isometric surface B-C-2-1, project downward (parallel to A-1 and B-2) to the place where the points intersect their specific projection line on the inclined face (A-B-C-D). Plot a point on this intersection. Using an irregular curve, connect the points on the inclined surface to complete the location of the cylindrical hole on the inclined surface.

Figure 12.27 shows the circular hole in the inclined surface without all of the construction required to create it. This looks as though it would be simple to create; but as you refer back to the steps, the process is very complex.

12.03 Oblique Drawings

Oblique drawings are forms of pictorial drawings that enable the viewer to see the most descriptive view of the object as a front view projected directly onto the plane of the paper. The depth of the object is shown at a receding angle. An advantage of oblique pictorials is that one surface appears as its true size and shape and is not distorted. This means that circular features such as holes and cylinders appear as circles in the plane of the paper and do not appear as ellipses. Objects with cylinders and holes are easier to show in a pictorial representation when the drawing is an oblique pictorial. A disadvantage of oblique pictorials is that they tend to be distorted and appear elongated when viewed because they are not a "true projection" even though they are dimensionally correct. Although any receding angle from 0° to 90° may be used for an oblique drawing, angles between 30° and 60° should be used, which minimizes the distortion and elongation, as shown in Figure 12.28.

12.03.01 Types of Oblique Drawings

There are generally two types of oblique drawings: **cavalier** and **cabinet**. Both types generate a pictorial drawing in a similar manner by showing the most descriptive view of the object in the plane of the paper in true size and shape and show a receding dimension along an axis at some angle between 30° and 60° (45° is preferred) to minimize distortion. The difference between cavalier and cabinet oblique drawings lies in the measurements made along the receding depth axes. A cavalier oblique drawing is generated when the true length of the depth dimension is measured along the receding

FIGURE 12.28. Example of an oblique pictoral.

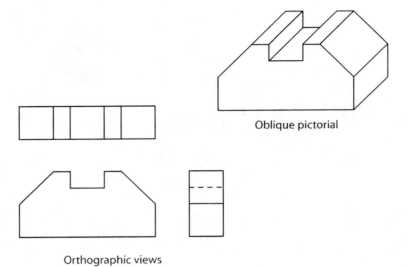

Oblique pictorial

Orthographic views

axes, as shown in Figure 12.29. The cabinet oblique is generated when half the true length of the depth is measured along the receding axes, as shown in Figure 12.30. The cavalier oblique shows the most distortion and elongation, while the cabinet oblique shows the least. For this reason, the cabinet oblique tends to be selected most often.

12.03.02 Construction of Oblique Drawings

An oblique drawing can be constructed using the "framing" technique, which is similar to the technique used when creating an isometric drawing. Essentially, an oblique prism is constructed and then the features are cut away to show the 3-D aspects of the object. Figure 12.31 illustrates the following steps in constructing an oblique drawing.

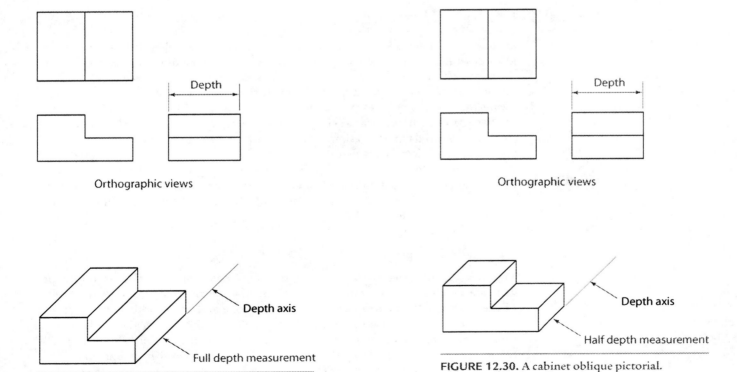

Orthographic views

Depth

Orthographic views

Depth

Depth axis

Full depth measurement

Depth axis

Half depth measurement

FIGURE 12.29. A cavalier oblique pictorial.

FIGURE 12.30. A cabinet oblique pictorial.

FIGURE 12.31. The steps required to construct an oblique pictorial.

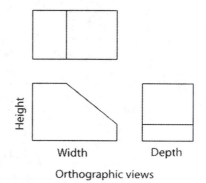

Orthographic views

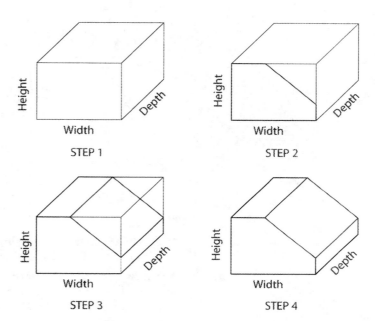

Step 1: Determine the height, width, and depth of the object and frame these dimensions. The width and height should be in the plane of the paper. Draw the receding axis at 45° and measure the depth dimensions along this axis using the true length of the depth.

Step 2: Draw the front view of the object, which matches the orthographic front view.

Step 3: Draw the inclined surface by laying out its location on the front surface and then on the right surface as displayed on the receding axis.

Step 4: Darken all visible lines and erase construction to complete the drawing.

12.03.03 Construction of an Object with Circular Features

The "boxing-in" technique can be used to create an oblique drawing of an object that has circular features such as holes or cylinders. The orthographic views shown in Figure 12.32 indicate that you will have to frame the cylinder with the hole as one step and frame the rectangular prism that also has a hole as another step. This object will need to have two "box-in" steps. Figure 12.32 illustrates the following steps.

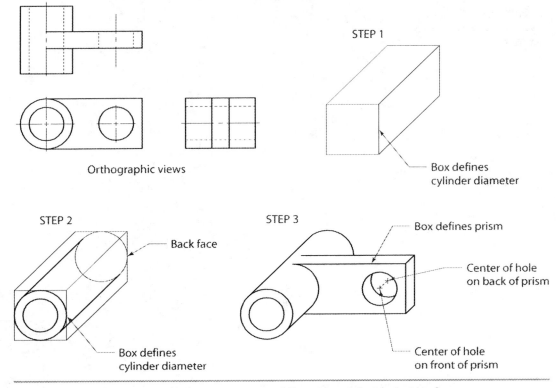

STEP 1

Box defines
cylinder diameter

Orthographic views

STEP 2

Back face

Box defines
cylinder diameter

STEP 3

Box defines prism

Center of hole
on back of prism

Center of hole
on front of prism

FIGURE 12.32. The steps required to construct an oblique pictorial with circular features.

Step 1: Frame the diameter of the cylinder and draw it in the plane of the paper with a 45° angle for the receding axis.

Step 2: On the front face, locate the center of the hole and cylinder. Frame both the hole and the cylinder. Draw the circles that define the hole and the cylinder on the front face. Frame the cylinder on the back surface and draw the circle (lightly) to define its depth. Connect the front surface cylinder with the back surface cylinder.

Step 3: Frame the rectangular prism and show the circular features that intersect the cylinder. Frame the hole that goes through the prism and show the back edge of the hole as it passes through the far side of the prism. This is done by offsetting the center of the hole by the depth of the prism.

Step 4: Darken all visible lines to complete the drawing.

When a circular feature such as a hole or cylinder appears in a view that is not in the plane of the paper, an ellipse must be drawn using the four-center method discussed in the section describing isometric drawings.

12.04 Perspective Drawings

Perspective drawings and sketches are some of the most lifelike pictorials created. Someone with a great deal of skill can create a perspective drawing that looks as detailed as a photograph. Perspectives incorporate the concept of vanishing points to produce the 3-D shape of an object on the plane of the paper or the computer screen. The concept of a vanishing point is very simple. Suppose you are standing in the middle of a railroad track in flat terrain so you can see where the sky intersects the terrain. The line where the sky intersects the terrain is called the horizon. As you look down the railroad toward the horizon, the outside rails seem to converge to a single

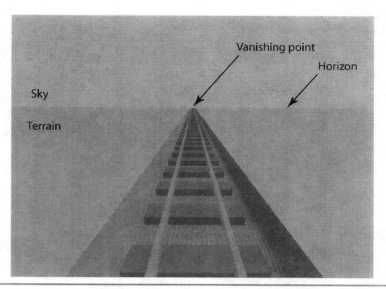

FIGURE 12.33. An illustration showing railroad tracks converging to a vanishing point on the horizon.

point as the railroad intersects the horizon. This point is called the **vanishing point (VP)**, as shown in Figure 12.33. Perspective pictorials employ the use of vanishing points to create a 3-D effect.

12.04.01 Types of Perspective Drawings

There are three types of perspective drawings: one-point perspectives, two-point perspectives, and three-point perspectives. A one-point perspective is illustrated in Figure 12.33. There is one vanishing point at the horizon, and all of the lines converge to this vanishing point. Figure 12.34 shows a two-point perspective. In this type of perspective, there are two vanishing points—one on the right and one on the left. Lines that define the 3-D object converge at the vanishing points. A three-point perspective is shown in Figure 12.35. In this type of perspective, there is a right and left vanishing point and there is a central vanishing point.

Of the three types of perspectives that can be drawn, the two-point perspective is the one most often used to show an object as a pictorial. The one-point and three-point perspectives are limited in their use and do not convey an image that the eye would be likely to perceive. Therefore, the two-point perspective will be the only type discussed in detail.

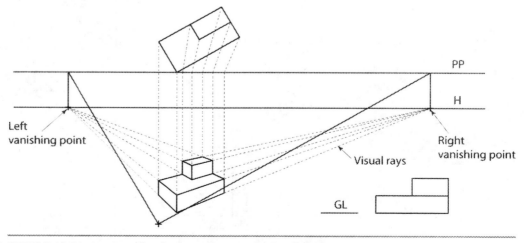

FIGURE 12.34. An example of a two-point perspective drawing.

FIGURE 12.35. An example of a three-point perspective drawing.

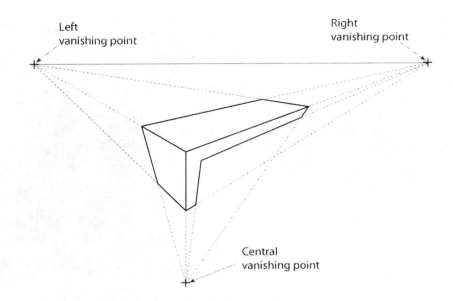

12.04.02 Two-Point Perspective Drawings

Generally, a two-point perspective is generated using the top (plan) orthographic view of the object and an elevation view. The **plan view** is rotated at an appropriate angle to enhance the 3-D aspects of the perspective. The **elevation view** is shown as it normally would be shown in its orthographic position.

An important feature in developing the two-point perspective drawing is the **picture plane (PP)**. The location of this vertical plane (shown as an edge) defines the size and position of the perspective when viewed from the **station point (SP)**. The PP can be located anywhere relative to the object. The simplest position is shown in Figure 12.36, where the PP goes through the corner of the object. When the PP is located in front of the object, the perspective appears farther away from the observer. When the PP is located behind the object, the perspective appears closer to the observer. Selection of the position of the PP controls the size of the perspective. At times, illustrators may choose to place the PP through the middle of the object, giving the appearance that one portion of the object is closer to the observer and one portion is farther away from the observer.

The **horizon line (HL)** is the line that defines where the ground meets the sky. It can be placed anywhere between the PP and the SP. The HL is important because it establishes the position of the left and right vanishing points that locate the position of the perspective drawing.

FIGURE 12.36. The relationship between the PP and the object.

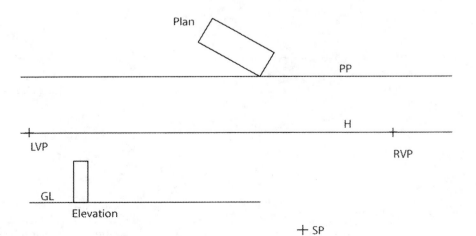

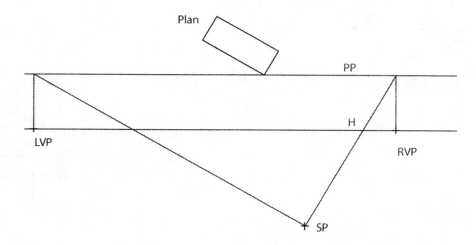

The **ground line (GL)** defines the position of the elevation view of the object. The GL is important because it determines the vertical location of the perspective drawing and serves as a starting point for the drawing, as shown in Figure 12.36.

12.04.03 Construction of a Two-Point Perspective Drawing

The two-point perspective drawing is constructed using steps similar to those for constructing the isometric pictorial and the oblique pictorial. You will progress through the steps to create a two-point perspective.

Step 1: Establish the vanishing points. Draw lines from the SP to the PP at angles parallel to the left and right visible planes in the plan view. Draw lines from these intersections with the PP vertically downward to the horizon. These intersections become the left vanishing point (LVP) and the right vanishing point (RVP), as shown in Figure 12.37.

Step 2: Establish the **measuring line (ML)**. When the corner of the plan view intersects the picture plane, draw the measuring line downward vertically from the intersection, as shown in Figure 12.38.

When the plan view is behind the picture plane, extend the corner of the plan view to the picture plane by drawing parallel to the line used when establishing the vanishing points (SP to PP). Then draw the measuring line downward vertically from the intersection with the picture plane, as shown in Figure 12.39.

FIGURE 12.38. Establishing the ML.

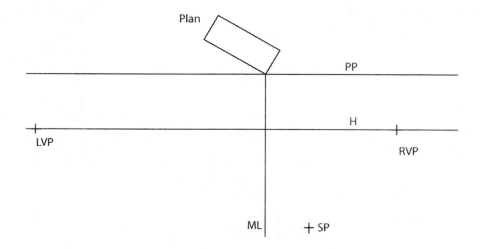

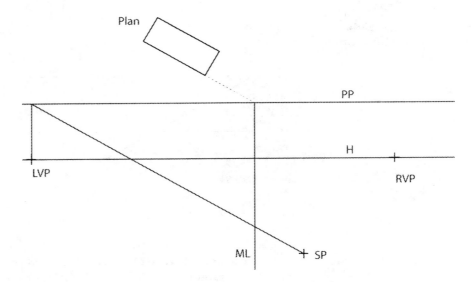

FIGURE 12.39. Establishing the ML when the object is behind the PP.

When the plan view is in front of the picture plane, extend the corner of the plan view to the picture plane by drawing parallel to the line used when establishing the vanishing point (SP to PP). Then draw the measuring line down vertically from this intersection with the PP, as shown in Figure 12.40.

Step 3: Project the height measurements to the ML from the elevation view. Project horizontally from the elevation view. Note the position of the GL to the elevation view, as shown in Figure 12.41.

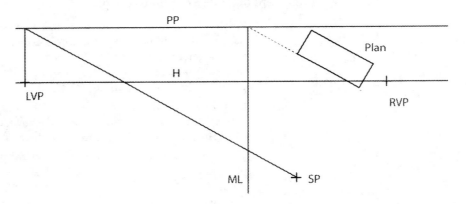

FIGURE 12.40. Establishing the ML when the object is in front of the PP.

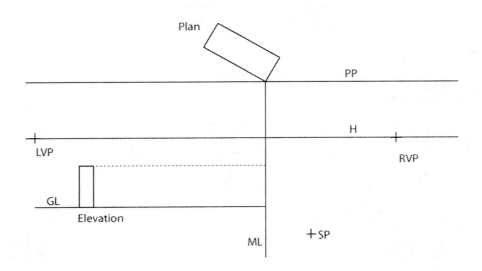

FIGURE 12.41. Establishing the height of the object on the ML.

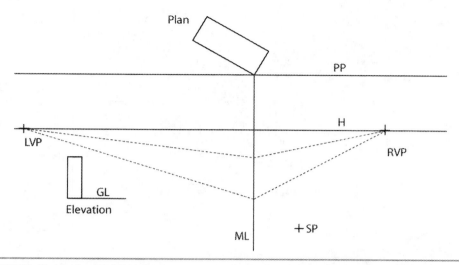

FIGURE 12.42. Establishing the measuring walls when the PP intersects the corner of the object.

Step 4: Establish the **measuring walls**. When the visible corner between the left and right visible planes touches the PP, the measuring walls originate at the ML. The lines may be drawn from the top and bottom of the ML to the left and right vanishing points to establish the left and right measuring walls, as shown in Figure 12.42.

When the corner that will be represented by the measuring line falls behind or in front of the PP, the measuring wall representing the extended visible plane in the plan view must be drawn first, as shown in Figure 12.43.

Special Note: The front-near corner must be projected (steps 5 and 6) before the measuring wall that represents the other visible plane can be drawn, as shown in Figure 12.44.

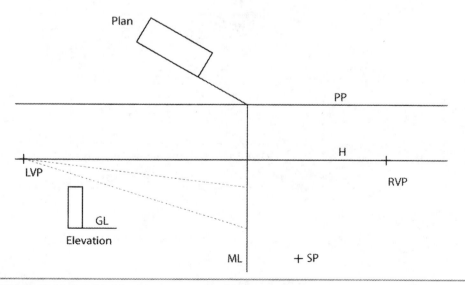

FIGURE 12.43. Establishing the measuring walls when the object is behind or in front of the PP.

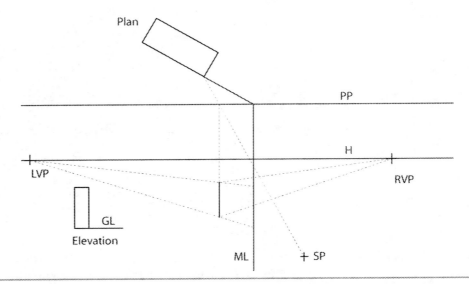

FIGURE 12.44. Projecting the front corner before the measuring wall can be drawn.

Step 5: Draw the visual rays. Align the straight edge from each object intersection in the plan view with the SP, but draw only the plan view intersections to the PP, as shown in Figure 12.45.

Step 6: Project the visual rays. Draw the PP intersections downward perpendicular from the PP to the measuring walls to establish the side details of the object, as shown in Figure 12.46.

Step 7: Lay out details. Repeat steps 3 through 6 to show details. Appropriate points will need to be projected to the vanishing points, as shown in Figure 12.47.

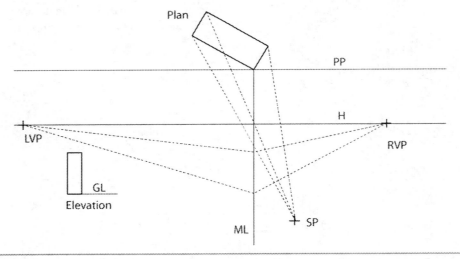

FIGURE 12.45. Drawing the visual rays of the object to the PP through the SP.

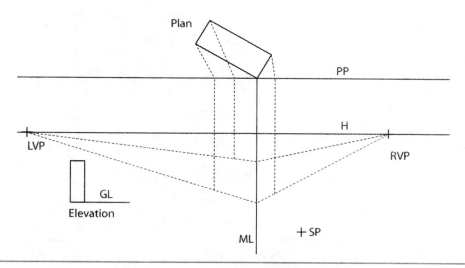

FIGURE 12.46. Projecting the intersection of the visual rays with the PP to the measuring walls.

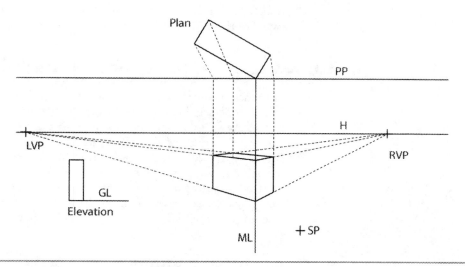

FIGURE 12.47. Completion of the perspective.

12.04.04 Complex Object in Two-Point Perspective

When a complex object is composed of more than one prism, the two-point perspective may require more than one measuring line. Figure 12.48 shows an object composed of two prisms, with one of the prisms behind the PP. When this happens, a second measuring line is required to establish the proper height of the prism located behind the PP. Note in Figure 12.48 that ML-1 establishes the height of the rectangular prism forming the base and ML-2 establishes the height of the prism containing the inclined surface

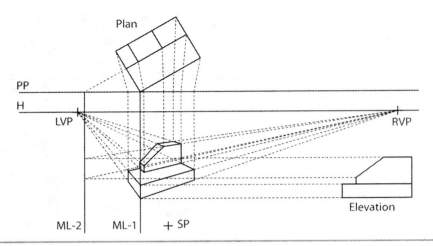

FIGURE 12.48. A two-point perspective drawing of a complex object.

that is behind the PP. The heights projected from the elevation view to ML-2 are transferred along a line from ML-2 to the right vanishing point. The projectors of the prism located behind the PP from the plan view are then drawn to the PP and projected downward to these lines to establish the position of the prism that is behind the PP.

12.05 Considerations for 3-D Modeling

The easiest way to create pictorial drawings is to extract them from solid models. Most solid modeling software has the capability to create engineering drawings from models. These drawings usually include not only traditional orthographic views but also pictorial views to increase the speed with which the parts and assemblies can be visualized. Creating a pictorial from a solid model usually is a matter of specifying the viewing orientation (many times predetermined to give a choice of an isometric or trimetric view) and the amount of perspective when a perspective view is desired. In fact, pictorial drawings are so easily extracted from solid models that it might be foolish not to include them with the orthographic views on working engineering drawings.

12.06 Chapter Summary

Pictorial drawings are designed to enhance your graphic communication skills. Since pictorial drawings describe all three dimensions on the plane of the paper, they are less likely to show the detail that would be expected in the orthographic drawings used in working drawings. Visualization and an understanding of the 3-D relationships of objects are greatly enhanced through the use of pictorial drawings. Different levels of complexity are involved in creating different types of pictorial drawings. For simple communication, isometric drawings usually can be created easily for most objects. Oblique drawings, albeit less realistic in their appearance, are even quicker and simpler to create. For applications that demand the most realistic appearance, especially for large objects such as buildings, perspective drawings can be used. With a solid modeler, pictorial drawings of any type can be created quickly (after the solid model is created) with a few commands. When 2-D CAD or manual drafting instruments are the only tools available, the traditional techniques presented in this chapter may need to be used. Regardless of the graphics tools available, pictorial drawings are now commonly included in formal engineering drawing to add clarity to the traditional orthographic multiview presentation.

12.07 glossary of key terms

axonometric drawing: A drawing in which all three dimensional axes on an object can be seen, with the scaling factor constant in each direction. Usually, one axis is shown as being vertical.

cabinet oblique drawing: An oblique drawing where one half the true length of the depth dimension is measured along the receding axes.

cavalier oblique drawing: An oblique drawing where the true length of the depth dimension is measured along the receding axes.

diametric drawing: An axonometric drawing in which the scaling factor is the same for two of the axes.

elevation view: In the construction of a perspective view, the object as viewed from the front, as if created by orthogonal projection.

ground line (GL): In the construction of a perspective view, a line on the elevation view that represents the height of the ground.

horizon line (HL): In the construction of a perspective view, the line that represent the horizon, which is the separation between the earth and the sky at a long distance. The left and right vanishing points are located on the HL. The PP and the HL are usually parallel to each other.

isometric drawing: An axonometric drawing in which the scaling factor is the same for all three axes.

isometric lines: Lines on an isometric drawing that are parallel or perpendicular to the front, top, or profile viewing planes.

measuring line (ML): In the construction of a perspective view, a vertical line used in conjunction with the elevation view to locate vertical points on the perspective drawing.

measuring wall: In the construction of a perspective view, a line that extends from the object to the vanishing point to help establish the location of horizontal points on the drawing.

oblique pictorial: A sketch of an object that shows one face in the plane of the paper and the third dimension receding off at an angle relative to the face.

perspective drawing: A drawing in which all three-dimensional axes on an object can be seen, with the scaling factor linearly increasing or decreasing in each direction. Usually one axis is shown as being vertical. This type of drawing generally offers the most realistic presentation of an object.

pictorial: A drawing that shows the 3-D aspects and features of an object.

picture plane (PP): In the construction of a perspective view, the viewing plane through which the object is seen. The PP appears as a line (edge view of the viewing plane) in the plan view.

plan view: In the construction of a perspective view, the object as viewed from the top, as if created by orthogonal projection.

station point (SP): In the construction of a perspective view, the theoretical location of the observer who looks at the object through the picture plane.

trimetric drawing: An axonometric drawing in which the scaling factor is different for all three axes.

vanishing point (VP): In the construction of a perspective view, the point on the horizon where all parallel lines in a single direction converge.

12.08 questions for review

1. Why are pictorial drawings useful?
2. When should pictorial drawing be used instead of pictorial sketches?
3. Why should pictorial drawings *not* be used as working drawings to produce parts?
4. What is an axonometric drawing?
5. How do isometric, diametric, and trimetic drawings differ?
6. How do isometric and oblique drawings differ?
7. In what way is an oblique drawing nonrealistic?
8. How do cabinet and cavalier oblique drawings differ?
9. How do isometric and perspective drawings differ?
10. In what way are perspective drawings more realistic than isometric drawings?
11. When should perspective drawings be used in favor of axonometric drawings?
12. Why are two-point perspective drawings more common than one-point or three-point perspective drawings?

12.09 problems

Measure the features shown in the front-, top-, and right- side views of the objects shown in Figure P12.1. Using drafting instruments or CAD, create the following scaled pictorials of each object that is represented.

1. An isometric drawing
2. A cabinet oblique drawing
3. A cavalier oblique drawing
4. A trimetric drawing using your choice of axes angles (one axis must be vertical).
5. A two-point perspective drawing using your choice of plan location and orientation, station point, and vanishing points. The height axis must be vertical, and the two vanishing points must be on the same HL.

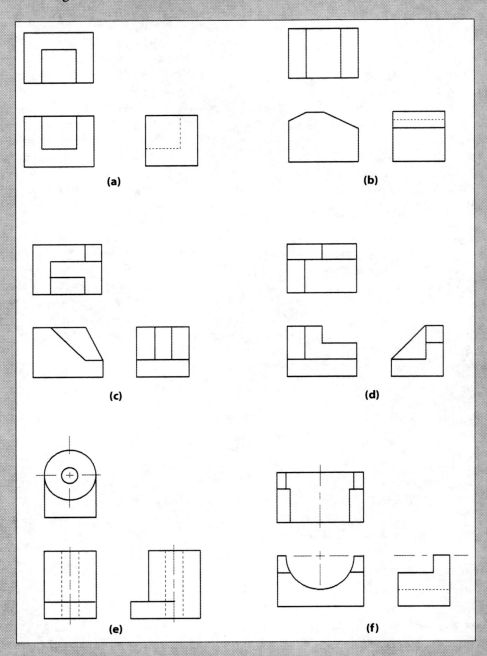

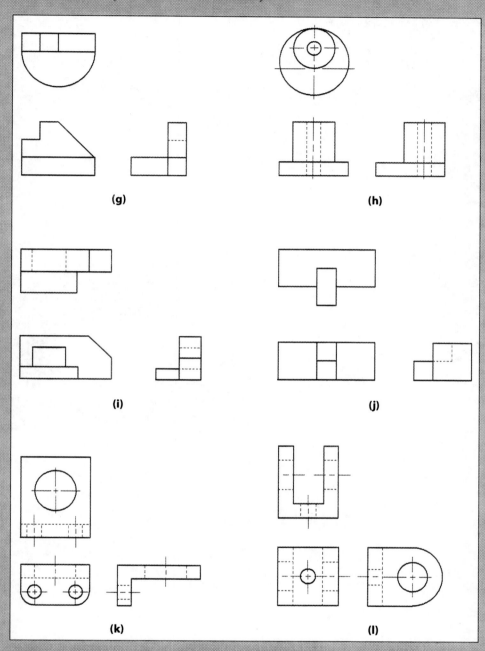

FIGURE P12.1.

Orthogonal Projection and Multiview Representation

objectives

After completing this chapter, you should be able to

- Discuss the principles of orthogonal projection
- Show how orthogonal projection is used to create multiple views of an object for formal engineering drawing
- Explain why orthogonal projection is necessary to represent objects in formal engineering drawing
- Create a multiview drawing from a 3-D object

10.01
introduction

The best way to communicate the appearance of an object (short of showing the object itself) is to show its image. For the purposes of the object's fabrication, analysis, or record keeping, this image must be precise. A precise description of an object begins with an accurate graphical representation of that object, which is what a formal engineering drawing is all about. It is a series of images that show the object viewed from different angles, every view accurately depicting what that object would look like from each view.

Whether you originated a drawing or you received one from the originator, the images represented in any engineering drawing must be interpreted the same way. Consistency is achieved by adhering to nationally and internationally accepted methods for creating and interpreting the images. Pictorial images, such as the isometric drawings first presented in Chapter 2 (and detailed in Chapter 12), quickly convey large amounts of qualitative information. However, pictorial images have the disadvantage of distorting the true size, configuration, and geometry of their features.

For an object to be represented without distortion or ambiguity, enough views must be provided such that all of the object's features can be clearly seen and accurately measured. In an engineering drawing, the choice of views is not arbitrary. Also, the views are carefully chosen such that the features on the object are aligned between the views and the geometries of the features are shown without distortion. With these views, size specifications can be added later to complete the description of the object.

10.02 A More Precise Way to Communicate Your Ideas

You have a wonderful idea for a new device. You believe in your idea. You want to have it fabricated. However, you must communicate to another party your thoughts about what the parts in the device will look like when they are fabricated. The other party may be another engineer who subjects your device to a more detailed analysis of what it should look like. The other party may be a fabricator who makes the device to your exact specifications. The other parties may be located in another area of the country or in another country. With the international scope of business today, design, analyses, and fabrication are commonly done in different locations around the world.

If questions arise concerning your idea, you may not be around to answer them. That is why all other parties involved in fabricating the object must envision it exactly as you do. One of your goals as the engineer or designer of a product, device, or structure is to represent it graphically in such a way (i.e., accurately) that it can be fabricated without any party misinterpreting how you want it to appear.

During the development of the Aerotec riser, the engineers at Hoyt USA faced the possibility that the product's geometry would be misinterpreted due to insufficient representation of what it would look like after fabrication. Creating a graphical image of the object in the form of a sketch or drawing as seen from only a single direction was not a good idea. The riser, which is shown in Figure 10.01, contains many features, such as cutouts and protrusions that could remain hidden when viewed from only one direction. The object had to be viewed from multiple directions to ensure that all of its features were revealed. If you were the engineer responsible for the design and manufacturing of a similar product, what would you do? How would you communicate what you want built to those who build it? How would you ensure that different people interpret and build the product the same way every time?

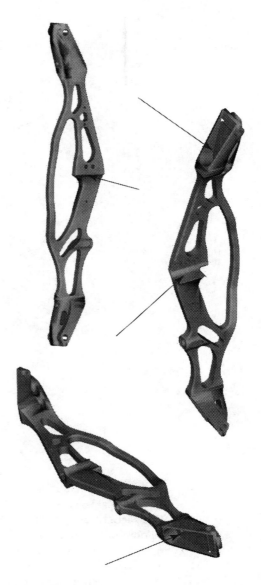

FIGURE 10.01. Viewing the Aerotec riser from different directions reveals previously hidden features. The arrows indicate details in each view that cannot be fully seen and described in the other views. (Model courtesy of Hoyt USA Archery Products).

10.02.01 Problems with Pictorials

One solution would be to use pictorials such as isometric or perspective view. These types of representations of an object offer the advantage of quickly conveying the object's 3-D aspects from one view. Even people who do not have a technical background can easily and quickly understand pictorials.

However, pictorial representations present problems that are inherent in the use of one view of an object's three dimensions. One problem is the distortion of angles, as shown in Figure 10.02. The use of right angles and perpendicularity between surfaces is common on many fabricated objects because surfaces having those relationships are easy to construct with machine tools. However, on pictorials, 90° angles do not appear as 90° angles. In fact, depending on the angle of viewing, a 90° angle can appear as more or less than 90°. On a pictorial, it is difficult to depict an object's angles correctly when angles are not 90°.

Another problem with pictorials is the distortion of true lengths. In any pictorial, a length of 1 m on an object, for example, is neither depicted nor clearly perceived as a 1 m length.

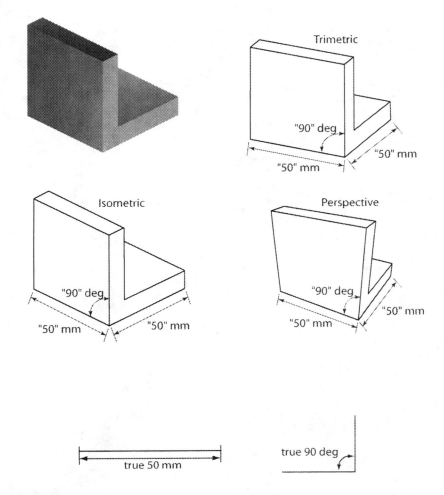

In some cases, such as an object with only rectilinear edges seen in the isometric view, this length distortion is the same in every direction. In this case, the real length can be obtained by multiplying the distorted edge length by a single correction factor. In Figure 10.02, for example, the length of each edge of the object shown in the isometric would need to be the actual edge length multiplied by a scaling factor of 0.612 if the object were drawn its full size. The formulas for getting this particular scaling factor is complicated, so do not worry about it for now. In general, however, the correction is not just a simple scaling factor. In a dimetric view, the correction factor for an edge of the object is dependent upon direction. The correction factor is more complicated for a trimetric representation, and the correction factor is even more complicated for a perspective representation.

Internal measurements also are distorted in pictorials. This distortion is dependent upon the direction of measurement, as shown in Figure 10.03. The location of the center of a hole placed at the center of a square face is, in reality, equidistant from each vertex of the square. However, in an isometric pictorial, the center of the hole must be drawn such that it is located a different distance from one vertex than from its adjacent vertices.

Figure 10.03 also shows the problem of curve distortion. The simplest curve—a circle or an arc of a circle—appears elliptical on a pictorial. On an isometric pictorial, the conversion from a circle to its representation as an ellipse is a matter of figuring out the scaling factors to calculate the major and minor axes and the orientation of the ellipse, both of which are dependent upon the circle's orientation in space. The calculation or construction is more complicated on a trimetric view because the scaling and orientation factors are different for different plane orientations on the object. On a perspective representation, the construction is more complicated

FIGURE 10.03. Distortion of internal lengths in pictorials. These different lengths on the same object represent the same length, which is the diameter of the holes in the cube.

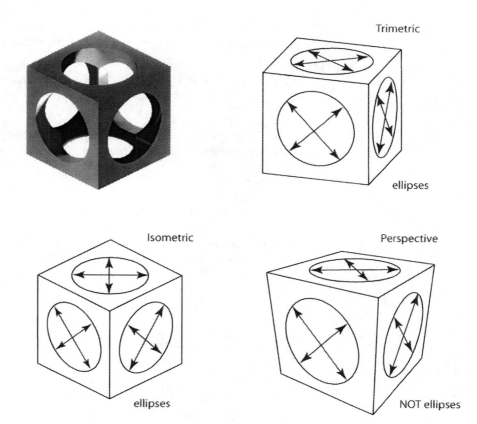

because the circle does not appear as an ellipse, but rather as an oval, or egg shape. (Remember, an egg shape is not an ellipse.)

The sum of the previous discussion is that although pictorials have the advantage of looking realistic, it is difficult or impractical to create an object with precision from them. Pictorials are subject to misinterpretation and errors in analysis and fabrication because the angles and distances are distorted. The most universally accepted solution to these problems is to use multiview representations, which are explained next.

10.02.02 Viewing Planes

A **multiview** representation depicts in one plane, such as a sheet of paper, many images of the same object, each viewed from a different direction. Pictorials can be used to enhance the clarity of the 3-D perception of an object; but the sizes of the object and its details are shown in a series of views, each view showing the sizes in their true length or shape. Any fabrication or analysis of the object's measurements can then be based on what is shown in the multiview projections, not on what is shown in the pictorial.

When you visualize an object in space, its appearance changes depending on the direction from which you view it. The lines and curves that form the graphical presentation of the object, such as the lines and curves shown in Figure 10.03, represent edges that are the intersections of surfaces. Now visualize a transparent plane, perhaps a sheet of glass, fixed in space between you and the object. This plane is called a **viewing plane**. Imagine the image of the object as seen through the plane is somehow painted onto the plane. Continuing to imagine, remove the object and look at the image painted on the viewing plane. What you see on that plane is a 2-D image of a 3-D object. The appearance of the image, however, would depend on the viewing angle of your head in front of that plane when you created the image. The simplest and most accurate view is from your head looking directly forward at the object. In general, to be accurate about the appearance of the object as seen through the plane, you would need to define the locations and orientations of the object, the viewing plane, and the viewer.

This is a great deal of information. But you would not need all of that information if you defined the image as one created by orthogonal projection, which is explained next.

10.02.03 Orthogonal Projection

In orthogonal projection, the image of an object is composed of points projected from individual points on the object onto the viewing plane such that the projection of each point is perpendicular to the viewing plane. Orthogonal projection of an object onto a transparent viewing plane is shown in Figure 10.04, where you can see the perpendicular relationship between the projection lines and the viewing plane when the plane is turned on edge.

An image created in this manner has two advantages. One advantage is that such an image is easy to create because you do not have to worry about defining the location or orientation of the viewing plane relative to the line-of-sight. The line-of-sight from a point on the object to the viewing plane is like the projection path; that is, it is always perpendicular to the viewing plane. The other advantage is that by turning the object such that an edge of the object is parallel to the viewing plane, the image of that edge shows its true length. Furthermore, the length of a projected edge is independent of its distance from the viewing plane. Both of these properties are shown in Figure 10.05.

10.02.04 A Distorted Reality

An image created by orthogonal projection is merely a convenience that allows you to analyze the image more easily when you are ready to make the object depicted. In the strictest sense, orthogonal projection does not accurately represent an image of the way a real object looks. In reality, parts of an object that are farther away appear smaller than the same-sized parts of an object that are closer. With orthogonal projection, all parts of the object appear in the same scale no matter how far the object is placed from

FIGURE 10.04. Using orthogonal projection to create an image of an object on a viewing plane. The object in (a) is in front of the viewing plane. The object in (b) is behind the viewing plane. In either case, the projection lines are perpendicular to the viewing plane, as shown in (c).

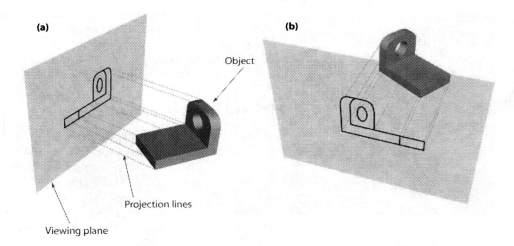

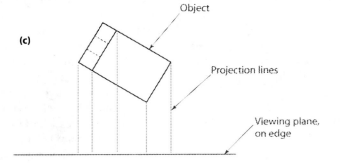

the viewing plane. But as in the case that follows and in most cases, the approximation is close and the convenience and ease of image creation and analysis far outweigh the need to see the image as it really appears.

The effect of an image created by orthogonal projection is similar to a photograph of an object taken at a long distance using a powerful telephoto lens. That type of picture lacks depth; that is, the object appears flat. This lack of depth is attributable to the fact that although the light rays actually extend radially from the surface of an object, the reflected light rays appear less like radial rays and more like parallel rays viewed at a great distances from the object. The greater the distance, the more parallel the light rays. At a long distance, where the light rays compose the image of the object, such as at a camera lens, the light rays are very nearly parallel to each other and very nearly perpendicular to the plane of the lens. This effect is shown in the bottom photograph in Figure 10.06; both photographs are the same object, each taken from a different camera distance. Even though the overall image size of the object is about the same, in the close-up photo, you should be able to see that the parts (for example, the wheels) of the object that are closer appear magnified when compared to the parts that are farther away.

10.02.05 Choice of Viewing Planes

From what was just explained, you should understand that an orthogonal projection of an object is a 2-D drawing of that object as it would appear on a viewing plane. To get a different view of the object, you need to move the object and/or the viewing plane to a different location.

Consider the case of keeping the viewing plane in the same place and rotating the object. One advantage of orthogonal projection is that an object's lines and curves can be seen in their true shape. For example, when the viewing plane is parallel to a circle, the circle actually appears as a circle rather than an ellipse. This may be important, for example, when you want to see how close the edge of a hole in an object actually comes to the edge of the object. It makes sense, therefore, to rotate the object into an orientation where the measurements, such as the diameter of the hole or its distance to the edge, can be seen to represent the true shape, distance, and size. Figure 10.07 shows an object rotated into the best position for this specific analysis versus the same object in

FIGURE 10.06. The top photograph was taken from up close. The bottom photo was taken from a long distance and enlarged so feature sizes could be compared. Can you see the lack of perspective in the long-distance photo?

a poor orientation. In general, in the creation of the first view of an object, it has become common practice to orient the object in a position that shows as many as possible of its lines and curves in their true shape.

However, a single view of an object is usually insufficient to specify all of its features and measurements fully. Figure 10.08 shows how different objects can appear the same using a single view only.

FIGURE 10.07. Good part placement shows most of the part edges in their true length.

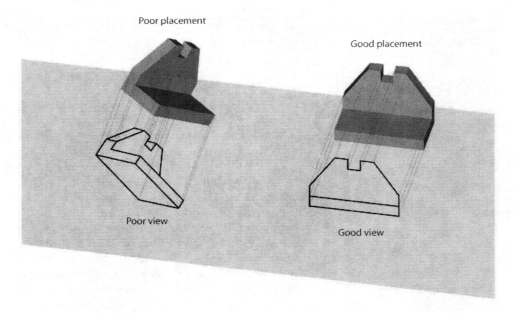

Poor placement

Good placement

Poor view

Good view

This single view...

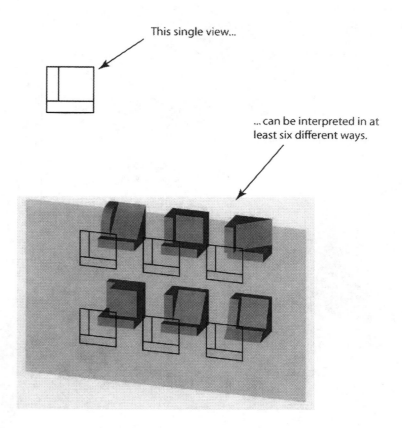

... can be interpreted in at
least six different ways.

To fully define the 3-D geometry of an object, it is necessary to depict the object in **multiple views**. This means there must be a viewing plane for each of the views. Specifying the location and orientation of each of the additional viewing planes must be done in a standardized way so that 2-D images can be extracted from the object easily. Also, the multiple 2-D images must contain enough information so that the original 3-D image can be re-created from them. One way to do this is to locate and orient the additional viewing planes so that each is orthogonal to the first viewing plane, as shown with a second and third viewing plane in Figure 10.09(a). The images on all of these viewing planes are created using orthogonal projection.

When the location and orientation of the intersection line between the first viewing plane and any one of the additional viewing planes are known, the location and orientation of each of the other additional images can be specified. The intersection line between the first viewing plane and any of the additional viewing planes can be imagined as a hinge between the two planes. By "unfolding" the additional planes at their imaginary hinges, as shown in Figure 10.09(b), the images on all of the viewing planes can be shown on a single plane, or in other words, a 2-D drawing.

Used this way, orthogonal projection and viewing planes offer you the advantage of seeing multiple views of the same object at the same time on a single sheet of paper. Orthogonal projection also can precisely identify the position and orientation of the viewing planes used to create those views by specifying on the single sheet the location of the intersection lines between the viewing planes.

10.02.06 Size and Alignment

When the second and third planes are completely unfolded and are coplanar with the first viewing plane, as shown in Figure 10.09(c), three images can be seen on a single plane. The images from the second and third planes are considered adjacent to (i.e., created immediately next to) the image from the first plane. Note that the size and orientation of the images are not arbitrary. Each image has the same scale (or magnification);

FIGURE 10.09. Two viewing planes that are orthogonal to the first (front) viewing plane (a) can be unfolded (b) to present the images on a single plane (c). The imaginary hinges for the two viewing planes are at the intersections of these planes with the front viewing plane.

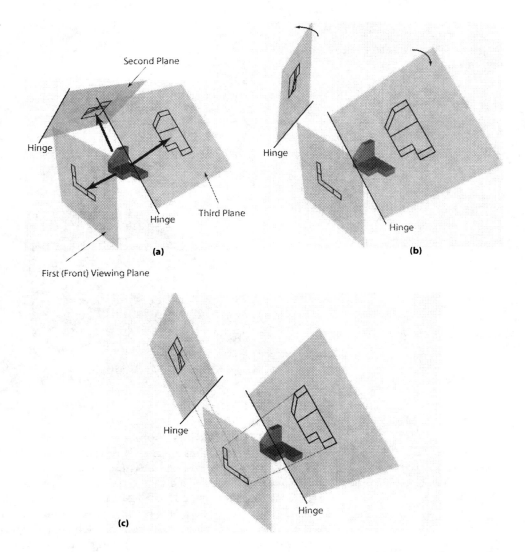

Second Plane

Hinge

Hinge

Third Plane

Hinge

(a)

First (Front) Viewing Plane

Hinge

Hinge

(b)

Hinge

Hinge

(c)

and the orientation of the image is dependent upon the original location of its viewing plane as defined by the location of the intersection line between the viewing planes, or their hinge. This alignment of the vertices of the object images in **adjacent views** is shown in Figure 10.10, where the three views are presented on a single sheet.

FIGURE 10.10. Viewing planes completely unfolded showing proper size, location, and orientation of the images on a single plane.

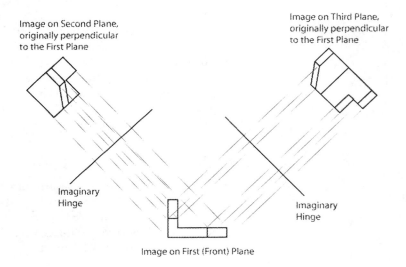

Image on Second Plane, originally perpendicular to the First Plane

Image on Third Plane, originally perpendicular to the First Plane

Imaginary Hinge

Imaginary Hinge

Image on First (Front) Plane

10.03 The Glass Box

Only three or four views are required to fully define most objects. Simple objects may require only one view; complicated objects may require six or more views. Objects such as engineered parts can usually be fully defined when they are viewed through a set of six viewing planes that together form a **glass box**, as shown Figure 10.11(a). The glass box has the unique property that for any viewing plane, all of its adjacent planes are perpendicular to each other and opposite viewing planes are parallel to each other.

When you open (or unfold) the panels of the box, as shown in Figure 10.11(b), you can view all six sides of the object simultaneously on a single plane, as shown in Figure 10.11(c). There is more than one way to unfold the box. Unfolding in the manner shown in Figure 10.11 is the standard way to do it according to accepted drawing practices. The top and bottom and right- and left-side views open about the front view; and the rear view is attached to the left-side view.

Make sure you see and understand that when the viewing planes are completely unfolded, the size and orientation of each image is not arbitrary. The scale in each view is the same. In the case of the complete glass box, each viewing plane is orthogonal to its adjacent viewing planes. When the box is unfolded and presented on a single sheet,

FIGURE 10.11. Viewing an engineered part through a glass box (a) that opens (b) to present the images on a single plane (c).

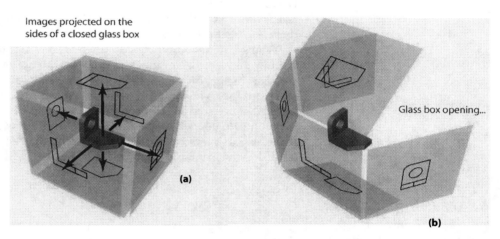

Images projected on the sides of a closed glass box

(a)

Glass box opening...

(b)

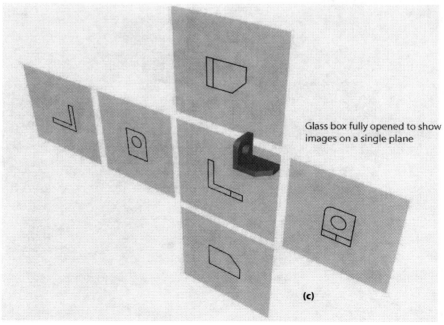

Glass box fully opened to show images on a single plane

(c)

as in Figure 10.12, adjacent images are aligned horizontally for horizontally adjacent views or vertically for vertically adjacent views. These alignment properties are very important when the object is analyzed. If you select any point on the object (assume point A on Figure 10.12), the images of that point will be horizontally aligned with each other on horizontally adjacent views and those images will be vertically aligned with each other on vertically adjacent views.

In general, the same point in space seen in adjacent views is aligned along a path that is perpendicular to the intersection line of the viewing planes, as shown in Figure 10.10. What this means for engineering drawing is that features on an object, such as edges or holes, shown in one view can be easily located on the adjacent view because the features are aligned between adjacent views. For complex objects with many features, the ability to identify the same feature on adjacent views is of tremendous utility.

10.03.01 Standard Views

The glass box yields six different views of an object. For a large percentage of engineered parts, six views are more than sufficient. Engineers typically like to design things that are easy and therefore inexpensive to make. Three-axis milling machines and single-axis lathes are common machines in any fabrication shop. These machines easily create surfaces on the workpiece that are parallel, perpendicular, or concentric to each other and that easily cut holes, slots, or other features that are perpendicular to the working surface.

The six views represented by the glass box are the front, top, left side, right side, bottom, and rear views. These views are known as the six standard orthogonal views or the six principal orthogonal views or more simply as the **six standard views** or the **six principal views**, respectively. When a formal drawing is created showing these views, the intersection lines and projection lines between views are not shown because these lines do not add much information to the drawing when it is already understood that adjacent views are orthogonal to each other. Also, each view does not need to be labeled as the front, top, right side, etc., views.

FIGURE 10.12. Alignment of points on adjacent views for all six standard views.

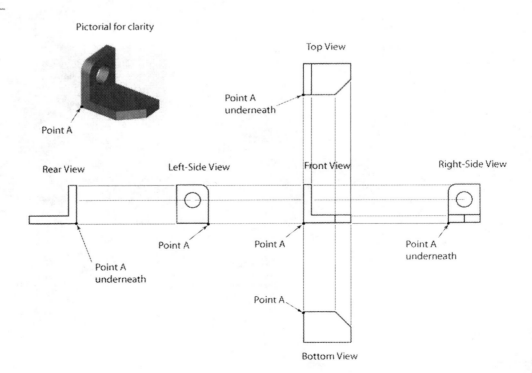

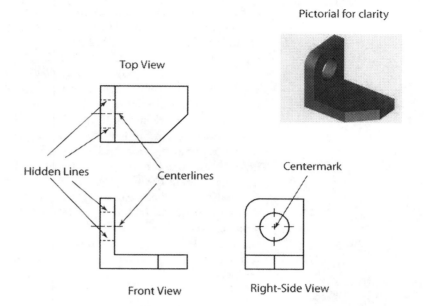

10.03.02 The Preferred Configuration

Are all six views necessary? Usually not. The great percentage of engineered parts can be fully defined geometrically with fewer than all six of the standard views. In fact, most engineered parts can be completely defined for fabrication using only three views.

Although there are no defined rules as to which views must be included or excluded in a formal engineering drawing, there is a **preferred configuration**—the front, top, and right-side views. Additional views are presented only when necessary to reveal and define features that cannot be shown in the preferred views. The preferred configuration for the object in Figure 10.12 is shown in Figure 10.13. Only the front, top, and side views are shown. Make sure every edge of the object can be seen in its true length in at least one view.

It is becoming increasingly popular to include an isometric or trimetric pictorial of the object somewhere on the drawing. When a pictorial is included, it serves only to aid in clarity; it does not need to be properly aligned or scaled with the standard views.

10.04 The Necessary Details

Only the minimum number of views needed to quickly and accurately communicate the geometry of an object should be created. Whenever possible, the preferred configuration of a front, top, and side view should be used unless fewer than three views are needed to see and define all of the features of the object. To minimize the number of required views on complicated objects and to reduce any possible ambiguity, some shorthand notation that describes common geometries such as certain types of holes and screw threads is used in drawing practice. Such notation is detailed in later chapters in this book. There will, however, be cases where additional views become necessary or when the preferred configuration may not be the best.

10.04.01 Hidden Lines and Centerlines

The dashed lines you see on the views shown in Figure 10.13 represent internal features or edges that are obscured by the object. These obscured features or edges are called **hidden lines** in these views. Hidden lines, which are denoted as equally spaced dashed lines on a drawing, represent the edges of an object or its features that cannot be seen on the real object but would be visible if the object were partially transparent. Hidden lines are used to emphasize an object's unseen geometry and thus speed the interpretation of its presentation. Hidden lines also are used to reduce the need for creating additional views. Although hidden edges cannot be seen on an opaque object, they are represented graphically the same way hidden lines are included in a view to emphasize that a feature cannot be seen in that view or to show that a feature cannot be seen from any of the other views. Later in this chapter, hidden lines will be discussed further as you encounter examples of the advantages and problems associated with them.

Looking closely at Figure 10.13, you will see lines located at the center axis of the hole. These are not hidden lines. They are **centerlines**, which are represented graphically by alternating short and long dashes along the length of the center of the circular hole. Centerlines cannot be seen on the real object, but they must be included on the drawing to identify where the center of the circular hole is located on the object. More generally, centerlines are used where there is a cylindrical surface such as a hole or a tube.

The reason for including centerlines is to make it easier for the reader to distinguish between edges, visible or hidden, that are part of a cylindrical surface and edges that result from the intersections of planes. Using centerlines also makes it easier to locate features such as holes, which are commonly defined by their diameters and center locations.

A **centermark**, the end view of a centerline, is identified by a right-angle cross such as that shown in the center of the circular hole in the right-side view of the object in Figure 10.13. Typically, centerlines and centermarks are used where the arc of a cylindrical surface is 180° or greater, although they can be used for lesser arcs as required for clarity in a drawing.

10.04.02 The Necessary Views

How many views should be created to fully define a object? In engineering practice, it is considered poor practice to create more views than are needed. Creating unneeded views means more work for which there is no payoff. However, having too few views can create problems when the fabricator tries to make the part. In the worst-case scenario, the fabricator will try to guess what you want, get it wrong, and deliver a potentially expensive part that cannot be used. In that case, the creator of the drawing would be at fault, not the fabricator. The party responsible for creating the drawing also may be legally responsible for paying for the services of the fabricator.

So how many views are needed to fully define an object? The number depends on how complicated the object is to depict in three dimensions. Start by creating the front, top, and right-side views. Remember, they represent the preferred configuration, which all engineering personnel like to see. Try to orient the object in such a way that these three views reveal as much of the object's features as possible. If you are lucky, these three views will fully define the object; but that is not always the case.

You should ask yourself the following two questions when you finish creating the drawing views:

1. Can the true size of all of the measurements needed to define all of the features of this object be seen in at least one of the views just created?

2. Is it impossible for the geometry of any feature to be misinterpreted as another type of geometry?

Yes to both questions means you have enough views. No to either question means you have more work to do.

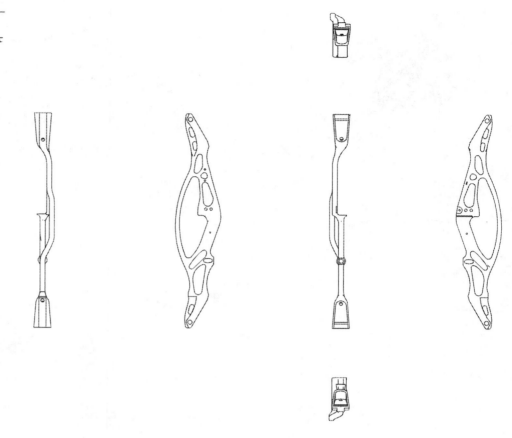

The multiview production drawing for the Hoyt Aerotec riser is shown in Figure 10.14. The complexity of this object requires that all six standard views be used because it has features that can be seen only from each of the six viewing directions.

Objects that are flat can be defined with a single view along with some sort of note specifying the thickness of the object. Flat sheet metal objects and objects that can be cut from a plate of uniform thickness fall into this category. The cuts must be through the entire thickness of the sheet or plate. An example of this type of object is shown in Figure 10.15. Because this object is made of very thin material, the adjacent orthogonal views would appear as lines.

Even when the thickness of the object is constant, a fabricator may find it helpful to see a second view; for example, to emphasize that the thickness of the object is a significant fraction of the object's planar geometry. See how the second view in Figure 10.16 helps depict the relatively large and uniform thickness of the object.

For objects that have 3-D features such as protrusions and cuts, each with a different depth, the problem of finding the proper number of views for a drawing becomes more difficult. Figure 10.17 shows an example of a drawing with two views. In this case, more than one interpretation of the object is possible. The addition of a third view is necessary to completely specify the desired object.

Figure 10.18 shows three original views that, in the absence of hidden lines, could be used to represent two possible objects. A fourth orthogonal view, a bottom view, is required in this case to distinguish between the two possibilities.

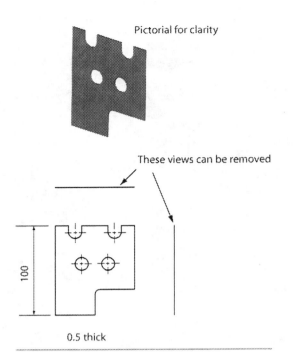

Pictorial for clarity

These views can be removed

100

0.5 thick

FIGURE 10.15. Additional views for very thin parts, such as sheet metal, add little information.

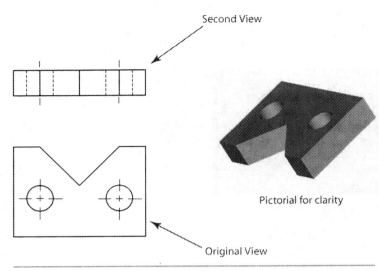

Second View

Pictorial for clarity

Original View

FIGURE 10.16. For a part with a constant but significant thickness, including a second view is a good idea to emphasize the 3-D nature of the part.

FIGURE 10.17. Different interpretations of a drawing with two views. A third view is necessary.

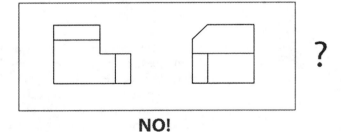

?

NO!

These two views alone are insufficient to define a three-dimensional object

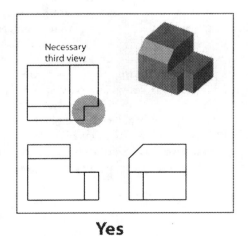

Necessary third view

Yes

Adding the third view uniquely defines the object shown

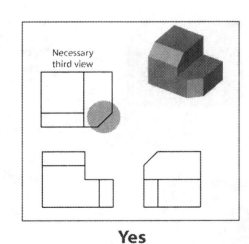

Necessary third view

Yes

Adding the third view uniquely defines the object shown

FIGURE 10.18. In the absence of hidden lines, four views are required to distinguish between these two parts. The fourth view is needed to distinguish the cutout on the underside as being diagonal instead of square.

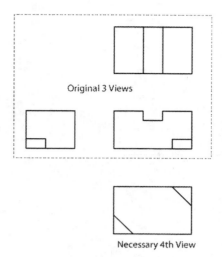

Original 3 Views

Necessary 4th View

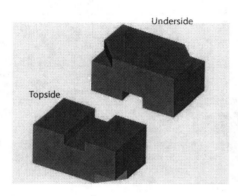

Underside

Topside

This one!

Underside

Topside

Not this one!

Figure 10.19 shows an example of an object where, in the absence of hidden lines, five views are necessary.

As a rule of thumb, when an object contains inclined surfaces with respect to the standard viewing directions, each of those inclined surfaces must appear inclined in at least one of the orthogonal views representing the object. When the inclined surface is not shown in one of the orthogonal views, a view needs to show the surface as being inclined (i.e., with at least one of its edges at an angle that is not 0° or 90°).

10.04.03 Hidden Lines versus More Views

One way to reduce the number of required views is to use hidden lines. The object shown in Figure 10.20 has some unique features. Try to imagine representing the object without using hidden lines. Without the hidden lines, five views would be required to define all of its features. With only the front, top, and right-side views and no hidden lines, the geometry of the keyway seen on the underside of the object cannot be defined. Moreover, without hidden lines, additional views would be required to show that the hole and slot extend all the way through the object.

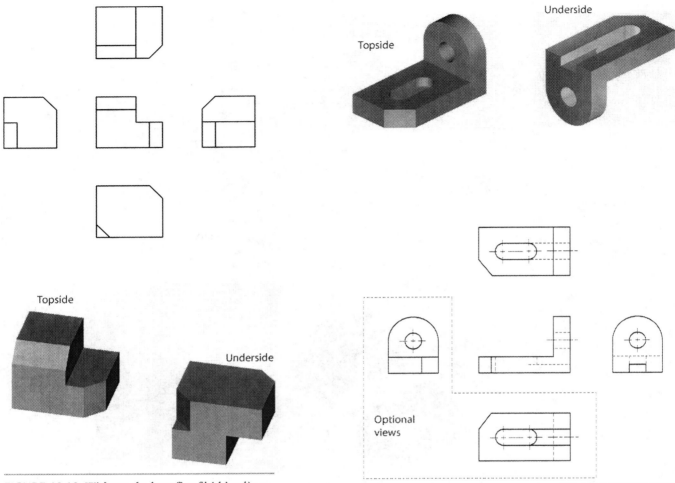

FIGURE 10.19. Without the benefit of hidden lines, five views are required to describe this object.

FIGURE 10.20. Hidden and internal features on a part. Using hidden lines makes the left side and bottom views optional.

Topside

Underside

Topside

Underside

Optional views

By using hidden lines, only three views are required—the preferred configuration of front, top, and side views. Whether you use all five views shown in Figure 10.20 or the preferred three-view presentation depends on your answer to this question: Which presentation would be clearer? You always select the presentation that has, in your opinion, the least ambiguity (and not necessarily the least amount of work to produce). In the case of the five-view presentation, although it would not be an absolute requirement, adding hidden lines would emphasize the internal geometry of the object. For the three-view presentation, adding the hidden lines would be an absolute necessity.

Another use of hidden lines is to reveal the details of internal features that cannot be easily seen in any of the standard orthogonal views. Such details would be, for example, the depth or the profile of holes and slots, as shown in Figure 10.21. Figure 10.20 demonstrates how hidden lines can be used instead of additional views, making the drawing easier to create and more compact without the loss of any information. For the object shown in Figure 10.21, the depth of the slot cannot be seen in any of the standard orthogonal views. If you look carefully at the views for the object shown in Figure 10.21, you see that hidden lines for different features can be separated into different views. But if all of the hidden lines were shown on all of the views, the result would be a jumble of so many hidden lines that it would be difficult to distinguish the different features that they represent.

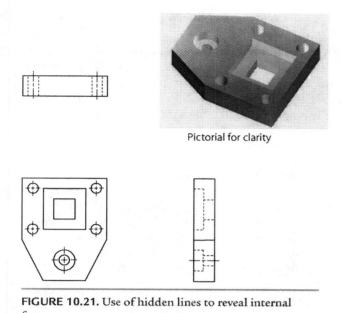

Pictorial for clarity

FIGURE 10.21. Use of hidden lines to reveal internal features.

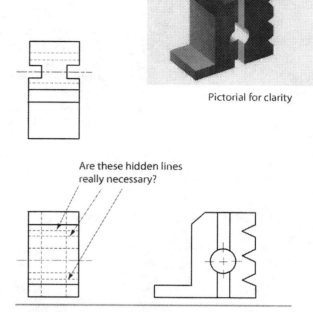

Pictorial for clarity

Are these hidden lines really necessary?

FIGURE 10.22. Overuse of hidden lines causes confusion. Exercise judgment. It might be better to create another view, such as a rear view in this case.

A common problem for inexperienced designers is deciding when to use hidden lines. Hidden lines should be used to add clarity to a drawing. Hidden lines should be used to emphasize a feature, even if that feature can be seen and defined in the existing orthogonal views. The goal of the creator or the drawing is to increase the speed at which the drawing can be interpreted. However, hidden lines must be used to add information when there is no way to obtain this information from the rest of the drawing.

Because hidden lines can be used to avoid creating another view, it is sometimes tempting to do just that, even when using another view would be better. Figure 10.22 shows that adding too many hidden lines create a complex, confusing drawing. With this result, it would be better to create extra views. When deciding whether to use hidden lines or to add additional views, simply do whatever will cause less confusion for the reader of the drawing. However, it is usually not a good idea to create hidden lines of different features such that the hidden lines cross each other, lie on top of each other, or even come close to each other.

The purpose of hidden lines is to define or emphasize details that cannot be seen, which is accepted as standard practice. Deleting unnecessary hidden lines and adding additional views are considered optional methods of reducing ambiguity when the use of hidden lines makes the presentation confusing. There must be no confusion as to which feature a hidden line represents.

10.05 First-Angle Projection versus Third-Angle Projection

The glass box representation of multiviews of an object is formally referred to as **third-angle projection**. Whenever third-angle projection is specified on a drawing, each view of the object was created by projecting the image of the object onto the glass box's transparent viewing plane between you and the object—the object is behind the transparent viewing plane. The viewing planes are then rotated about their intersection lines until all of the views are shown on a single plane or sheet. This interpretation is the one most commonly used in the United States.

However, in some parts of Asia and Europe, **first-angle projection** is commonly used. In first-angle projection, each viewing plane is behind the object, which means the object is between you and the viewing plane. With first-angle projection, the viewing plane is opaque and the image is projected back and transferred onto the viewing plane. One way to interpret first-angle projection is to imagine the object in front of the opaque panels, as shown in Figure 10.23(a). The image of the object, as seen by a viewer located directly in front of each panel (with the object directly in line between the two panels), is transferred to that panel. Opening the panels, as in Figure 10.23(b), begins to show how the front, top, and right-side views are presented on a single plane, as shown in Figure 10.23(c).

For drawings created using either first-angle or third-angle projection, the primary view is considered to be the front view. The front view in either projection is usually selected as the view containing the most features in their true sizes and shapes, thereby allowing for the most measurement extraction. As you saw earlier, for the six standard views using third-angle projection, the top view appears above the front view and the

FIGURE 10.23. Viewing an object in front of opaque panels for first-angle projection. The images are projected onto the panels (a), which open (b) to present the images on a single plane (c).

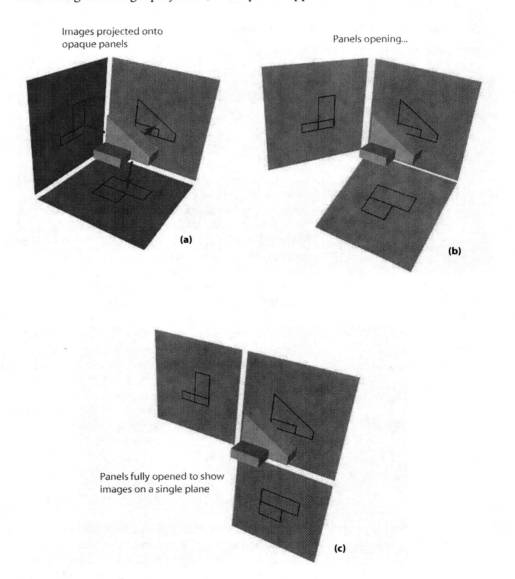

Images projected onto opaque panels

Panels opening...

(a)

(b)

Panels fully opened to show images on a single plane

(c)

bottom view appears below the front view. The right-side view appears to the right of the front view, and the left-side view appears to the left of the front view. The rear view appears, by practice and convention, attached to the left-side view and appears to its left.

Using first-angle projection, the top view of an object appears below the front view and the bottom view appears above the front view. The right-side view appears to the left of the front view, and the left-side view appears to the right of the front view. The rear view appears, by practice and convention, attached to the left-side view and appears on its right. The location of the first-angle projection views is shown in Figure 10.24.

The differences between first-angle projection and third-angle projection are sometimes subtle and confusing, particularly because the front view of the object is the same in both cases. To add further confusion, for a large percentage of engineered parts, the left side and right-side views or the top and bottom views are identical. These reasons explain why drawings need to clearly specify whether first-angle or third-angle projection must be used to interpret the views. Many large companies operate internationally, with engineering and fabrication facilities worldwide. In international business, drawings are often created in one country and the parts fabricated in another country. When a drawing is interpreted incorrectly, the resulting fabricated part may be the mirror image of what was desired. Figure 10.25 shows a multiview drawing of an object and the two different objects that are created when the drawing is interpreted using first-angle projection and third-angle projection.

The symbol added to a drawing to specify first-angle projection or third-angle projection is two views of a truncated cone, shown in Figure 10.26. This symbol depicts how a truncated cone would appear if a drawing of it were made using the projection method used for the entire drawing. The appropriate symbol and/or wording must be added to a formal drawing, usually somewhere in the title block (for which more detail can be found in Chapter 18) to eliminate ambiguities that may arise from misinterpreting which projection was used.

FIGURE 10.24. The six standard views, using first-angle projection, presented on a single sheet.

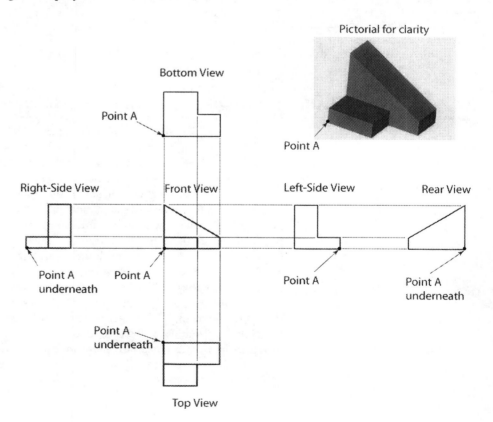

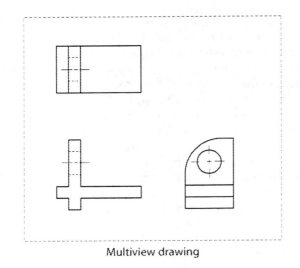

Multiview drawing

Object Represented

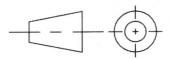

Symbol for First-Angle Projection

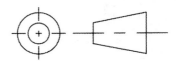

Symbol for Third-Angle Projection

FIGURE 10.26. Drafting symbols for specifying the use of either first-angle or third-angle projection in a drawing.

Interpretation using third-angle projection

Interpretation using first-angle projection

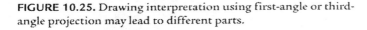

FIGURE 10.25. Drawing interpretation using first-angle or third-angle projection may lead to different parts.

10.06 Strategies for Creating Multiviews from Pictorials

Few people think of an object in terms of its multiview representation. If you are thinking about a pencil, for example, you probably do not imagine it in terms of a front, top, and side view. The image you have is likely to be three-dimensional, perhaps as a pictorial of some sort. Transforming that image into its multiview representation requires some skill. To develop this skill, some rules (and a great deal of practice) are required. And you need to remember that a pictorial image contains 3-D information that must be extracted from the way the pictorial looks in a 2-D medium. A multiview representation is merely a different, more accurate way of presenting this information. Exercises in converting pictorials to multiviews and multiviews to pictorials will help you develop practical skills, as well as improve visualization skills. Engineers should be able to quickly visualize 3-D objects from multiview drawings and quickly create multiview drawings for proposed or existing 3-D objects. You can begin developing these skills using the following step-by-step procedures. For the first few examples that follow, sketching techniques will be used because sketching, as opposed to drawing with instruments or CAD, is an excellent method for developing visualization skills. Later examples in this section will use more formal graphics so the drawings can be more clearly detailed.

Transforming a pictorial image into a multiview drawing usually involves keeping track of the vertices, edges, or surfaces of the object. Regardless of which elements are tracked, the process starts the same way. An eight-step process is used to create the drawing. The first two steps are as follows:

Step 1:   On the pictorial, specify the viewing directions that you intend to create (e.g., front, top, right side, etc.) and create a sheet with areas reserved (and labeled) for the appropriate orthogonal views based on the projection method used.

Step 2:   Find the maximum size of the object in each of the three directions of your coordinate system and in each view, sketch the limits of a rectilinear box that will contain only the entire object in all three directions.

A typical problem of multiview creation is shown in Figure 10.27. An isometric image of an object is presented, and the goal is to create the necessary orthogonal views to specify all of its features completely. Assume that all of the hidden surfaces are flat and that there are no hidden features.

This object is basic, considering all of its surfaces are perpendicular or parallel to each other. When this is the case, the edges of all of the surfaces will appear to be horizontal or vertical in all of the orthogonal views created. The true length of each feature must be shown in at least one view. For convenience in measuring the lengths of the edges on the object, an isometric grid has been placed on the isometric view. Placed on each of the orthogonal views is a corresponding rectangular grid that in each plane direction represents the same grid spacing as the isometric grid, as shown in Figure 10.28. The edge lengths as seen in the isometric view then can be conveniently transferred to the corresponding edges on the orthogonal views.

As an alternative to creating grids, you also can measure the edges in the isometric view using drafting instruments or CAD and transfer these measurements to the corresponding edges on the orthogonal views. When the edge lengths are otherwise specified, such as with notes, the specified edge lengths should be used in the orthogonal views. Carefully note the viewing directions for each view on the orthogonal views and the pictorial and make sure these directions are consistent.

You need to make clear from which point to which other point you are measuring any line in the pictorial —that is, the direction of your measurement—so you can incorporate the same information (direction of point-to-point measurement) in any of the

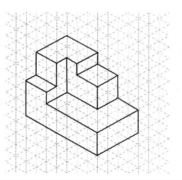

FIGURE 10.27. How would you create a multiview drawing of this object? The isometric grid is to be used for sizing.

FIGURE 10.28. Defining the foundation space, axes, viewing directions, and anchor point A.

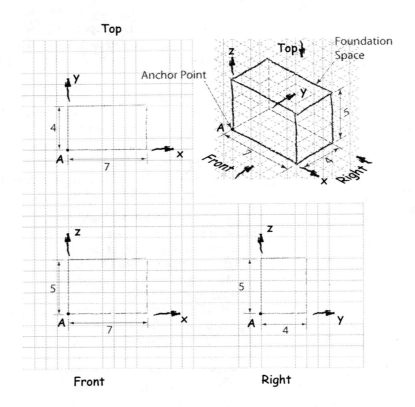

orthogonal views. For example, in Figure 10.28, as you measure from one point to another in the pictorial, you must be able to follow the same direction of measurement in the orthogonal views. For this purpose, it may be convenient to use a set of coordinate axes initially to help you with the directions of measurements until you become more familiar with the directions in the orthogonal views in your drawings. In Figure 10.28, a right-handed Cartesian coordinate system is placed with the origin coincident to one of the corners of the object in the pictorial. This same coordinate system is placed in all three orthogonal views. Make sure you maintain alignment of the origin of the coordinate system in each of the three views (step 1).

For this point to be in the same place in each view, it must be aligned on a vertical line between the top and front views and on a horizontal line between the front and right-side views. The top view looks straight onto the xy plane, so the z-axis points out of the page. The front view looks straight onto the xz plane, so the y-axis points into the page. The right-side view looks straight onto the yz plane, so the x-axis points out of the page.

The next step in creating the multiview drawing is to mark the limit of the size of the object in all three directions (step 2). These limits define a **foundation space**, which represents the rectilinear limits occupied by the object in each view. Although the foundation space is not the outline of the object itself, it helps you visualize the object in each view by delineating the volume that the object can and cannot occupy. If in the process of creating the orthogonal views you start creating lines or points for the object outside its foundation space, you will know you are doing something wrong. The foundation space for the object in Figure 10.27 is shown in Figure 10.28. Examine the foundation space on the pictorial. It extends 7 units in the x-direction, 4 units in the y-direction, and 5 units in the z-direction. Make sure these limits are marked off properly in each of the orthogonal views.

Once the foundation space is defined, there are different ways you can proceed. Students who have practiced and completed many problems in drawing orthogonal views from pictorials are able to proceed intuitively. Most beginners need a little help getting started before intuition kicks in.

10.06.01 Point Tracking

One way of continuing beyond step 2 is to label each vertex on the pictorial as a point, keep track of each point on every orthogonal view, and then connect the points in the views to form an image of the object in these views. (Keep in mind that all of an object's points may not be visible on the pictorial.) This process is called the **point tracking** method. Here is how it works.

After you have established the viewing directions and foundation volume in step 1 and step 2, you are ready to follow the next six steps to complete the drawing. The general procedure is outlined below. Each step is explained in detail in the paragraphs that follow.

Step 3: Define an anchor point.

Step 4: Locate a vertex adjacent to the anchor point and draw that edge.

Step 5: Successively locate other vertices and draw the edges between those vertices.

Step 6: Convert hidden lines.

Step 7: Add internal features.

Step 8: Check model validity.

A point on the object must be selected as an **anchor point** (step 3). There is an anchor point in each of the orthogonal views, and it is the same point in space as is seen from the different views. An anchor point is a point whose location you feel certain you can identify on each of the orthogonal views. Such a point is commonly a vertex located on one of the bottom corners of the object. Call this point A; then locate and label the point on each of the orthogonal views and on the pictorial. Remember, point A in views that are left or right of each other must be aligned horizontally; and in views that are above or below each other each, point A must be aligned vertically. In this case, but not necessarily in all cases, point A also is the origin of the coordinate axes.

Select another point on the pictorial (step 4) near point A, which can be located by traveling along one edge of the object, as shown in Figure 10.29. Call this point B; then locate it with respect to point A in each orthogonal view. You do this by noting on the

FIGURE 10.29. Defining and tracking points on the same surface near the anchor.

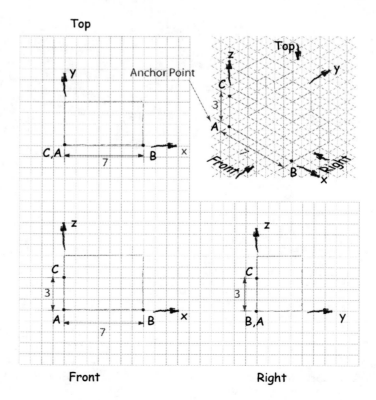

pictorial the direction and distance from point A to point B. From the measurements on the pictorial, you can see that to reach point B from point A, you need to travel 7 units in the positive x-direction. In the top view, the location for point B is 7 units to the right on a horizontal line from point A, which is the x-axis in that viewing plane. In the front view, the location of B also is 7 units to the right on a horizontal line from point A, which is the x-axis in that viewing plane. In the right-side view, the x-axis points out of the page; so point A and point B appear coincident in that view, although point B would actually be closer to you. Finally, connecting point A and point B in each orthogonal view creates an edge in each view.

Next, select another point (step 5) on the object near point A or point B that can be located by traveling along an edge of the object. It does not matter if the point is closer to point A or to point B because eventually all of the points on the object will be selected. Call this point C and locate it on each of the orthogonal views by noting the distance and direction you must travel to get to it from point A or point B. Point C is located 3 units from point A in the positive z-direction. In the front and right-side views, this direction is upward on a vertical line from point A. On the top view, point A and point C appear coincident because the z-axis points out of the page. Once point C is located in each view, its corresponding edge can be created.

The object's other edges are created in the same manner. You should select the points and edges to outline one entire surface of the object before moving to another surface of the object, as shown in Figure 10.30. In this way, you can see the surfaces appear one at a time instead of having a series of connected edges that extend in different directions. This process continues until the entire object is created in all of the views, as shown in Figure 10.31.

Inspecting the object's pictorial for any hidden edges (step 6) reveals that all edges shown are visible; they should be shown with solid lines. There are no internal features (step 7) on the object. As a final check (step 8), make sure each vertex in every view has at least three edges connected to it. Remember, one of these edges may be oriented into the page and thus appear as a point coincident with the vertex. If you determine that no

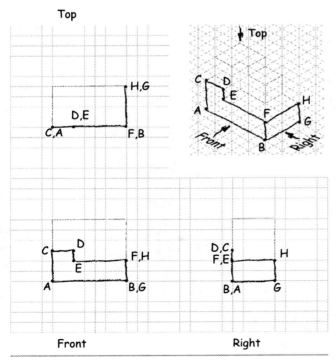

FIGURE 10.30. Connect the points to form edges of a complete surface before proceeding.

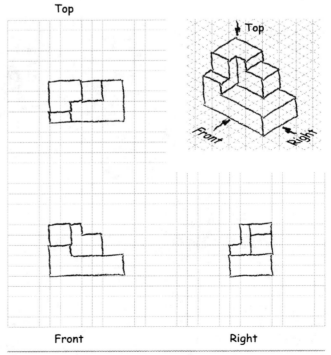

FIGURE 10.31. Continue tracking points, creating edges and surfaces until all points are accounted for.

edges are oriented into the page and only two edges are connected to a vertex, then a line must be missing.

You may have realized that even though three orthogonal views were created, this particular object could have been described using only two orthogonal views—the front and right-side views, shown in Figure 10.32. When only two views are used, it makes a difference as to which two views are used. In the example shown in Figure 10.32, specifying the front and right-side views is correct. If you were to use the front and top views, the possibility exists of either an inclined surface or a step feature, as shown in Figure 10.33.

FIGURE 10.32. Two orthogonal views, the front and the right, define all of the features of the object and are an acceptable presentation on an engineering drawing. The use of three views is more common.

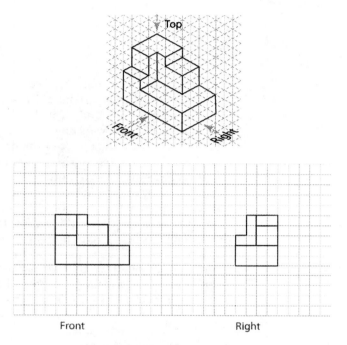

FIGURE 10.33. The wrong two views, the top and the front, lead to ambiguity. These views can represent either of two objects.

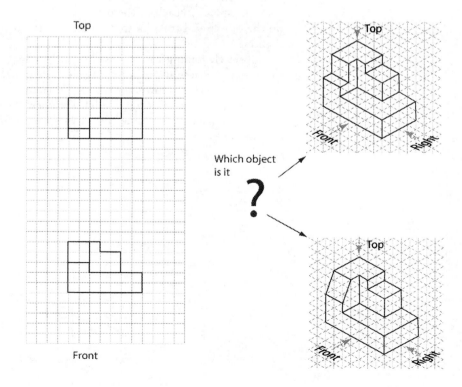

FIGURE 10.34. By keeping track of individual points, how would you create a multiview drawing of this object?

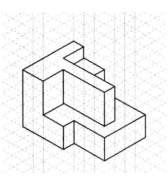

A slightly more complicated object is shown in Figure 10.34. You will try to build the multiview drawing of this object with three views.

The three views and their directions are shown in Figure 10.35. Note that the definitions of the viewing directions for this object are different from the definitions of the directions for the object in the preceding example. This does not matter as long as the definitions are consistent within the same presentation; that is, the right-side view is always on the right of the front view, the top view is always above the front view, etc., on the drawing. Whenever possible, the front, top, and right-side views should be used to represent the object unless one or more of the other standard views offers a better representation of the object's features. This example will proceed using the front, top, and left-side views to show how other views can be created and used.

A set of coordinate axes is defined on the pictorial and then transferred to the orthogonal views (step 1). Note that these directions are different from the coordinate directions in the preceding example. The location and orientation of these axes must be consistent in all views—that is what matters. In fact, as long as you are sure of the travel directions in each view, you can skip the use of coordinate axes altogether.

The foundation space is outlined in each view (step 2); and a convenient anchor point, designated A in the views, is selected (step 3). This time assume you know how to locate points on the pictorial and then transfer the location of each point to its corresponding place in each of the orthogonal views. Points near the anchor are identified on the object and then located on each of the orthogonal views (step 4), as shown in Figure 10.36.

Correctly joining the points creates the edges. The process of successively locating the object's vertices and creating edges on the multiview drawing is then extended to the rest of the object, as shown in Figure 10.37 (step 5). If you carefully examine Figure 10.37, you will notice that although the left-side view shows all of the edges of the object that can be seen in that view, some of the edges would not be seen if the object were solid and opaque. The edges that cannot be seen are hidden lines and should be shown as dashed lines for clarity (step 6).

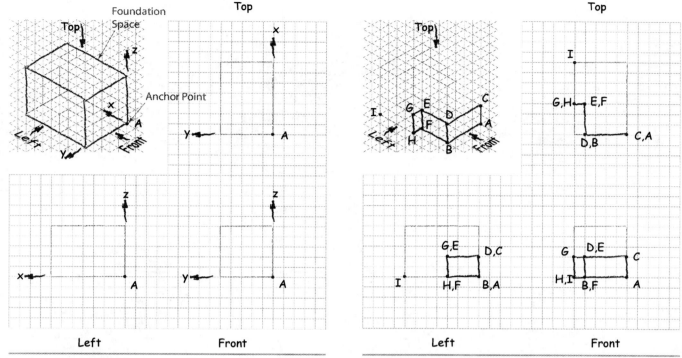

FIGURE 10.35. Defining the foundation space, viewing directions, and anchor point.

FIGURE 10.36. Designate each vertex as a point. Working with one surface at a time, locate the points and then the edges that make up each surface.

An alternative presentation is shown in Figure 10.38, where the right-side view has been added. This additional view allows you to see solid edges that are hidden in the left-side view. Note that the right-side view also has hidden lines, which are edges seen as solid lines in the left-side view. When you add the right-side view in this example, the hidden lines on both side views are no longer mandatory; but it would be wise to keep them since they do not clutter the drawing and would speed its interpretation. With the use of hidden lines, either the left- or right-side view can be deleted without harming the information conveyed about the object's geometry. Or both side views can be presented for additional emphasis to this geometry.

When internal features in this object are examined, none are found (step 7). As a final check, make sure each vertex in every view has at least three edges connected to it (step 8), keeping in mind that one of these edges may be oriented into the page and thus appear as a point coincident with the vertex. When this is not the case, a line is missing.

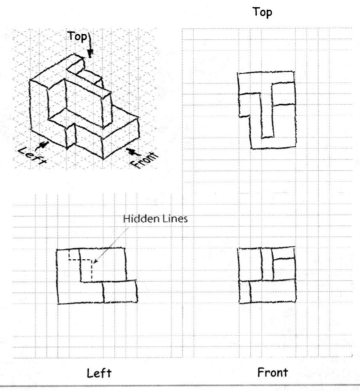

FIGURE 10.37. Continue tracking points, creating edges and surfaces until all points are accounted for. Edges that are obscured are represented with hidden lines.

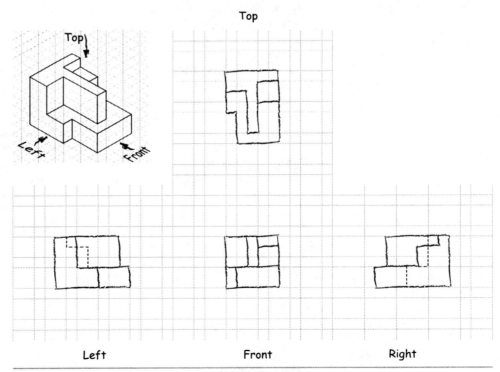

FIGURE 10.38. When a right-side view is added, the hidden lines are no longer necessary but still recommended to show all of the edges of the object.

10.06.02 Edge Tracking

Tracking individual points on an object to create its orthogonal views is a reliable method of creating the views. However, this process is slow and boring. After several trials at using this method, you will be anxious to try something faster. One way is to track an edge instead of tracking two points along the edge. This process is called **edge tracking**. It is like the eight-step process used for point tracking, where steps 1, 2, 6, 7, and 8 are the same, but steps 3, 4, and 5 are modified as follows:

Step 3: Define an anchor edge.

Step 4: Locate an edge adjacent to the anchor point, and draw that edge.

Step 5: Successively locate other adjacent edges.

To create a multiview drawing of the object in Figure 10.39, decide how many orthogonal views you may need; then create the foundation space and directions (steps 1 and 2), as shown in Figure 10.40. Locate and label all of the edges on the object pictorial, keeping in mind that all of its edges may not be visible.

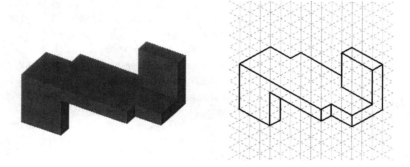

FIGURE 10.39. By keeping track of individual edges, how would you create a multiview drawing of this object?

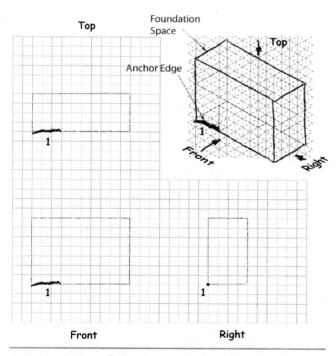

FIGURE 10.40. Defining the foundation space, viewing directions, and anchor edge. The selected anchor edge must be identifiable with confidence in all views.

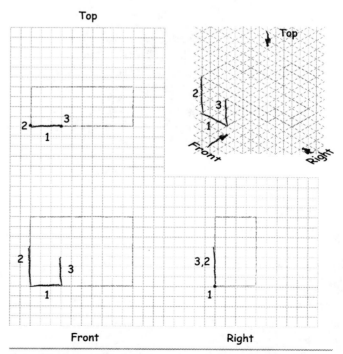

FIGURE 10.41. Defining and tracking edges near the anchor edge on the same surface.

Next, instead of selecting a convenient anchor point, select a convenient edge to use as an **anchor edge** (step 3). A good choice would be an edge whose length, location, and orientation you can easily and confidently find on each of the orthogonal views. For the object in this example, such a choice might be a straightedge on the bottom of the object. Call this edge 1 and locate and label the edge on each of the views, as shown in Figure 10.40.

Next, select an edge on the object that is connected to edge 1 (step 4). Call this edge 2 and note the size, location, and orientation of this edge with respect to edge 1. Find the same location and orientation of edge 2 in each of the orthogonal views and create this edge in those views. Keep in mind that if the edges of the object are parallel to a viewing plane, it will appear as its true length when it is viewed through that plane. If an edge on the object is perpendicular to a viewing plane, that edge will appear with both of its endpoints coincident when viewed through that plane. Note that edge 2 on the object is parallel to the front and side views; so in those views, that edge appears as its true length. Edge 2, however, is orthogonal to the top view. In that view, edge 2 appears as coincident endpoints, which would be drawn as a single point.

Continue to locate each of the object's edges on the respective orthogonal view until the object is completely represented in all orthogonal views (step 5). In the edge tracking method, you should select the edges to outline one entire surface of the object before moving on to outline another surface, as shown in Figure 10.42.

Notice on the completed multiview drawing in Figure 10.43 that for the object in this example, an edge that was originally visible during its creation later became obscured by another surface. The resulting hidden line (step 6) can be removed because the existence of that edge can be easily ascertained from the information already in the drawing. However, in this case, it would be better to leave this hidden line in place because its inclusion would facilitate the interpretation of the drawing.

There are no internal features (step 7) on this object. As a final check, make sure each vertex in every view has at least three edges connected to it (step 8).

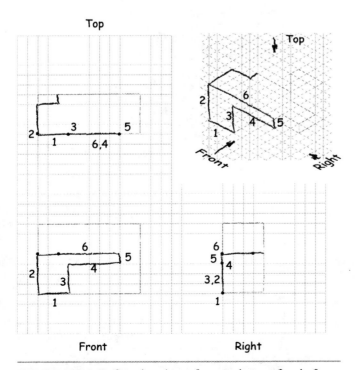

FIGURE 10.42. Define the edges of a complete surface before proceeding to the next surface.

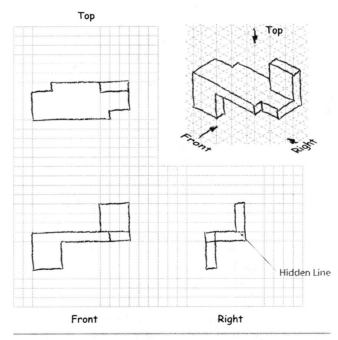

FIGURE 10.43. Continue tracking edges and surfaces until all edges are accounted for.

10.06.03 Surface Tracking

As you gain more experience and become faster at creating orthogonal views using the point tracking or the edge tracking approach, you may want to use an even faster technique. Instead of tracking an object's points or edges, you may want to track its surfaces. This is called **surface tracking**. The initial steps are the same as for point and edge tracking: first, decide how many orthogonal views you may need; then create the foundation space and directions on those views (step 1 and step 2). Steps 6, 7, and 8 are also the same; but steps 3, 4, and 5 are modified as follows:

Step 3: Define an anchor surface.

Step 4: Locate a surface adjacent to the anchor surface and draw its boundary.

Step 5: Successively locate other adjacent surfaces and draw those boundaries.

For the object shown in Figure 10.44, the viewing directions and foundation are shown in Figure 10.45 (steps 1 and 2).

Note that two pictorial views are required to reveal all of the features of this object. This is a clue that more than three orthogonal views (or some use of hidden lines) will be required to specify all the features of this object completely. In addition to front, right side, and top views, the left side and bottom views also will be included. Later the drafter can eliminate views that are unnecessary if she decides they will provide no useful information or function. For surface tracking, you must locate and label all of the surfaces on the object's pictorial, keeping in mind that all of the surfaces may not be visible.

For surface tracking, the first surface selected will be the **anchor surface** (step 3). A good choice would be a surface whose length, location, and orientation you can easily and confidently find on each of the orthogonal views, such as one of the surfaces located on the bottom of the object in this example. Call this surface A and locate and label this surface on each of the orthogonal views. Note that on the top and bottom views, surface A appears as its true shape. On the front and two side views, the surface appears on edge and is represented by a line.

FIGURE 10.44. By keeping track of individual surfaces, how would you create a multiview drawing of this object?

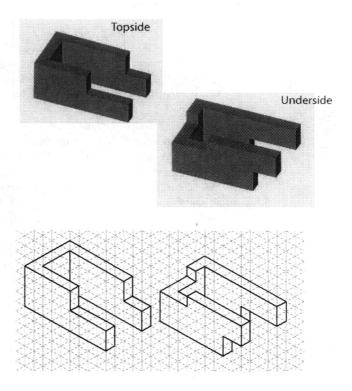

Topside

Underside

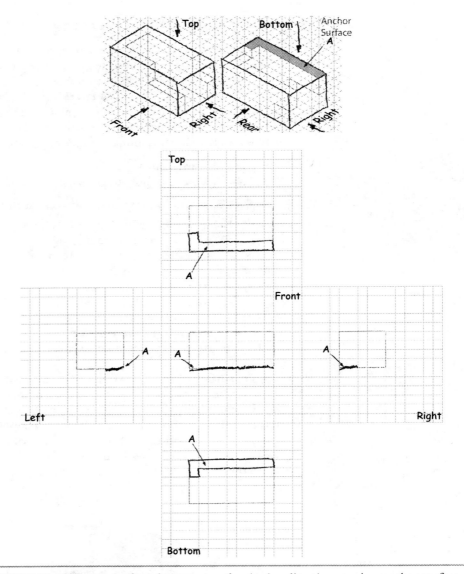

FIGURE 10.45. Create the foundation space, the viewing directions, and an anchor surface. The selected anchor surface must be identifiable with confidence in all views.

Next, select a surface that is adjacent to the anchor (step 4). Call this surface B, locate and orient this surface relative to the anchor surface, and create surface B in each of the orthogonal views. Keep in mind that object surfaces that are parallel to a viewing plane will appear as their true shape when viewed through that plane. If an object surface is perpendicular to a viewing plane, that surface will appear as a single edge when viewed through that plane. Surface B on the object is parallel to the front plane; so in the front view, that surface appears in its entirety. All of its lines will appear as their true length in the front view, and all of its angles will be appear as their true values. Surface B, however, is orthogonal to the top, bottom, and both side views.

In those four views, surface B will appear as an edge, which would be drawn as a line. Creating surface B by surface tracking is shown in Figure 10.46.

Locating each of the object's other surfaces on the orthogonal views is continued until all surfaces have been selected and the drawing is complete (step 5). Be aware that each surface that is created may partially or completely obscure surfaces that have been completed. The edges that have been obscured must be converted to hidden lines (step 6).

Step 7 and step 8 for surface tracking are the same steps used in the point tracking and edge tracking methods. The hidden lines are identified or additional views are created so that hidden lines are not necessary. The completed drawing is shown in Figure 10.47.

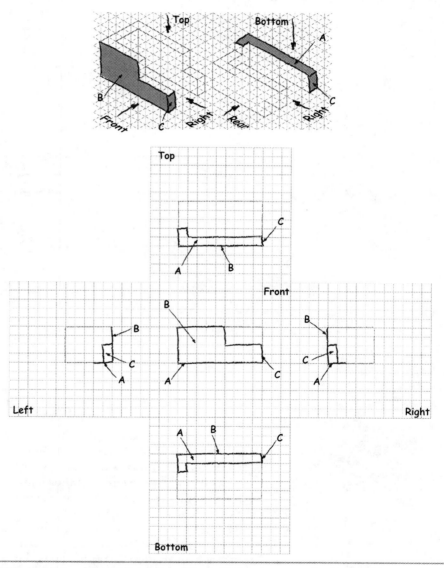

FIGURE 10.46. Locating additional surfaces adjacent to the anchor surface.

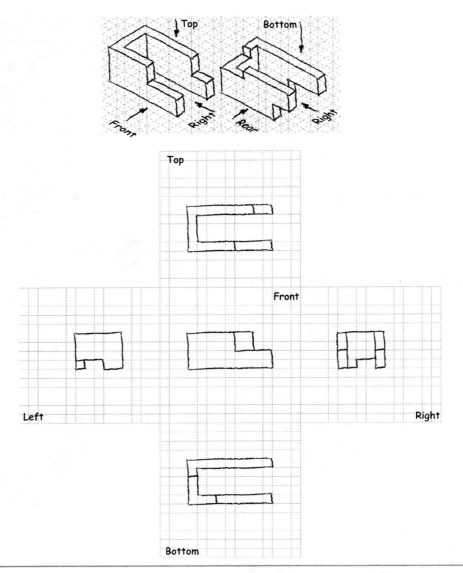

FIGURE 10.47. Continue tracking surfaces until all surfaces are accounted for.

In Figure 10.48, an alternative presentation method is shown. The rear view eliminates the need for a bottom view and a right-side view. The rear view also provides a better description of the rear of the object, which is partially obscured in the front view.

Using hidden lines (step 6), as shown in Figure 10.49, can further reduce the number of views and present the object in the preferred format of the front view, top view, and right-side view.

Whichever presentation method is used, your final step is to assure that each vertex in every view has at least three edges connected to it (step 8). Any vertex not having three edges connected to it means a line is missing. But you need to keep in mind that an edge may be oriented into the page, which means it will appear as a point coincident with the vertex.

In the preceding examples, the problems were simple because all of the surfaces on the object were parallel or perpendicular to each other and, thus, either parallel or perpendicular to the orthogonal views. These orientations are common for many but not all engineered parts.

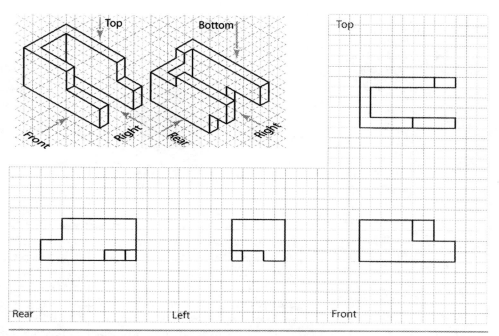

FIGURE 10.48. An alternative presentation using a rear view.

Next, you need to consider more complex objects, starting with an object that has surfaces inclined with respect to one another. That means you have to learn how to represent those surfaces in the orthogonal views of the object. Figure 10.50 shows an object with normal and inclined surfaces. For an object with inclined surfaces, the edges of the surfaces will appear to be inclined in one or more orthogonal views.

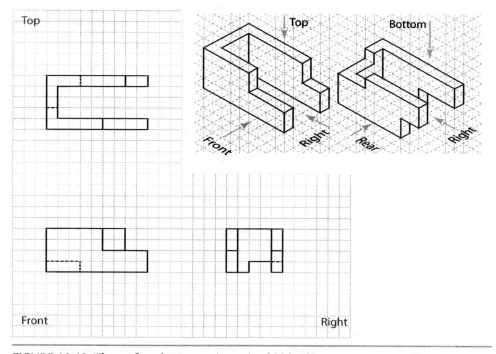

FIGURE 10.49. The preferred presentation using hidden lines.

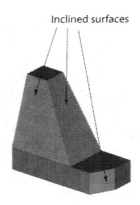

FIGURE 10.50. Considering the existence of inclined surfaces, how would you create a multiview drawing of this object?

Inclined surfaces

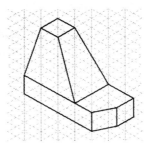

The initial steps to solving this problem are the same as with the preceding problems. Decide how many orthogonal views you think you will need to represent the object completely; then define the space and directions occupied by the object in each of those views, as shown in Figure 10.51. Point tracking, edge tracking, or surface tracking can be used. Assume you have a little experience now and surface tracking can be used for a quicker solution. An anchor surface is necessary. This time, for convenience, surface A will be used, as shown in Figure 10.51.

One way to approach a problem with inclined surfaces is to create the surfaces that are not inclined (i.e., the normal surfaces—parallel and perpendicular surfaces—as was done in the earlier examples). This is done in Figure 10.52. When only one inclined surface is on the object, such as when one edge of the object has been beveled, or chamfered, there is no need to consciously discover the location of the object's edges. Because the other surfaces completely surround the one inclined surface, the edges of the inclined surface are formed by the edges of the other surfaces. The same would be true if there were multiple inclined surfaces on the object, unless the inclined surfaces share a common edge.

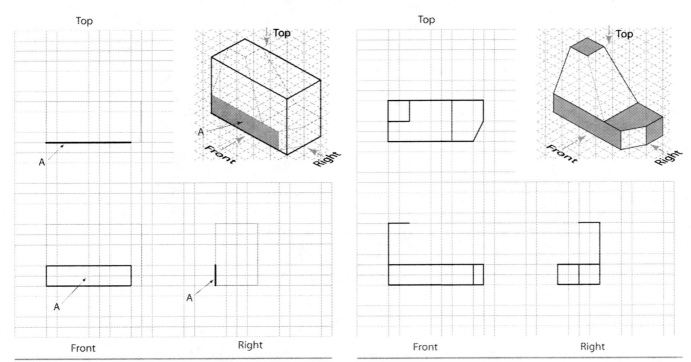

FIGURE 10.51. Define the foundation space, viewing directions, and anchor surface.

FIGURE 10.52. Continue the process of surface location for the noninclined surfaces.

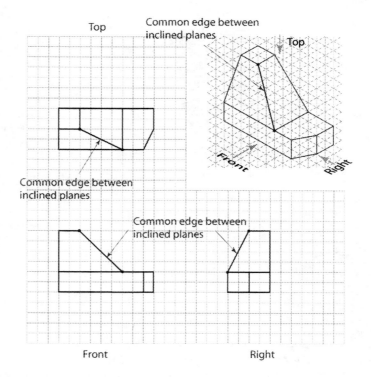

On this object, there are, indeed, two inclined surfaces that share a common edge. Once the parallel and perpendicular surfaces have been created, the shared edge of the inclined surfaces must be located. You can do this by either point tracking or edge tracking. The result is shown in Figure 10.53.

For more complicated objects, the hidden lines are identified or additional views are created so that hidden lines are not necessary.

For any object, no matter which method of tracking you use to create orthogonal views, your final step is to assure that each vertex in every view has at least three edges connected to it and to be aware that one of the edges may be oriented into the page and thus appear as a point coincident with the vertex. When this is not the case, a line is missing.

In the previous example, the inclined surfaces were inclined in a single direction only; that is, each was still perpendicular to one of the three preferred viewing planes. In this case, the entire inclined surface can be seen as an edge from two of the six standard views.

The next example is slightly more complicated. The object in Figure 10.54 has surfaces that are inclined in two directions (i.e., oblique surfaces). Neither of the two oblique surfaces is perpendicular to any of the six standard views; therefore, neither surface appears as an edge view in any of those views. Although creating the multiview drawing of this object may seem daunting, the procedure is the same as that used for creating surfaces inclined in only one direction.

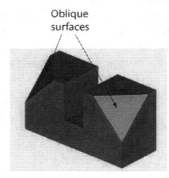
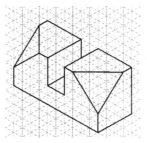

Oblique
surfaces

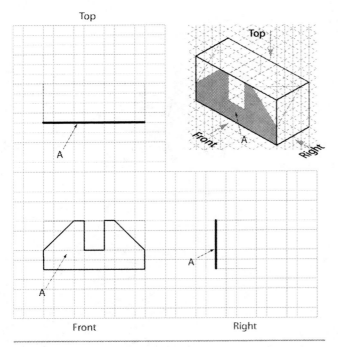

FIGURE 10.55. Define the foundation space, viewing directions, and anchor surface.

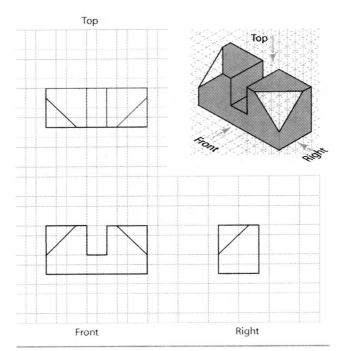

FIGURE 10.56. Continue the process of surface location for the noninclined surfaces. Since the oblique surfaces do no intersect, their boundaries are automatically formed by the normal surfaces.

Create the views for the noninclined surfaces by temporarily ignoring the oblique surfaces and using the surface tracking procedure, which is shown in Figure 10.55.

For the object in this example, the inclined surfaces do not intersect; so their boundaries are formed by the edges of the noninclined surfaces and the drawing is complete, as shown in Figure 10.56.

Next, consider how to represent in orthogonal views an object that has curved surfaces. Although there are an infinite number of types of curved surfaces, the most common are surfaces that are either cylindrical or conical; the most common curved surface is a simple round hole. Drawing a curved surface is unusual because in addition to an edge being shown where it intersects another surface, an artificial edge is drawn where there is an optical limit to the object. Examining Figure 10.57, make sure you understand that the indicated edge is not an intersection of any of the surfaces. This particular edge is the visible limit between the object and the surrounding air when the object is seen in that particular orientation. The location of this limit on the object changes when the orientation of the object changes.

When creating a multiview drawing of an object such as this, you must include one of these limits in each view of the drawing. For the object shown in Figure 10.57, the process of creating the four curved surfaces is made easier by the fact that each surface is orthogonal to one of the standard viewing planes. Therefore, the curved edges will appear in the orthogonal views as their true shape or as an edge view. When viewed as

FIGURE 10.57. Considering the existence of curved surfaces, how would you create a multi-view drawing of this object?

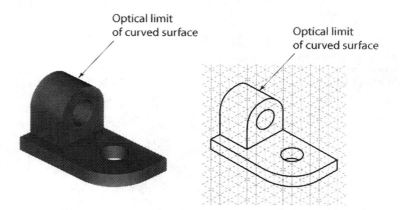

Optical limit of curved surface

Optical limit of curved surface

FIGURE 10.57. Considering the existence of curved surfaces, how would you create a multi-view drawing of this object?

its true shape, a circle will appear as a true circle, with its correct geometry, size, and location. In an edge view, the circle will appear as a straight line. Selecting the necessary number of views, creating the foundation space, defining their directions, and selecting an anchor surface are done as before, which is shown in Figure 10.58.

Holes and rounds appear distorted as ellipses or parts of ellipses in the pictorial. In the process of surface tracking, when a surface contains a circle or a part of a circle, that edge can be drawn as a circle by locating its center point and tangent points to the other edges on the surface. This process is shown in Figure 10.59. In this example, the two holes are internal features; thus, step 7 in the eight-step drawing creation process cannot be dismissed when the views are completed.

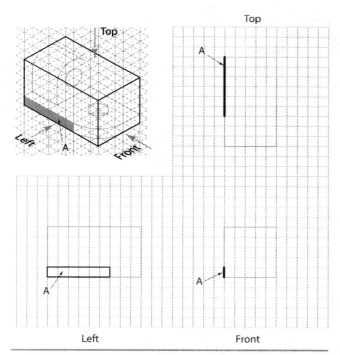

FIGURE 10.58. Define the foundation space, viewing directions, and anchor surface.

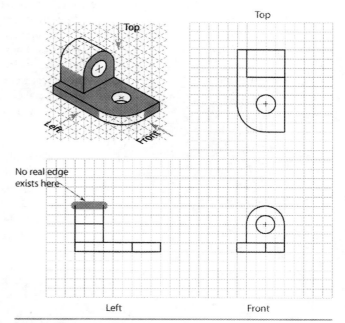

FIGURE 10.59. Locate the remaining planar surfaces of the object in all views.

FIGURE 10.60. Add the optical limits of the curved surface, add hidden lines to show hole depths, remove tangent edges, and add centerlines to the centers of the holes.

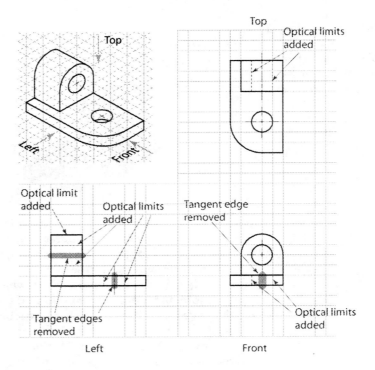

FIGURE 10.60. Add the optical limits of the curved surface, add hidden lines to show hole depths, remove tangent edges, and add centerlines to the centers of the holes.

When the orthogonal views are completed, as with the pictorial, additional line segments must be added to delineate the physical limits of the object, as shown in Figure 10.60. Even though an actual edge may not exist there, it is nevertheless what would be seen if the object were real.

The hidden lines are identified or additional views are added to eliminate the need for hidden lines. For this example, it is convenient to use hidden lines to show the depth of the holes. These hidden lines do not represent true edges; rather, the hidden lines delineate the optical limits of curved surfaces internal to the object (i.e., as would be seen if the object were partially transparent).

During the final check, which involves ensuring that each vertex on the object has at least three edges connected to it, it is important to remember that an edge is formed where a curved surface is tangent to a plane. This type of edge is called a **tangent edge** and customarily is not shown on either the pictorial or its multiview drawing, except for objects where not showing the tangent edges deletes key features that may lead to misinterpretation of the drawing.

When an internal feature such as a hole or a round is located on an inclined plane on the object, as shown in Figure 10.61, creating the multiview drawing becomes more difficult. For this problem, the views of the basic object will be created first; then the

FIGURE 10.61. Considering the existence of cutouts on an inclined surface, how would you create a multiview drawing of this object?

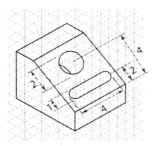

circular features (in this case, a hole and a circular slot) will be added. Because the hole and slot are located on the inclined plane, it is difficult to ascertain their true sizes even with an isometric grid. For convenience, the sizes and locations of these features are given. The center of the hole and slot are otherwise assumed to be symmetrical around the center of the inclined surface.

Determining the necessary number of views, creating the foundation space, defining their directions, and selecting an anchor surface are done as before. The multiview drawing, less the hole and slot, are shown in Figure 10.62.

Because inclined planes are not parallel to any of the six standard orthogonal views, they are not shown in their true shape in any of these six views. This means a circle on an inclined plane will appear not as a circle but as an ellipse and a circular edge will appear as a portion of an ellipse. A circle on an inclined plane will appear as a circle only in an auxiliary viewing plane created to be parallel to the inclined surface, but this is the topic of Chapter 14. The true location of the hole center, as given by the measurements on the pictorial, can be measured only in the front view, where the inclined plane is shown on its edge. The centers of the holes can be found in the other views by point tracking, as shown in Figure 10.63. The fact that points in adjacent views must be aligned vertically or horizontally greatly aids in locating the circle centers on all of the views.

Because the plane containing the circle in Figure 10.63 is inclined in one direction only (i.e., it can be seen as an edge in the front view), you can create the ellipses representing the circle in the other views by realizing that the major axis of the ellipse on the inclined surface will be the same size as the diameter of the circle.

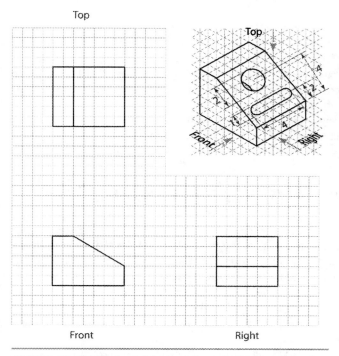

FIGURE 10.62. The basic block without the hole and slot is created.

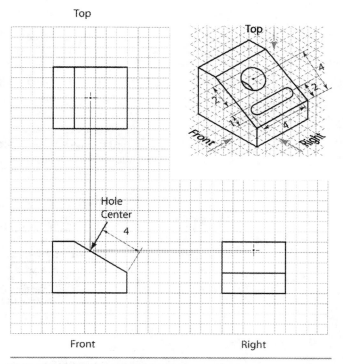

FIGURE 10.63. Locating the hole center by feature alignment in each view.

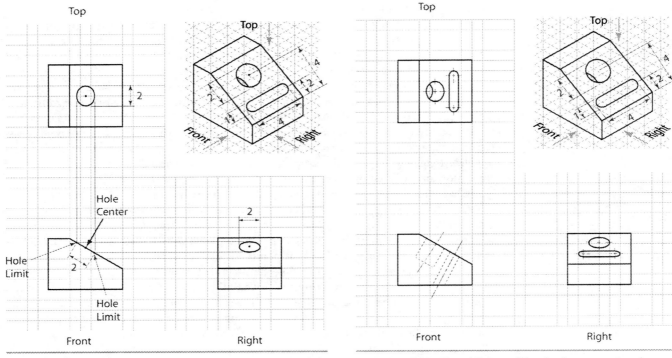

FIGURE 10.64. Construction of the major and minor axes of the ellipse in each view.

FIGURE 10.65. The addition of the slot by converting the circular edges to elliptical shapes, addition of hidden lines to indicate depth, and addition of centerlines. Note the addition of the hole bottom in the top view.

The measurements of the major and minor axes of the ellipse can be deduced graphically. You do this by marking the limits of the circle on the inclined surface in the front view, as shown in Figure 10.64, and projecting these limits into the right side and top views. Mathematically, the size of the minor axis of the ellipse will be the circle diameter multiplied by the cosine of the inclination angle of the plane from a horizontal plane.

The slot is added to the right-side view, as shown in Figure 10.65, by converting its circular edges to elliptical edges. The depth of the hole and slot are specified using hidden lines in the front view.

10.07 Breaking the Rules—and Why It Is Good to Break Them Sometimes

Creating an engineering drawing using orthogonal views is sometimes a balance between how accurately the drawing can be interpreted and how easily the drawing can be created. Strictly following some of the guidelines presented so far may lead to problems. To avoid those problems, you should consider some generally accepted exceptions to the guidelines, which are usually graphical shortcuts or approximations. These exceptions can reduce the time it takes to create a drawing and/or minimize possible misinterpretation of a drawing. With all of the exceptions that follow, the main question you need to ask yourself before using any of them is whether the approximation or shortcut could lead to misinterpretation of the drawing. If the answer is yes, the exception should not be used.

10.07.01 Threaded Parts

The first shortcut is in the representation of a threaded part, such as the bolt shown in Figure 10.66. A thread is essentially a helical mating surface for a fastener. The thread may be external, such as on the outside of a bolt or screw, as shown in Figure 10.66, or internal, such as on the inside of a nut. An accurate drawing of all surfaces on such an object would result in a very complicated drawing, especially if the drawing had to be created with manual instruments or 2-D CAD software. A much simpler representation of the external thread is shown as the schematic representation in Figure 10.66. For internal threads, the schematic representation is shown in Figure 10.67. These schematic representations are much simpler to construct with very little loss of information, especially since thread sizes are, for the most part, standardized based on the diameter of the part. A note (and arrow) is required to specify the precise thread sizes. Methods for the complete specification of thread sizes are found in Chapter 17 of this book. You can also find thread specifications in most machinists' or engineers' handbooks.

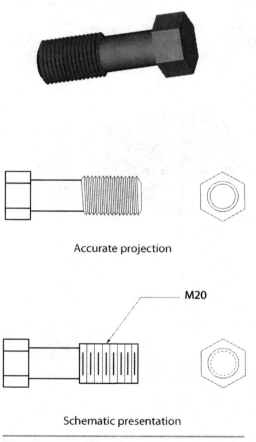

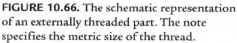

FIGURE 10.66. The schematic representation of an externally threaded part. The note specifies the metric size of the thread.

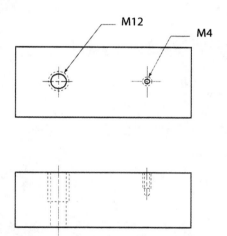

FIGURE 10.67. The schematic presentation of internal threads. The notes specify the metric sizes of the threads.

10.07.02 Features with Small Radii

An exception to the guidelines is in the representation of edges with small radii. Consider the object shown in Figure 10.68, which has small rounds on some of its edges. Based on the guidelines established in this chapter, a multiview drawing of the object should look like the drawing in Figure 10.68. Recall that cylindrical surfaces have no defined edges and that the tangent lines between curved and planar surfaces are not shown. Following the established guidelines, the top view should look like a featureless plane. Such a presentation, however, would likely cause confusion because upon initial inspection, the front view contains features that are absent in the top view.

A better, albeit not accurate, representation would be a presentation where the small rounds are represented as if they were true edges. The rounded edges are still shown in the front view, where their measurements can be specified. However, the approximation of the small rounds as edges enables the reader of the drawing to grasp the larger shape of the object more quickly. But what exactly is a "small" radius, and when should a small round be approximated as an edge on a drawing? The purpose of the approximation is to clarify the drawing. When the approximation clarifies the drawing, it should be used. As a rule of thumb, when the radius is less than about 5 percent of the overall size of the object, consider using the approximation.

10.07.03 Small Cutouts on Curved Surfaces

An approximation also is allowed when there is a small hole or another cutout on a curved surface. Figure 10.69, for example, shows a small hole and slot on a tube as compared to larger cutouts.

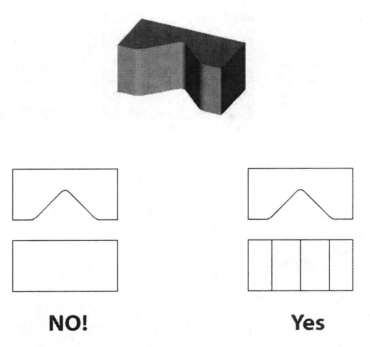

NO!

Not showing the tangent edges on small radii is an accurate projection but creates a deceiving presentation

Yes

Although not a true projection, small radii shown as edges present a clearer representation of the object geometry

FIGURE 10.68. The representation of small radii on a part.

If a true projection were made of these features, the orthogonal views would show a curved depression on the surface of the tube. The shape of this curve is complex and would take time to create. In most applications, the size of the depression on the surface is unimportant; so the depression is not shown on the orthogonal views. The true projection of these features and the accepted shortcut are shown in Figure 10.69. This approximation makes the drawing easier to create, with very little loss of information. However, when the cutouts are large or the size of the depression cannot be ignored in the function of the object, the true projection should be used. Within these guidelines, what is considered "small" is up to whoever is creating the drawing. The question that must be asked is this: Will this approximation possibly lead to misinterpretation of the drawing? If the answer is yes, the shortcut should not be used.

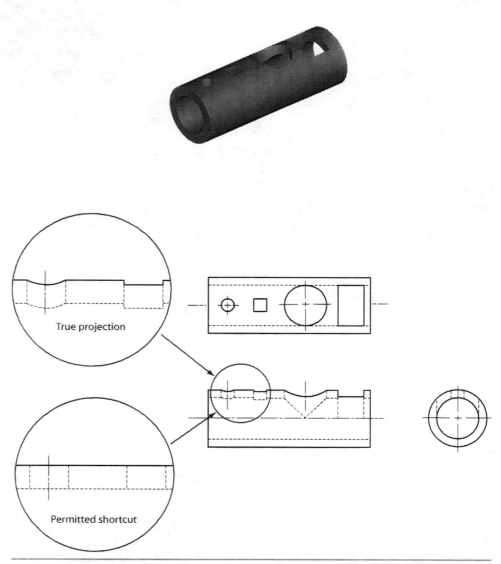

FIGURE 10.69. The true projection and an acceptable shortcut for small holes and slots on a curved surface. The shortcuts should not be used for large holes and slots because the geometric inaccuracies would be too obvious.

10.07.04 Small Intersections with Curved Surfaces

A similar approximation is allowed for small protrusions that extend from a curved surface, as shown in Figure 10.70. As with small cutouts on a curved surface, the appropriate use of this approximation is subjective. When the protrusions are small relative to the arc of the surface, their intersections on the curved surface can be shown as lines without affecting the intended representation of those features. When the protrusions are large relative to the arc of the surface, the approximation cannot be made. Again, the question that must be asked is whether this approximation could lead to misinterpretation of the drawing. If the answer is yes, the shortcut should not be used.

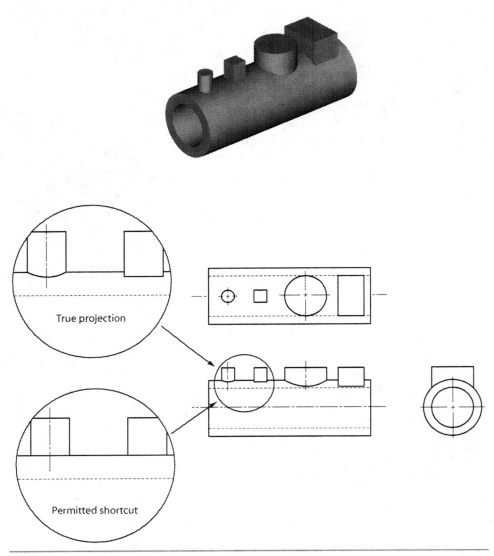

FIGURE 10.70. The true projection and an acceptable shortcut for small protrusions from a curved surface. The shortcuts should not be used for large protrusions because the geometric inaccuracies would be too obvious.

10.07.05 Symmetrical Features

An interesting exception to the rules of true projection occurs in the representation of objects with symmetry, as shown in Figure 10.71. This object has one-third rotational symmetry, which means the object can be divided into three identical sections about its axis of rotation, with three support ribs about the center tube.

An accurate multiview drawing would be the true projection drawing shown in Figure 10.71 using a front and top view. However, using a true projection for the front view in this case has two problems. One problem is that when instruments or 2-D CAD is used, an accurate projection is difficult to create. The other problem is that the true projection of the side view may be incorrectly interpreted as representing a nonsymmetrical object.

A preferred presentation for this drawing is shown in Figure 10.71. This drawing is easier to create and gives the impression that the object is symmetrical. The top view clarifies any possible misinterpretation about the number and locations of the support ribs. This may seem strange, but if the object had one-quarter rotational symmetry, for example, with four equally spaced support ribs instead of three, the front view would be the same as the view for the three support ribs.

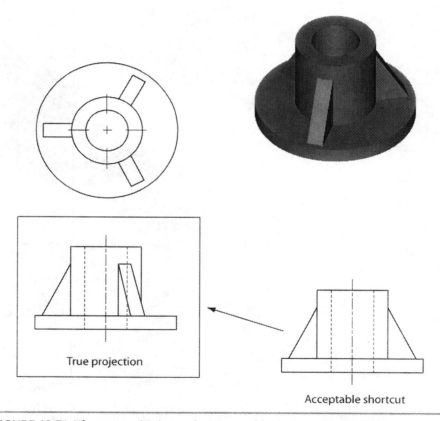

True projection

Acceptable shortcut

FIGURE 10.71. The true projection and an acceptable shortcut for an object with prominent symmetry. This property is emphasized by the use of a projected view that is modified to appear symmetrical.

10.07.06 Representation of Welds

Objects that contain welds, which are very common in civil engineering and some mechanical engineering applications, use special notation to specify the geometry of the weld. The use of this notation increases the speed of drawing creation with little loss of information. A simple object made from individual pieces that are welded together is shown in Figure 10.72. Even though a welded object is composed of two or more smaller pieces, it is common that such an object be fabricated at a single shop and delivered as a single unit. Thus, a single drawing showing the final welded configuration is often desirable.

Drawing the geometry of the welds on the multiview drawing takes time and effort, especially when the object contains many welds. So instead of the weld being drawn, a shorthand symbol is used. The notation specifies the geometry and locations of the weld, as well as any necessary modifications to the individual pieces in preparation for welding.

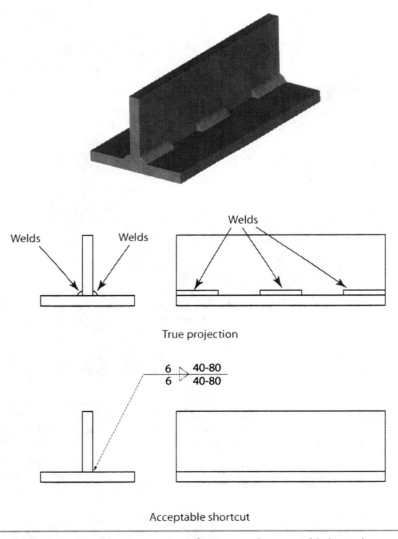

FIGURE 10.72. The acceptable presentation of two parts that are welded together to make a single part. The note specifies the size and location of the welds.

CAUTION   Inexperienced engineers, designers, and drafters can unwittingly introduce errors to their drawings. Despite the errors, the person reading the drawing probably will interpret it as intended because the necessary information is contained on the views not having an error. Nevertheless, errors can cause confusion and slow down interpretation of the drawing. A more serious case of errors can result with an ambiguity that makes the drawing impossible to interpret correctly. In a worst-case scenario, the errors may cause the object to be interpreted as an entirely different object than what was desired. The following sections are a compilation of the most common beginners' errors and ways to fix them.

Missing Lines

A common problem with hand-created or 2D CAD-created drawings is that one or more line segments may be missing from one or more of the orthogonal views. This error is especially difficult to correct when someone else made the drawing. As an example, examine the drawing shown in Figure 10.73, which shows the top, front, and right-side views of an object. Two lines are missing from the side view, and one line is missing from the front view.

The general procedure for locating a missing line is to examine the vertices in the adjacent views, as shown in Figure 10.74. Vertices are formed when surfaces or edges intersect as features on the object. A vertex in one view means there must be a corresponding vertex or edge in its adjacent views. Also, vertices representing the same point or edge on the object must be aligned horizontally or vertically in adjacent views. To discover any missing features, you can start with any view; but eventually you have to examine all of the views. From each vertex in a view, create horizontal or vertical alignment lines into the adjacent view. In the adjacent views along each alignment line, you should see the meeting of two surfaces to form an edge or the meeting of multiple surfaces to form another vertex.

Two vertices in the front view are missing some corresponding feature in the side view. The top view reveals that these vertices are the intersections of perpendicular edges. A horizontal line representing an edge must be added to the side view to keep the

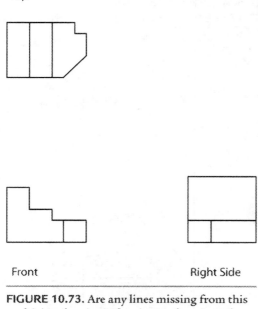

FIGURE 10.73. Are any lines missing from this multiview drawing? If so, insert them into the views at their correct locations with their correct visibilities.

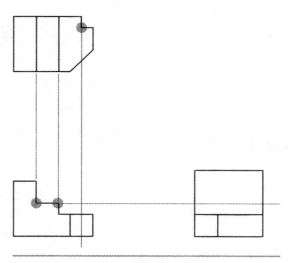

FIGURE 10.74. These vertices do not have corresponding features (i.e., another vertex or edge) in all views.

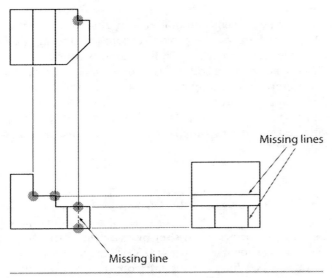

Missing lines

Missing line

FIGURE 10.75. The missing lines are shown here. The vertex in the top view produces a hidden line in the front view, which, in turn, shows that another line is missing in the side view.

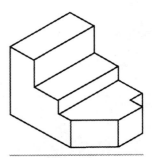

FIGURE 10.76. An isometric presentation of the object shown in the previous figure.

features consistent between the front and top views. Keep in mind that when a line appears to be missing, the next step is to determine whether that line should be visible; that is, the missing line might actually be a hidden line. Because the front view is uncluttered, it would be best to include the hidden line because it would reinforce the presence of the rectangular cutout on the back of the object. This hidden line produces two new vertices, which are missing some corresponding feature in the side view. A vertical line representing an edge must be added to the side view to maintain feature consistency between the front and side views. Figure 10.75 shows the drawing with the missing lines added. Figure 10.76 shows an isometric presentation of the complete object.

As another example, the drawing in Figure 10.77 has two lines missing from the front view. You can find the missing lines by examining the vertices in each view to ensure that a vertex in one view leads to some corresponding feature in an adjacent view, as shown in Figure 10.78. Note that hidden lines are used to show the depth of the

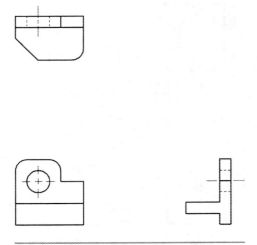

FIGURE 10.77. Are any lines missing from this multiview drawing? If so, insert them into the views at their correct locations with their correct visibilities.

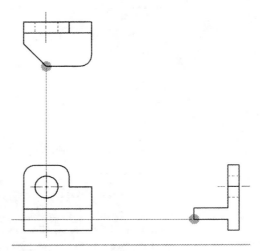

FIGURE 10.78. These vertices do not have corresponding features in all views.

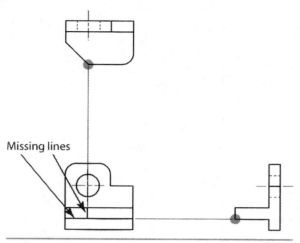

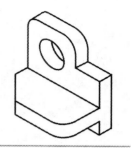

FIGURE 10.80. An isometric presentation of the object in the previous figure.

Missing lines

FIGURE 10.79. The missing lines are shown here. Tangent edges are not shown.

hole. These hidden lines are optical limits, not true edges; therefore, they do not form vertices or intersections as with true edges. Also observe that tangent edges are not shown even though they form intersections and vertices. Figure 10.79 shows the drawing with the missing lines added. Figure 10.80 shows an isometric presentation of the complete object.

Solving problems of missing lines is an excellent way to develop your skills with multiview projection.

Missing Views

When an entire view is not shown, consider it an opportunity to challenge your ability to find missing lines. Figure 10.81 is the drawing of an object where the front view is not shown. Although a missing view of this type rarely occurs in real-world engineering, this is the kind of problem for homework and exams. These types of problems are a test of your ability to recognize and extract 3-D data from 2-D views.

The procedure for finding the missing view in Figure 10.81 is to locate identical vertices in the given views and then transfer the locations of these vertices into the missing view. One way to proceed in this example is to select, one at a time, vertices that

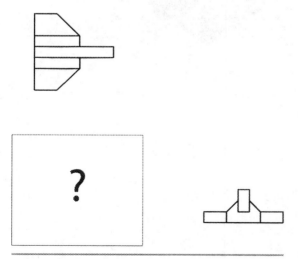

FIGURE 10.81. Create the front view of this object from the top and side views.

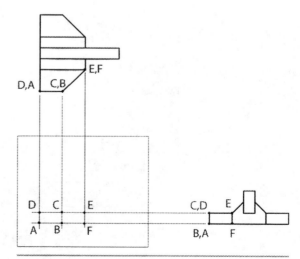

FIGURE 10.82. Locate corresponding vertices by alignment in the given views.

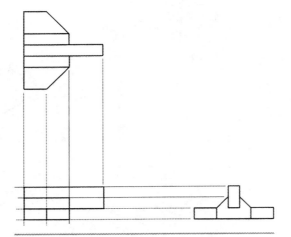

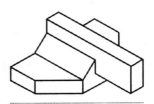

FIGURE 10.84. An isometric presentation of the object in the previous figure.

FIGURE 10.83. Continue locating vertices, adding edges in the front view when they exist in either of the given views.

are closest to the front view and then proceed toward the back of the object. Edges between the vertices in the front view are produced when the existence of the edge is evident for one of the given views. This process is shown in Figure 10.82.

Figure 10.83 shows the drawing with the missing view added. Figure 10.84 shows an isometric presentation of the complete object.

Incorrect Visibility

Sometimes all of the lines are there, but the visibility of one or more lines is incorrect. This means lines that are suppose to be shown dashed (representing hidden lines) are erroneously shown as solid (representing visible lines) or vice versa. Figure 10.85 shows an example of a drawing with an incorrect line visibility in the front view. One of the hidden lines is erroneously shown as a visible edge. Even though a person reading

FIGURE 10.85. Care must be taken to ensure that the visibility of edges is correct.

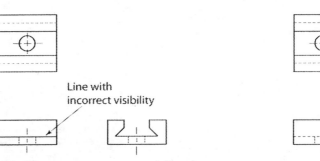

Line with incorrect visibility

 NO!

A hidden edge is incorrectly displayed as a solid line

 Yes

Hidden edges displayed as dashed lines, visible edges displayed as solid lines

FIGURE 10.86. Overuse of hidden lines causes confusion.

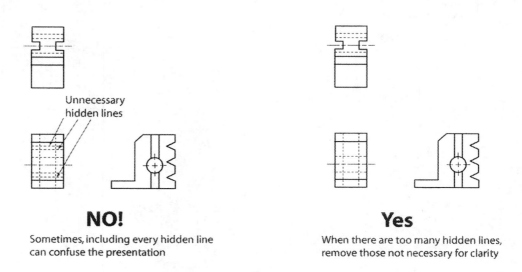

Unnecessary hidden lines

NO!

Sometimes, including every hidden line can confuse the presentation

Yes

When there are too many hidden lines, remove those not necessary for clarity

the drawing would probably figure out the error when it is realized that features between the views are not consistent, the error does create some confusion.

Too Many Hidden Lines

Although hidden lines usually aid in the interpretation of a drawing, using more hidden lines than are necessary can lead to confusion. For example, in Figure 10.86, the original front view shows the hidden lines representing the internal features (the hole and slots), as well as the V-grooves on the back of the object, resulting in a large number of hidden lines in that view. There should be no confusion about which feature a hidden line represents. For such cases, consider using hidden lines to emphasize only the most important features or use additional views to characterize the features fully. In this case, limiting the hidden lines in the front view clarifies the presentation. Hidden lines are used for the hole and the two slots in the front view to confirm that these features extend straight and all the way through the object. The fact that the three V-grooves also extend straight and all the way through the object can be confirmed from the hidden lines used in the top view.

Too Few Hidden Lines

Anyone reading a drawing not having any hidden lines, as in Figure 10.87, may have to guess the geometry of features. In this figure, without hidden lines or additional views for clarification, the drawing has two possible interpretations, as shown; the reader will have to guess which interpretation is corect. Never make the reader guess because that guess may be wrong. And if you made the drawing, the wrong guess would be your fault, not the reader's. Legally, a drawing's creator is responsible for ensuring that accepted guidelines for geometry presentation are followed so the drawing's contents cannot be misinterpreted. Just because something is obvious to you does not mean it will be obvious to someone else. Figure 10.88 shows the correct drawing for the desired object, using hidden lines.

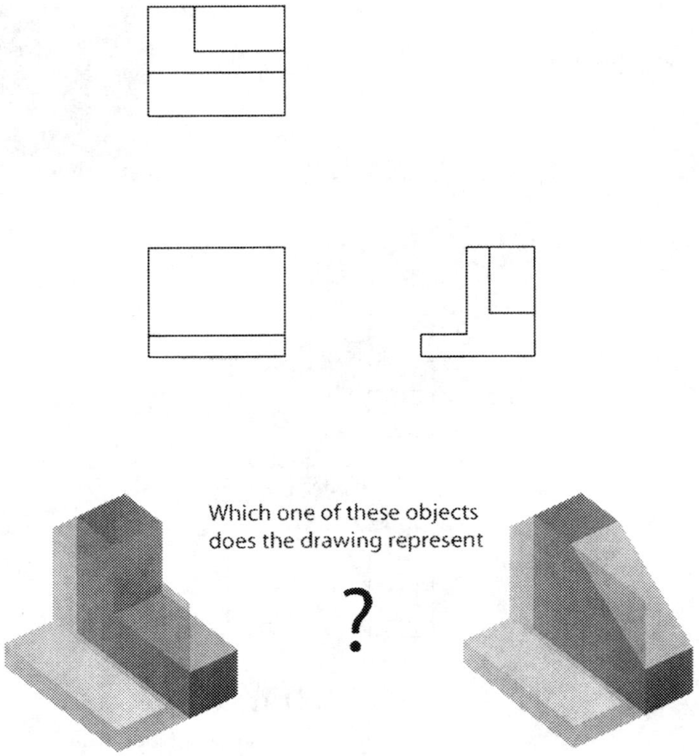

FIGURE 10.87. Underuse of hidden lines may delete critical information.

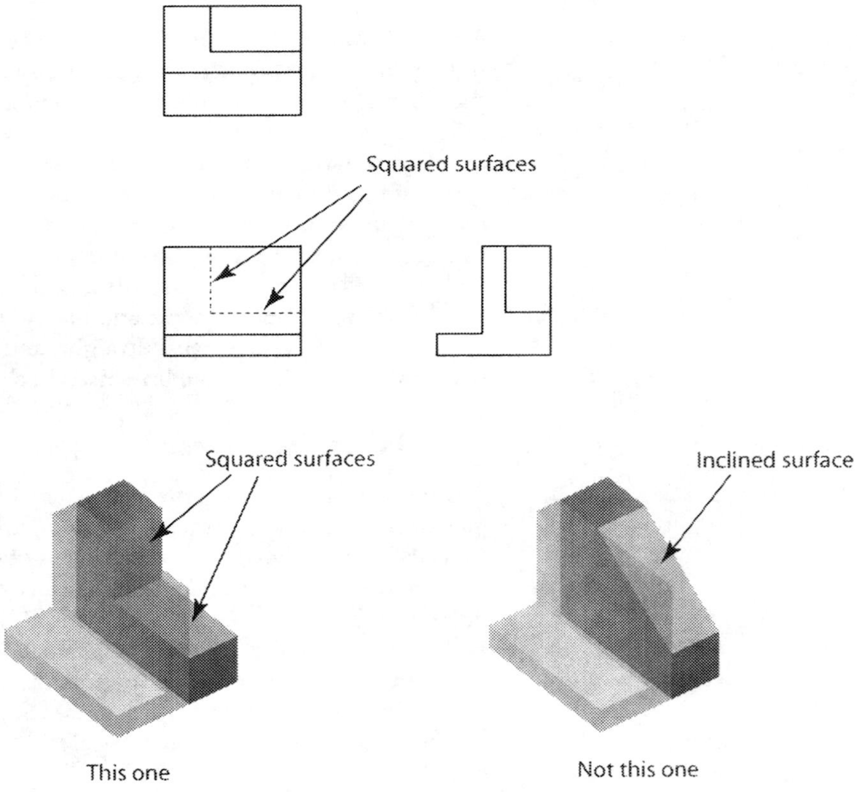

Which one of these objects does the drawing represent

?

FIGURE 10.88. Use hidden lines as often as practical to define and reinforce features.

Squared surfaces

Squared surfaces

Inclined surface

This one

Not this one

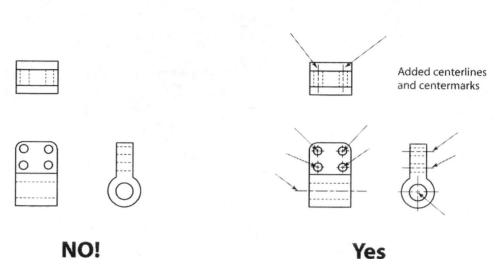

Added centerlines and centermarks

NO!

Centerlines and centermarks are missing from cylindrical surfaces

Yes

Centerlines and centermarks are present on cylindrical surfaces

No Centerlines and/or No Centermarks

To aid in the interpretation of a drawing, centerlines and centermarks mark the location of an axis of rotational symmetry. A centerline on a feature alerts the reader that the edges seen next to the centerline may be optical limits of a surface, not true edges. Without these marks, a drawing cannot be interpreted as quickly, as shown in Figure 10.89. With centermarks and centerlines added, the hidden lines and circles are quickly identified as having been created by holes.

Showing Tangent Edges

A tangent edge is formed when two curved surfaces or a curved surface and a plane are tangent to each other on a line. Tangent edges are normally not shown on drawings because they cannot be seen on a real object. Showing tangent edges, as in Figure 10.90, gives the false impression of the existence of a visible edge. Ideally, a tangent edge on a real object is smooth, without any abrupt changes in surface direction; and the drawing is made to reflect this attribute of real surfaces.

Not Showing Tangent Edges

Some exceptions exist as to when tangent edges should be shown to aid in interpreting the drawing. There are cases, for example, where the precise locations of tangent edges are important for the proper function of the object; and those locations must be emphasized for clarity, as shown in Figure 10.91. In this case, the tangent edges show precisely where the curved surfaces and the flat surfaces intersect. Also, when pictorials of objects that contain many rounded edges are created, the absence of tangent edges can produce relatively featureless presentations. In these cases, it is better to make the tangent edges visible.

FIGURE 10.90. On a real part, tangent edges cannot be seen and thus, in most cases, are not shown on a drawing.

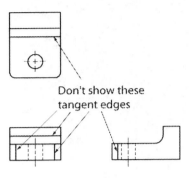

Don't show these tangent edges

Tangent edges deleted

NO!

Tangent edges have incorrectly been included

Yes

Tangent edges generally should not be shown

FIGURE 10.91. In a some cases, tangent edges may be shown to emphasize surface geometry; otherwise, views may appear to be featureless.

Missing tangent edges

Show tangent edges

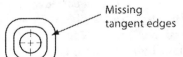

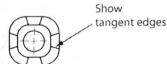

NO!

Removal of tangent edges results in deceptively featureless views

Yes

Including the tangent edges reinforces the existence of curved surface features

FIGURE 10.92. Small radii between surfaces should be shown as edges; otherwise, views may appear featureless.

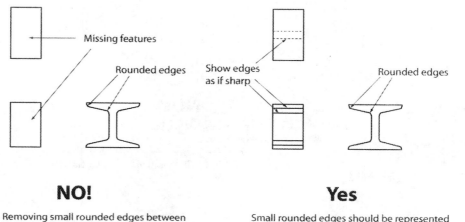

Missing features

Rounded edges

NO!

Removing small rounded edges between intersecting surfaces results in deceptively featureless views

Show edges as if sharp

Rounded edges

Yes

Small rounded edges should be represented as simple visible edges to empahsize their existence

Not Showing Small Radii

The intersection of two surfaces is not usually a sharp edge, but rather a smooth transition with a small radius between the surfaces. The general purpose of this transition is to reduce the number of external sharp edges for safety during use and handling of the object and to eliminate breakage by reducing stress concentrations that exist at sharp internal corners. When the tangent edges of these transitions are removed, the result is a drawing devoid of features in certain views, especially when the object has inclined surfaces, such as the object shown in Figure 10.92. When the radius of a transition is very small relative to the remainder of the object, instead of the object's tangent edges being shown, it is acceptable to show the transition as a single edge, as if the radius is a sharp edge.

Mismatched View Scales

When the scale, or object magnification, in each view of a drawing is different, as shown in Figure 10.93, it becomes very difficult to align features between views. Consequently, when an object has many features, it becomes difficult to identify and characterize those features correctly. All of the orthogonal views on a drawing must have the same scale.

Unaligned Views

When the views are not aligned, as shown in Figure 10.94, it is difficult to align the same features in each view so that each feature can be uniquely identified. The rules of orthogonal projection and multiview presentation mandate that orthogonal views be aligned.

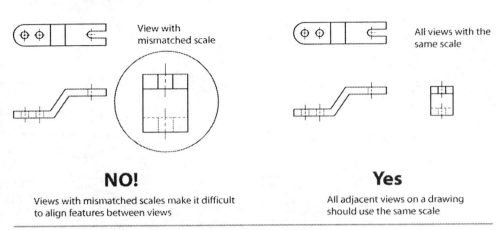

NO!

Views with mismatched scales make it difficult
to align features between views

Yes

All adjacent views on a drawing
should use the same scale

FIGURE 10.93. Orthogonal views must have the same scale.

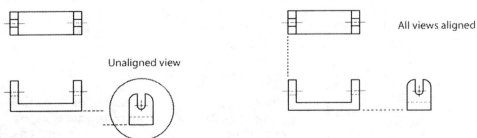

NO!

Unaligned views make it difficult
to align features between views

Yes

All adjacent views on a drawing
should be aligned

FIGURE 10.94. Orthogonal views must be aligned.

Views in Incorrect Relative Locations

The rules of first-angle or third-angle projection dictate that different views on a drawing must be located in certain positions with respect to each other. Consequently, people who read drawings have learned to expect certain views to appear in certain locations, such as a top view located above a front view (using third-angle projection). When the locations of the views are different from what is expected, as shown in Figure 10.95, the reader may become confused because the same features on the object are no longer properly aligned horizontally and vertically between these views.

Poor Choice of Object's Original Orientation

A poor choice in the original orientation of the object leads to a drawing with many hidden lines and/or inclined surfaces, as shown in Figure 10.96. The choice of object orientation should be such that the use of hidden lines and/or inclined surfaces is minimized.

Incorrect Rotational Orientation within a View

Inexperienced drafters may rotate a view by 90 or 180 degrees from its correct orientation with respect to the other views, as shown in Figure 10.97. An indication that this has happened is when the outer edges of the object are not aligned horizontally or vertically in adjacent views or when features on the object do not align. Such a rotation would confuse the person trying to read the drawing. Care should be taken to ensure that the rotational orientation of every view is correct with respect to first-angle or third-angle projection.

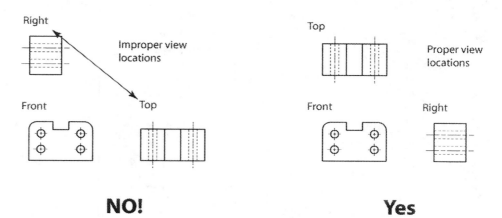

FIGURE 10.95. Orthogonal views must be in their proper locations with respect to one another.

FIGURE 10.96. The part should be oriented to show as many visible lines as possible in their true length.

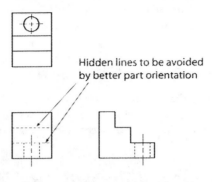

Hidden lines to be avoided by better part orientation

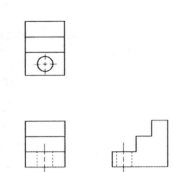

NO!

This object orientation generates many hidden lines which can be avoided by using a differnt orientation

Yes

This object orientation minimizes the number of hidden lines that are generated

FIGURE 10.97. The rotational orientation within each view must be consistent with proper orthogonal projection, as seen in the glass box.

Incorrect rotational orientation of view

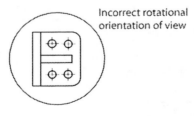

NO!

Views in incorrect rotational orientations make it difficult to align features between views

Yes

All adjacent views on a drawing should be in their correct rotational orientation

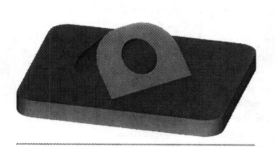

FIGURE 10.98. An object such as this one cannot be fully described by the six standard views.

FIGURE 10.99. An object with internal features such as this one cannot be fully described by the six standard views.

10.08   When Six Views Are Not Enough

It would seem that the six orthogonal views provided by the glass box would be sufficient to specify the geometry of any object. But the views are not sufficient for every object.

10.08.01 Features at Odd Angles

An example of an object requiring more than six views or nonstandard views is shown in Figure 10.98, where features are located on surfaces that are inclined or oblique. For this object, none of the six standard orthogonal views would show these features in their true shape. A supplementary view, known as an auxiliary view, must be created before measurements can be specified for the feature represented in that view. Auxiliary views are covered in detail in Chapter 14 of this book.

10.08.02 Internal Features

Certain internal features, such as holes, bores, or cutouts with an irregular wall profile and details that are hidden from view, cannot be seen in any of the six standard views. An example of an object with internal features is the wheel shown in Figure 10.99. For this object, the geometry of spokes cannot be seen because the rim of the wheel obscures it. Although hidden lines can sometimes be used to show such features, those features will appear more clearly in a cutaway, or section view. Section views of all sorts are covered in detail in Chapter 13 of this book.

10.09   Considerations for 3-D Modeling

The proliferation of 3-D solids modeling software, especially in mechanical engineering applications, has made the process of creating drawings much easier than in the past. Typically, with solids modeling software, objects are initially modeled as a series of protrusions and cuts to create their 3-D graphical representation. The solids modeling software creates a mathematical model of the geometry from which the projections of the object are used to create drawings. The model can be scaled and rotated for viewing from any orientation direction. Once the solids model is created, it usually is simple to specify the viewing directions needed to for the software to create isometric and other pictorial views. It also is easy to extract a front view, side view, or any of the other orthogonal views from a solids model.

The ease with which pictorials and multiview drawings can be created from a solids model has many advantages, but also some disadvantages. The greatest advantage is the speed and accuracy with which orthogonal views can be created. With most software, additional views can be created by specifying the location of the viewing plane and then picking a location on the drawing where the additional view is to appear. Usually this is done by striking a few keys on a keyboard or making a few clicks with a mouse or another pointing device. The time required to produce the additional view is usually only a few seconds. Hidden lines can be added or removed for individual features or for an entire view. Also, accurate orthogonal projections of features that were previously represented by shortcut practices, such as small cutouts in curved surfaces or thin symmetric features, are easily created. In fact, with most software, it would be difficult to create a view that is *not* an accurate projection.

But there is a disadvantage to having so much ease in creating drawings. Remember, the original process of manually creating projected views from pictorials and mental images and pictorials from projected views depended on the drawer's developed skills of spatial reasoning and mental imaging. When software makes the process of creating drawings too automatic, a person may not be able to apply these skills in the absence of the software because she did not develop adequate drawing skills. In other words, the person may have become too dependent on the software. That person, when faced with a multiview drawing in the shop, may not be able to create a mental image of the object or may not develop the skills necessary to interpret standard drawings. Eventually, the person will develop these skills, but it may require experience with many solids models and their drawings. Whether you are working with instruments, 2-D CAD, or solids modelers, the key to successful development of mental imaging skills is simply to practice—a lot.

10.10 Chapter Summary

Orthogonal projection and the use of the standard views of an object are accepted nationally and internationally as the formal means of creating and presenting images for the purpose of producing the original object. Constructed correctly, these views are used to re-create the same 3-D object, no matter who is viewing the images. Care must be taken to ensure that the rules for view creation, orientation, scale, and alignment are followed. Hidden lines are used for completing the description or for additional emphasis of certain features on the object. Extra views are used as necessary for completing the description of these features. From these formal views, the original 3-D object can be re-created. When done successfully, whether you are the person making the drawing or the person reading the drawing, you will find that the interpretation of the views and the object they represent are the same.

10.11 glossary of key terms

adjacent views: Orthogonal views presented on a single plane that are created immediately next to each other.

anchor edge: The same edge that can be easily and confidently located on multiple views and on a pictorial for an object.

anchor point: The same point, usually a vertex, that can be easily and confidently located on multiple views and on a pictorial for an object.

anchor surface: The same surface that can be easily and confidently located on multiple views and on a pictorial for an object.

centerline: A series of alternating long and short dashed lines used to identify an axis of rotational symmetry.

centermark: A small right-angle cross that is used to identify the end view of an axis of rotational symmetry.

edge tracking: A procedure by which successive edges on an object are simultaneously located on a pictorial image and on a multiview image of that object.

first-angle projection: The process of creating a view of an object by imprinting its image, using orthogonal projection, on an opaque surface behind that object.

foundation space: The rectilinear volume that represents the limits of the volume occupied by an object.

glass box: A visualization aid for understanding the locations and orientations of images of an object produced by third-angle projection on a drawing. The images of an object are projected, using orthogonal projection, on the sides of a hypothetical transparent box that is then unfolded into a single plane.

hidden lines: The representation, using dashed lines, on a drawing of an object of the edges that cannot be seen because the object is opaque.

multiple views: The presentation of an object using more than one image on the same drawing, each image representing a different orientation of the object.

multiview: Refers to a drawing that contains more than one image of an object and whose adjacent images are generated from orthogonal viewing planes.

orthogonal projection: The process by which the image of an object is created on a viewing plane by rays from the object that are perpendicular to that plane.

point tracking: A procedure by which successive vertices on an object are simultaneously located on a pictorial image and a multiview image of that object.

preferred configuration: The drawing presentation of an object using its top, front, and right-side views.

six standard views (or six principal views): The drawing presentation of an object using the views produced by the glass box (i.e., the top, front, bottom, rear, left-side, and right-side views).

surface tracking: A procedure by which successive surfaces on an object are simultaneously located on a pictorial image and a multiview image of that object.

tangent edge: The intersection line between two surfaces that are tangent to each other.

third-angle projection: The process of creating a view of an object by imprinting its image, using orthogonal projection, on translucent surface in front of that object.

viewing plane: A hypothetical plane between an object and its viewer onto which the image of the object, as seen by the viewer, is imprinted.

10.12 questions for review

1. What is orthogonal projection?
2. What are the advantages and disadvantages of using pictorial images, such as isometric images, for the graphical representation of an object?
3. What is a multiview presentation?
4. What are the advantages and disadvantages of using a multiview presentation for the graphical representation of an object?
5. How are different views located with respect to each other on the same drawing?
6. Why should features be aligned between views in a multiview presentation?
7. Why is it important that different views have the same scale?
8. What are the advantages of having features of an object aligned between views?
9. What are the standard (or principal) views?
10. What is the preferred configuration?
11. When should extra orthogonal views be used?
12. When should hidden lines be used?

10.12 questions for review (continued)

13. When should hidden lines not be shown?
14. When should tangent edges be shown?
15. When should tangent edges not be shown?

16. What is the difference between first-angle projection and third-angle projection?
17. When can the rules of orthogonal projection be bent? What are the advantages of doing so?

10.13 problems

The following exercises may be done with instruments, with CAD, or on square and isometric grids. Use third-angle or first-angle projection as specified by your instructor.

1. From the isometric pictorials shown in Figure P10.1, create accurate multiview drawings with a sufficient number of views to specify all details of the object completely. Do not use hidden lines.

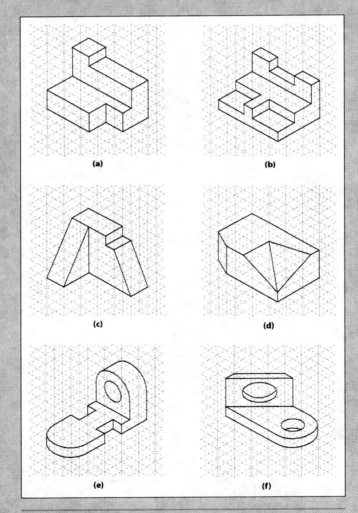

FIGURE P10.1.

10.12 questions for review (continued)

2. From the isometric pictorials shown in Figure P10.2, create accurate multiview drawings in the preferred format of front view, top view, and right-side view. Use hidden lines as necessary to specify all details of the object completely.

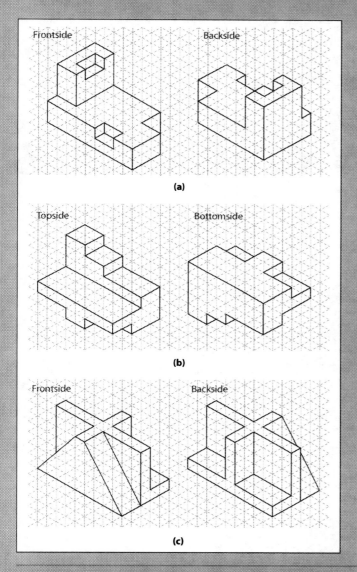

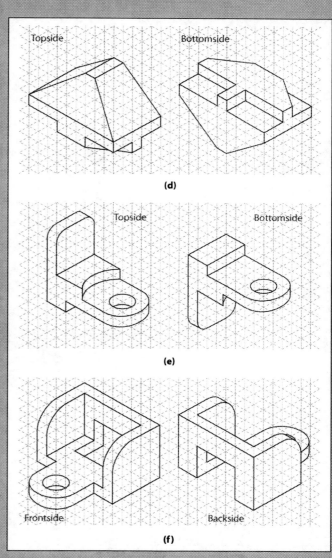

FIGURE P10.2.

10.13 problems (continued)

3. Each set of multiview drawings shown in Figure P10.3 may have visible or hidden lines missing. Add the missing lines to the drawing. An isometric pictorial has been included for clarity.

10.13 problems (continued)

4. For each front view shown in Figure P10.4, draw the top view (in the correct scale, location, and orientation) that corresponds to each of the possible side views that are shown.

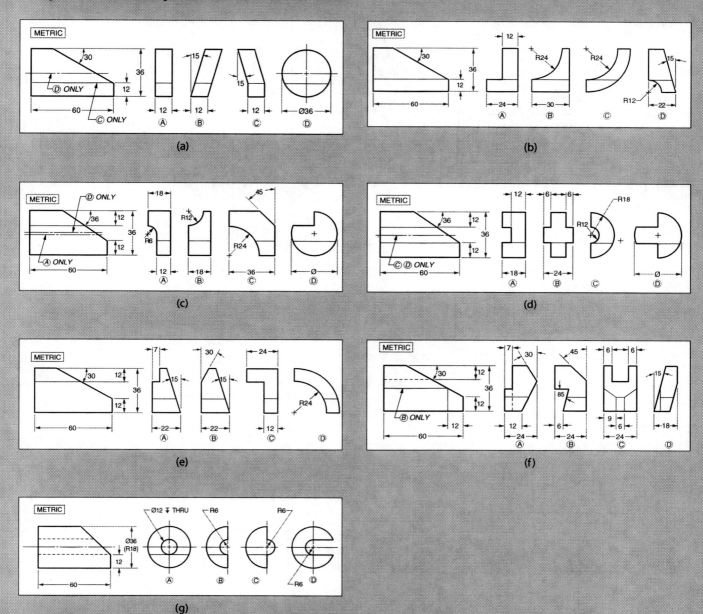

FIGURE P10.4.

10.13 problems (continued)

5. For each set of multiview drawings shown in Figure P10.5, add the missing view to the drawing in the indicated location. An isometric pictorial has been included for clarity.

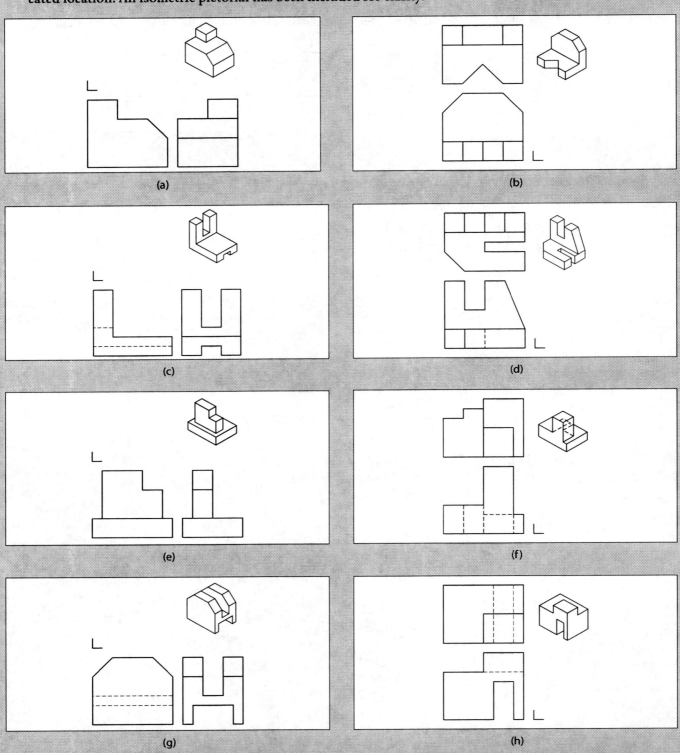

(a)

(b)

(c)

(d)

(e)

(f)

(g)

(h)

10.13 problems (continued)

6. Create correctly scaled multiview orthogonal drawings of the objects shown in Figure P10.6. Show at least the front, top, and right-side views. Include hidden lines. Recommend when additional views would be useful to clarify the presentation and add these views to the drawing.

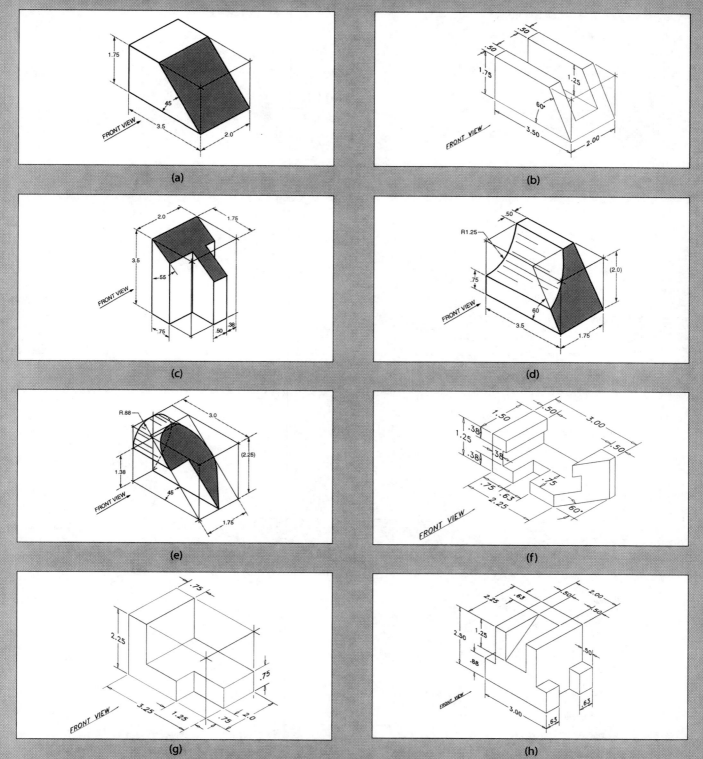

(a)

(b)

(c)

(d)

(e)

(f)

(g)

(h)

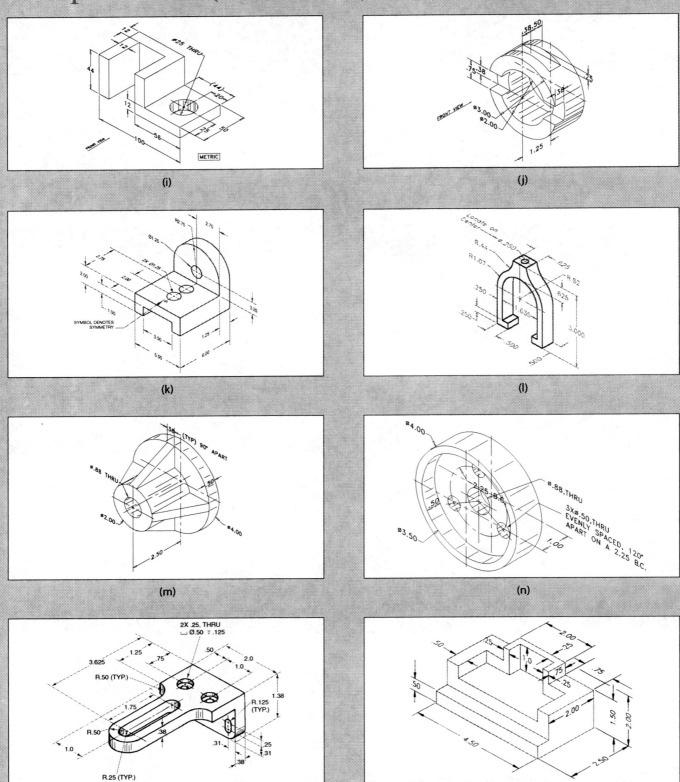

(i)

(j)

(k)

(l)

(m)

(n)

(o)

(p)

10.13 problems (continued)

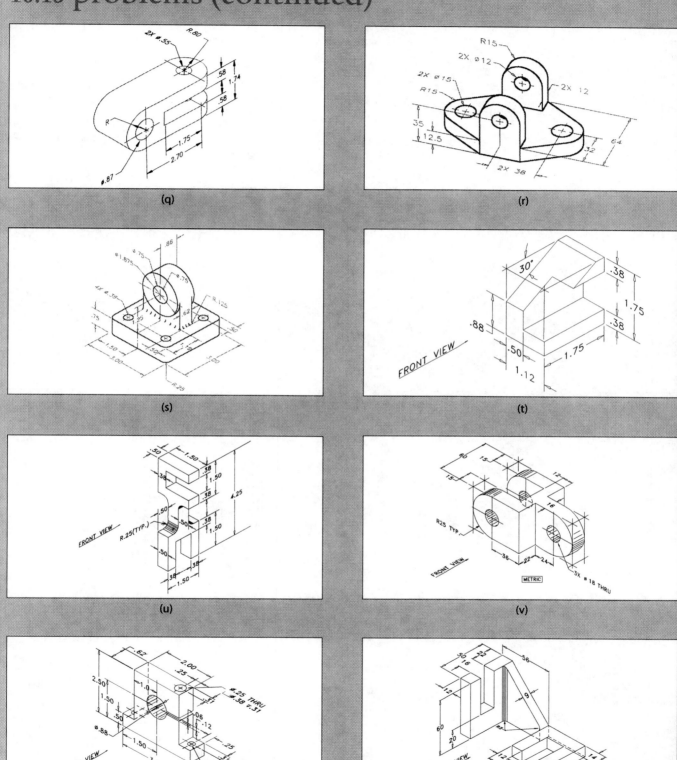

(q)

(r)

(s)

(t)

(u)

(v)

(w)

(x)

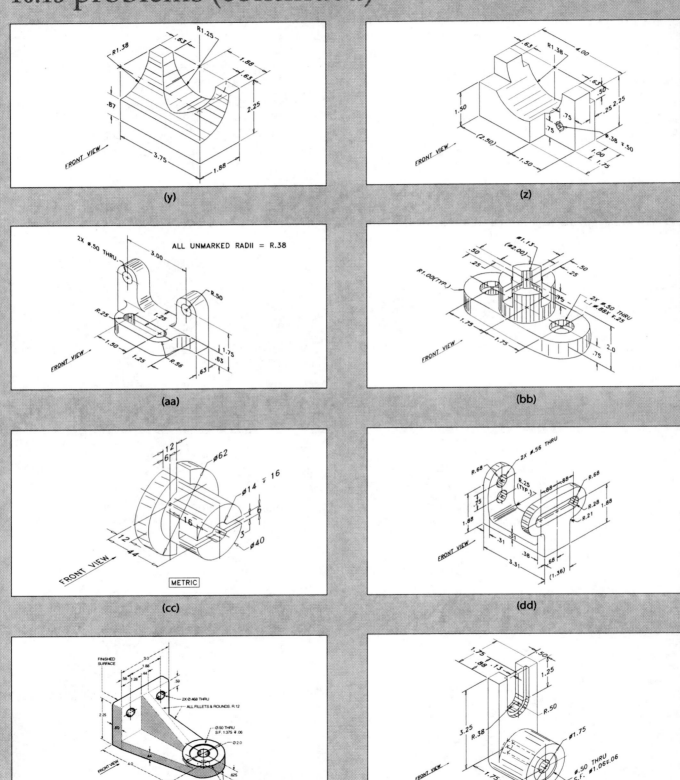

(y)

(z)

(aa)

(bb)

(cc)

(dd)

(ee)

(ff)

10.13 problems (continued)

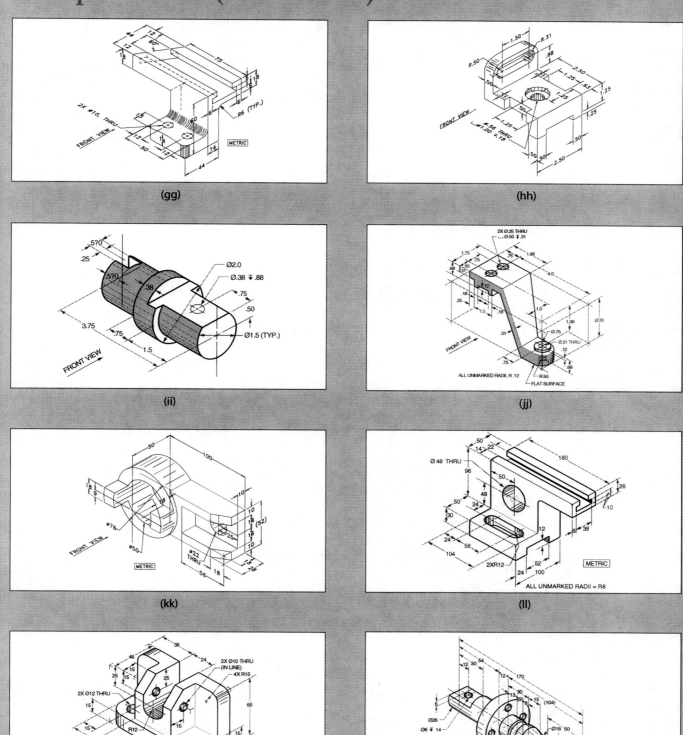

(gg)

(hh)

(ii)

(jj)

(kk)

(ll)

(mm)

(nn)

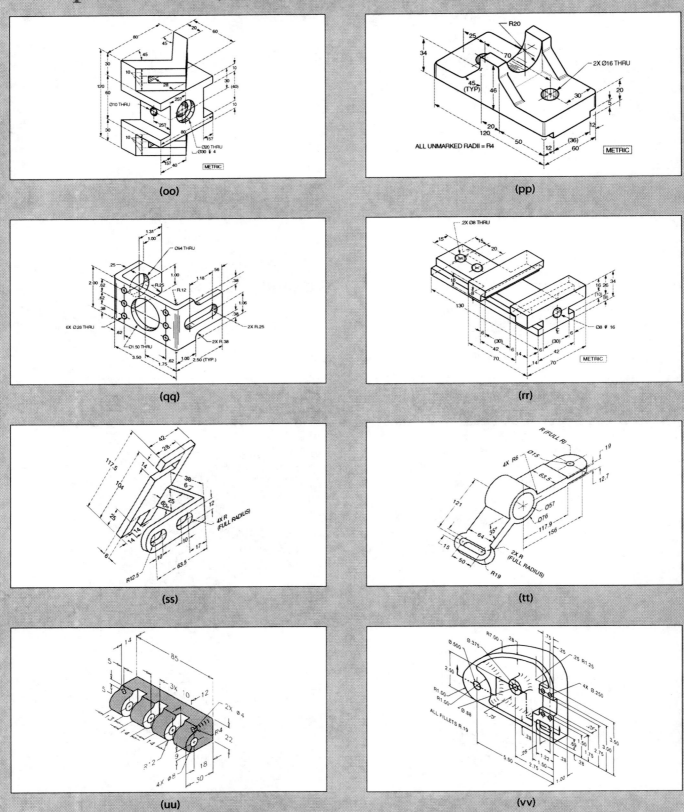

(oo)

(pp)

(qq)

(rr)

(ss)

(tt)

(uu)

(vv)

10.13 problems (continued)

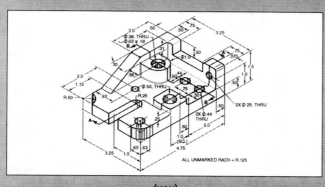

(ww)

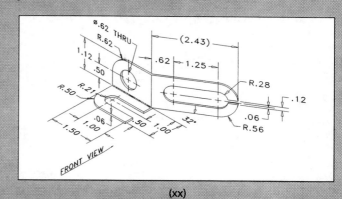

(xx)

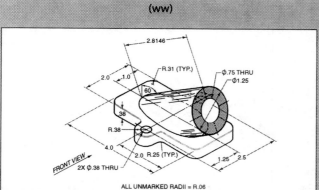

(yy)

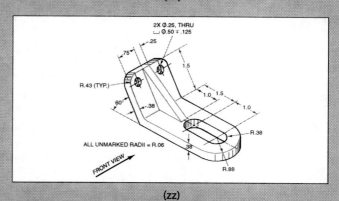

(zz)

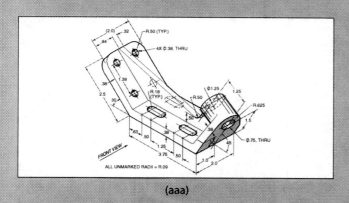

(aaa)

FIGURE P10.6.

Auxiliary Views

objectives

After completing this chapter, you should be able to

- Describe an auxiliary view
- Describe situations where an auxiliary view is desired
- Locate top-adjacent, front-adjacent, and side-adjacent auxiliary views constructed from primary views
- Create an auxiliary view of an inclined surface

Auxiliary views are most commonly used to determine the true shape of inclined or oblique surfaces. Auxiliary views also are used to locate characteristics and relationships between lines and planes, such as:

- Visibility of lines and planes. For example, at a chemical facility, you will find buildings containing pumps and pipes crossing over and under each other. Auxiliary views and visibility principles are used to determine whether a pipe is on top or in front of another pipe.
- The shortest distance between two lines; for example, designing a brace to separate two pipes at their closest point.
- The shortest distance from a point to a plane. For example, in an ore mine, the entrance tunnel leading to a vein of ore should be short for economic reasons, but it also should have the optimal slope for the transportation of the ore.
- The slope of a line or plane; for example, the downward angle of a feeder that delivers parts to a conveyor belt.
- The angle between two planes, also called a dihedral angle. For example, the angle between the face and flank of a tool bit is ground to 62° to cut steel and 71° to cut cast iron.
- The intersection of two planes; for example, the intersection of one tube with another on a bicycle frame.

In this chapter, you will learn about the basics of using auxiliary views for examining inclined surfaces on solid objects. A supplemental chapter covers fundamentals in descriptive geometry, a graphical technique that was developed to explore characteristics and relationships between lines and planes. In descriptive geometry, auxiliary views are constructed to define relationships between points, lines, and planes in space; however, here you will focus on the fundamentals in creating auxiliary views of object surfaces, leaving the more advanced techniques for your later exploration.

14.02 Auxiliary Views for Solid Objects

In a previous chapter, you learned about multiview drawings of objects. You learned how to construct the top, front, and side views of an object by projecting these views onto the surfaces of a glass box surrounding the object and then unfolding the panes of glass so all of them were in the same plane. You also learned that normal surfaces are parallel to one of the six primary views, inclined surfaces are perpendicular to one of the primary views but are not parallel to any of the primary views, and oblique surfaces are neither parallel nor perpendicular to any of the primary views.

For normal surfaces, a frontal surface is parallel to the front view (or front pane on the glass box). A frontal surface is seen as an edge in the top and side views and is seen in its **true shape** and size in the front view. Likewise, horizontal surfaces are seen in true shape and size in the top view (they are parallel to the top view), and profile surfaces are seen in true shape and size in the side view (they are parallel to the side view). Thus, for a surface to be seen in its true shape and size, it must be parallel to the given view.

What about an inclined or oblique surface? You learned previously that these types of surfaces are not parallel to any of the primary views. Because they are not parallel to any of the primary views, they are seen **foreshortened** in the primary views—they are not seen in their true shape or size in the top, front, or side views. In the remainder of this chapter, you will learn about the creation of auxiliary views that show inclined surfaces in true shape and size. The creation of auxiliary views to determine the true size

FIGURE 14.01. The image of
the object is projected onto a
horizontal surface to create
the top view in (a). The front
and top views are shown in (b).

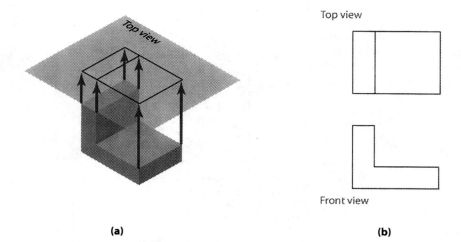

(a)

Top view

Front view

(b)

and shape of oblique surfaces will not be covered here. If you want to create successive auxiliary views to obtain true size and shape of an oblique surface, you can refer to the supplementary chapter on descriptive geometry.

Before you dive into understanding how auxiliary views are created, step back and think about the creation of the primary views. A horizontal surface is parallel to the top view. When you constructed the top view, you projected it onto the top pane of the glass box using **projection rays** that were perpendicular to the pane. In the front view, these projection rays extended perpendicularly from the horizontal **edge view** of the normal surface toward the top viewing plane. When the top pane was unfolded, the projection rays from the front view defined the outer limits of the surface as seen in the top view. The horizontal pane of glass also appears as an edge in the front view—an edge that is parallel to the surface in question. Figure 14.01a shows a simple object with the projection rays used to create the top view indicated, and Figure 14.01b shows the top and front views of the object after the imaginary glass box has been unfolded.

Figure 14.02 shows the top, front, and right-side views of a drill jig; a pictorial view of the jig is also shown for clarity. Surface A on the drill jig is seen as an edge in the front and side views and is seen in its true shape in the top view, signifying that surface A is

FIGURE 14.02. An object with
an inclined surface shown in the
preferred orthogonal view configuration with top, front, and
right-side views. Surface A is
parallel to the top viewing plane
(and, therefore, will be shown in
its true shape in the top view)
and in its edge view in the
front and right-side views.

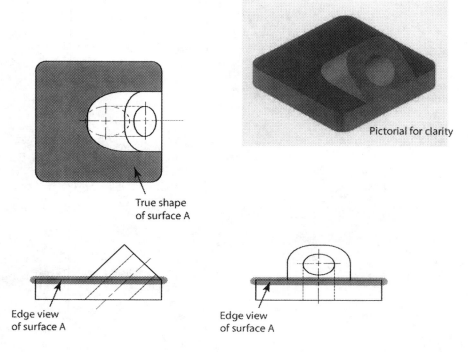

Pictorial for clarity

True shape
of surface A

Edge view
of surface A

Edge view
of surface A

FIGURE 14.03. Surface B is seen in an edge view in the front view but is not seen in its true shape in either the top or right-side views.

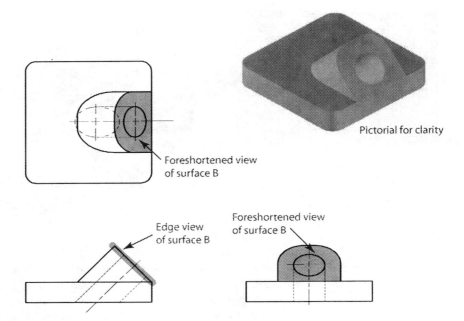

Foreshortened view of surface B

Pictorial for clarity

Edge view of surface B

Foreshortened view of surface B

parallel to the top plane. The edge view of inclined surface B is seen in the front view as indicated in Figure 14.03; however, since neither the top nor right-side views of the object are parallel to the surface, you are not seeing surface B in its true shape and size in either view. Surface B is foreshortened in both the top and side views.

To manufacture this part (you learned about manufacturing processes in an earlier chapter), a machinist will need to know exactly where the hole through the inclined surface B is located. However, since none of the views show the surface in its true shape and size, it would be difficult for the machinist to make this part accurately, based on the given information. If a view that is parallel to this inclined surface could somehow be constructed, surface B would be seen in its true shape and size in this new view, solving the problem of accurately locating the hole for the machinist. Because this new view is not one of the primary views of the object, it is called an auxiliary view—essentially any extra view, other than a pictorial, which has been constructed for overall clarity.

To understand how auxiliary views are created, it is useful once again to think about the object as if it were surrounded by a glass box. This time, however, imagine an extra pane of glass has been added to the glass box that is parallel to the inclined plane as shown in Figure 14.04. The inclined surface can be projected perpendicularly onto

FIGURE 14.04. An additional plane (pane) added to the glass box to show the true shape of the inclined surface.

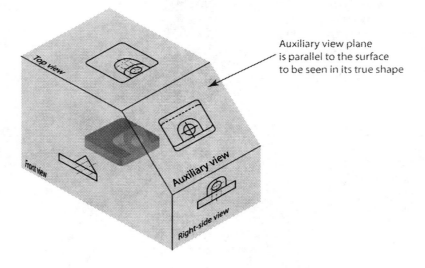

Top view

Auxiliary view plane is parallel to the surface to be seen in its true shape

Front view

Auxiliary view

Right-side view

FIGURE 14.05. The glass box
unfolded, showing the top,
front, right-side, and auxiliary
viewing planes on a single plane.

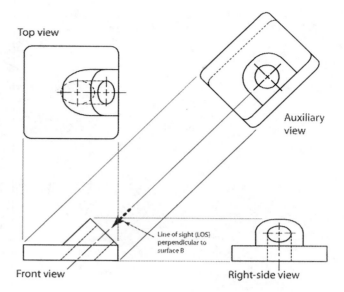

Top view

Auxiliary
view

Line of sight (LOS)
perpendicular to
surface B

Front view

Right-side view

this angled pane of glass, resulting in a view of its true shape and size. The glass box can
now be unfolded to show all views, including the auxiliary view, on a single plane.
Figure 14.05 shows the glass box with the panes of glass unfolded, including the pane
with the auxiliary view on it.

Figure 14.06a shows a full auxiliary view of the drill jig, while Figure 14.06b shows
a partial auxiliary view of the drill jig. The difference is that the full auxiliary view
shows all surfaces of the object, whether they are true shape or not, whereas the partial
auxiliary view shows only the surface for which the true shape and size are required—
the inclined surface. Full auxiliary views are usually not necessary to construct because

FIGURE 14.06. A full auxiliary
view is shown in (a). A partial
auxiliary view, showing only the
inclined surface, is shown in (b).

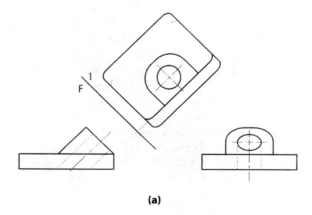

(a)

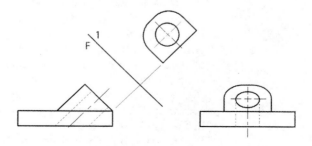

(b)

FIGURE 14.07. The glass box planes labeled.

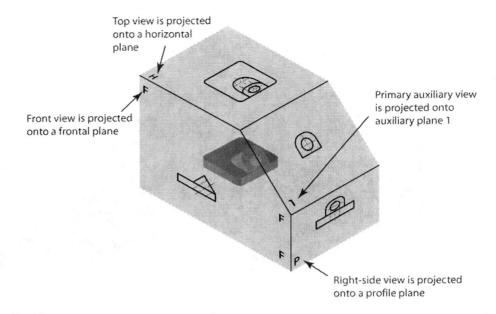

Top view is projected onto a horizontal plane

Front view is projected onto a frontal plane

Primary auxiliary view is projected onto auxiliary plane 1

Right-side view is projected onto a profile plane

you do not gain additional information from including other surfaces , which may even serve to clutter the drawing in such a view—the primary views show you what you need to know about the other surfaces on the object. Since your primary purpose in creating an auxiliary view is for clarity and not for confusion, partial auxiliary views are the most common type of auxiliary views you will create.

Some conventions have been developed to enable you to organize your work when you are working with auxiliary views. One of the conventions is in labeling views. You know the glass box is composed of six principal planes—two horizontal planes (the top and bottom planes), two frontal planes (the front and back planes), and two profile planes (the right and left-side planes). To help identify which views you are working with, when creating auxiliary views, it is standard practice to label the top, front, and side planes with the capital letters *H*, *F*, and *P*, respectively. (In this case, *H* represents the horizontal, or top plane; *F* represents the front plane; and *P* represents the side, or profile plane.) Any auxiliary planes you create should be numbered sequentially.

Figure 14.07 shows the three principal planes of the glass box labeled H, F, and P and the angled glass plane for the auxiliary view labeled 1. Figure 14.08 shows what these planes look like after the glass box has been unfolded. The glass box hinges are referred to as **reference lines** or fold lines and will be used to transfer measurements as you construct your auxiliary views. One of the other conventions that have been developed for work with auxiliary views is that the fold lines are usually shown in the multiview drawings. This is in contrast with standard practice for constructing multi-view drawings that you learned about in a previous chapter, where fold lines are not usually shown.

Understanding an auxiliary view is simple if you remember the principles of ortho-graphic projection. Any view that is projected from one view into the next is *adjacent* to the first view. The auxiliary view showing the inclined surface B in true size and shape is adjacent to the front view; the top and side views are also adjacent to the front view. In general, **adjacent views** are aligned side by side and share a common dimension. For example, the right and front views that are adjacent to each other show the height of the object in common. **Related views** are adjacent to the same view and share a common dimension. For the drill jig, the top and auxiliary views are adjacent to the front view. In this case, the top and auxiliary views are related to each other and share a common dimension—the object depth. The depth that point A is away from the fold line is visible in the top view, and this distance is preserved in the related auxiliary view. Figure 14.09 shows how the depth dimension for point A is preserved from the top into the auxiliary view.

FIGURE 14.08. The glass box
opened to show proper view
alignment.

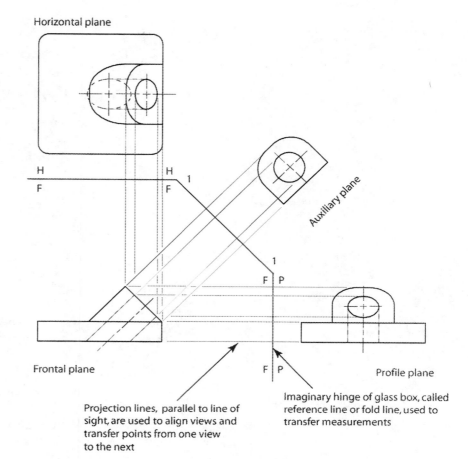

Horizontal plane

Auxiliary plane

Frontal plane

Profile plane

Projection lines, parallel to line of
sight, are used to align views and
transfer points from one view
to the next

Imaginary hinge of glass box, called
reference line or fold line, used to
transfer measurements

FIGURE 14.09. Comparison
between adjacent and
related views.

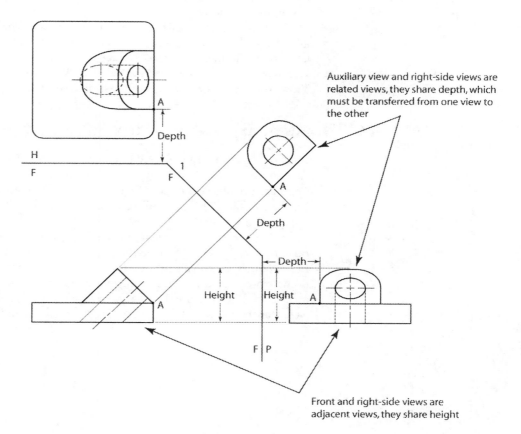

Auxiliary view and right-side views are
related views, they share depth, which
must be transferred from one view to
the other

Depth

Depth

Depth

Height

Height

Front and right-side views are
adjacent views, they share height

FIGURE 14.10. A profile-adjacent auxiliary view of surface B.

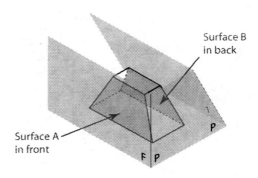

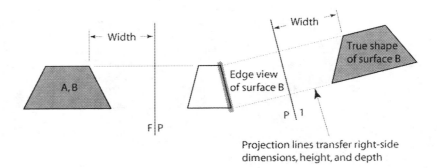

The auxiliary view you have been working with is called a front-adjacent view because it was constructed adjacent to the front view. It also is possible to draw top-adjacent and side-adjacent views, depending on which primary view shows the inclined surface in question as an edge. For example, if the inclined surface is an edge view in the top view, you would project the auxiliary view from the top view to obtain its true size and shape, thus creating a top-adjacent view. Similarly, if the inclined surface is seen as an edge in the side view, a side-adjacent auxiliary view would be used to show the surface in its true size and shape. Figure 14.10 illustrates a side-adjacent auxiliary view that shows the true size and shape of the indicated inclined surface.

14.03 Auxiliary Views of Irregular or Curved Surfaces

Most of the time, you will need to construct an auxiliary view of a surface on an object that shows a curved or irregular feature, like the drill jig from the previous example. Consider the object shown in Figure 14.11. This object contains two holes through an inclined surface. The inclined surface is seen in edge view in the top view, and the holes appear as ellipses in the front view.

When creating an auxiliary view of this surface, you should project several points on the curved edges to define them in the new view. For a circular hole, usually four radial points are sufficient; but, for an irregular curve, you may need to locate several points to obtain an accurate projection. Figure 14.12 shows an auxiliary view of the inclined surface for the object shown in Figure 14.11. In this case, four radial points were transferred into the auxiliary view for each circular hole on the surface.

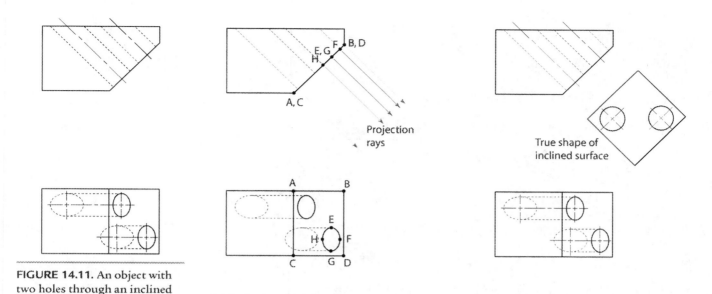

FIGURE 14.11. An object with two holes through an inclined surface.

(a) Projection of four points on each circle.

(b) Completed auxiliary view.

FIGURE 14.12. An auxiliary view of an inclined surface with holes in it.

14.04 Strategies for Auxiliary Views

How do you construct an auxiliary view that shows an inclined surface in true size without the aid of a glass cube? Review what you know so far. To see a surface in true size and shape, you must view it from a plane that is parallel to the surface. Since this viewing plane is parallel to the surface, the edge view of the pane of glass defining the new view also will be parallel to the surface. Finally, the points on the surface will project perpendicularly into this new view, similar to the way points are projected perpendicularly from the front into the top view (or from the front into the side view).

In general, the procedure used to create an auxiliary view that shows an inclined surface in true size and shape is as follows:

1. Identify the edge view in one of the primary views of the surface to be projected.
2. Sketch a "fold" line parallel to the edge view of the surface.
3. Label all of the fold lines, including the one you just created.
4. Project the points that define the surface along rays that are perpendicular to the fold line for the auxiliary view.
5. Obtain the projected dimensions of the surface into the auxiliary view by observing the same dimension in a related view. (Another way to think of this is that the dimensions are found in a view that is two views back from the auxiliary view in which you are working.)

In the case of curved or irregular surfaces, the first step in the procedure is to segment the curved edge into several points and to locate these in the primary views. The points defining the segments also can be projected into the auxiliary view in step 4 of this procedure.

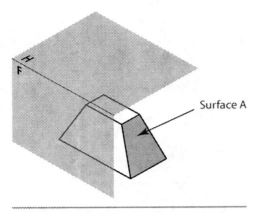

FIGURE 14.13. A truncated pyramid for constructing an auxiliary view.

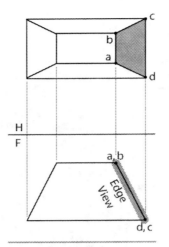

FIGURE 14.14. Top and front views of the truncated pyramid.

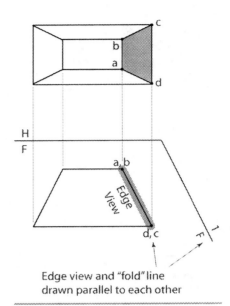

Edge view and "fold" line drawn parallel to each other

FIGURE 14.15. The fold line for the auxiliary view, with labels added.

Figure 14.13 shows a truncated pyramid, and you want to sketch an auxiliary view of the plane A that shows its true size and shape. Figure 14.14 shows the horizontal and front views of the pyramid. Notice that the front view includes the edge view of the surface in question. Also notice for this application the inclusion of the fold line between the top and front views.

To begin the construction of the auxiliary view, sketch a line parallel to the edge view of the surface in the front view. This line represents the fold line for the auxiliary view—the edge view of the pane added to the glass box. After you sketch the fold line, you should label the views appropriately. Figure 14.15 shows the two views of the object with the added fold line and the labels for the fold lines.

The surface will be projected into the auxiliary view along perpendicular projection rays. Only four points define the surface; but in the front view, these points are on top of each other—the endpoints of the line representing the edge view of the plane. Lightly sketch the projection rays from the endpoints of the line into the auxiliary view, keeping in mind that the direction of the projection rays is perpendicular to the fold line. Since the fold line was drawn parallel to the edge view of the plane, the projection rays also are perpendicular to the edge view of the surface. Figure 14.16 shows the two views of the object with the projection rays extending into the auxiliary view.

FIGURE 14.16. Projection rays added, extending from the edge view into the auxiliary view.

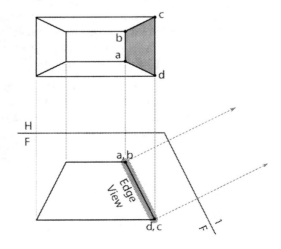

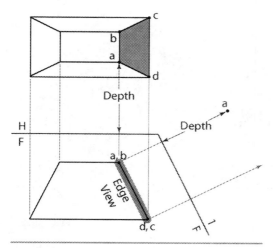

FIGURE 14.17. Point "a" transferred into the auxiliary view.

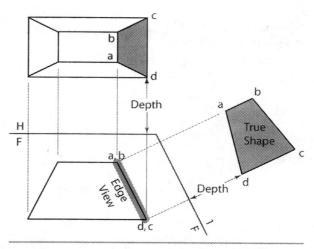

FIGURE 14.18. The auxiliary view showing surface A in true shape.

Transfer the depth dimensions that define the surface in question by looking in the related view (two views back). In this case, the depth is obtained in the top view for transfer into the auxiliary view. Figure 14.17 shows the first point for the surface, point "a," transferred into the auxiliary view.

Continue transferring the remaining points that define the surface into the auxiliary view, each time transferring the depth dimension from the top view. Figure 14.18 illustrates the completed auxiliary view showing the true size and shape of the inclined surface.

Follow this same procedure to obtain the true size and shape of the irregular inclined surface on the object shown in Figure 14.19.

Before you begin, you need to locate several points along the curved edge that you will subsequently project into the auxiliary view. Figure 14.20 shows the same object except that five points along the curved edge have been located and labeled A–E in the top and front views.

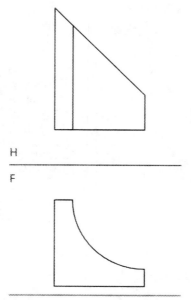

FIGURE 14.19. Top and front views of an object with an irregularly shaped surface for the auxiliary view.

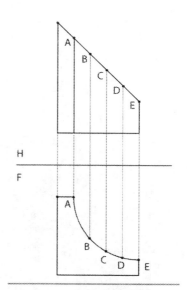

FIGURE 14.20. A curved edge with points A–E located.

FIGURE 14.21. The fold line and projection rays added.

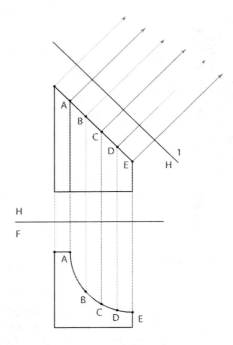

Sketch the fold line parallel to the edge view of the inclined surface and project the points into the auxiliary view using perpendicular projection rays as you did before. Also, make sure you label the fold lines appropriately according to the conventions described earlier. The result is shown in Figure 14.21. When projecting the points, make sure you project each of the points from the segments defining the irregular curved edge.

Locate each of the points in the auxiliary view by measuring the distance each point is from the fold line for the related view (in this case, the front view) and transferring those distances into the view you are creating. Figure 14.22a shows the distance transferred for point A, and Figure 14.22b shows the remainder of the points defining the curved edge transferred into the auxiliary view. Figure 14.22c shows the remaining points defining the surface transferred into the auxiliary view.

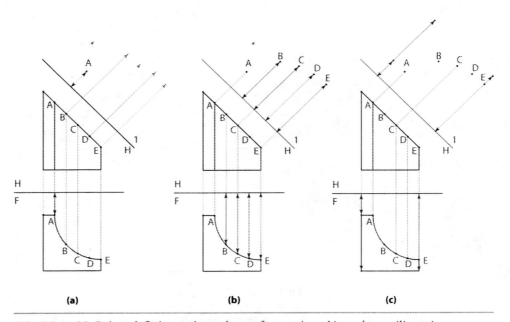

(a)   (b)   (c)

FIGURE 14.22. Points defining an irregular surface projected into the auxiliary view.

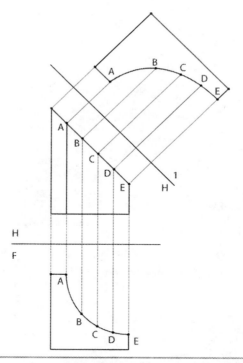

FIGURE 14.23. The completed auxiliary view of the irregular surface.

Finally, connect the dots to create a smooth curved edge and complete the auxiliary view that shows the surface in true shape and size. The completed view is shown in Figure 14.23.

CAUTION

The most common error that students make in creating auxiliary views is when transferring distances into the new view. A typical mistake involves trying to measure the distance from the adjacent view instead of from a related view. For example, Figure 14.24 shows an object with an inclined surface. The parallel fold line is easily created, as are the perpendicular projection rays shown in Figure 14.25.

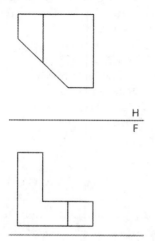

FIGURE 14.24. An object with an inclined surface for auxiliary view.

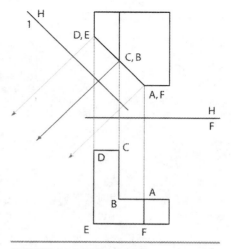

FIGURE 14.25. The fold line and projection rays for auxiliary view creation.

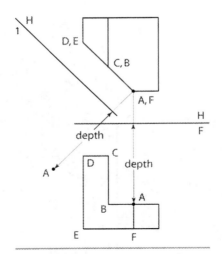 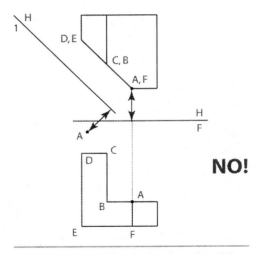

FIGURE 14.26. The depth distance for point A found in the front view.

FIGURE 14.27. The incorrect transfer of distance to point A in the auxiliary view.

NO!

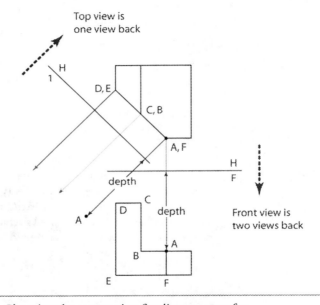

FIGURE 14.28. Choosing the correct view for distance transfer.

To establish point A along the projection ray, you need to determine the distance that it lies from the H/1 fold line. To do this, you need to measure the distance that the point is from the H/F fold line; however, it is the distance from the H/F fold in the *front* view, as shown in Figure 14.26. Many times students incorrectly transfer the distance that the point is from the H/F fold line in the *top* view, as shown in Figure 14.27.

Remember, when transferring distances into the auxiliary view, go back *two* views, not just one, as shown in Figure 14.28.

Solid Modeling Considerations in Creating
14.05 Auxiliary Views

The procedure followed to create an auxiliary view by hand is sometimes tedious and often prone to errors. In the era of 3-D solid modeling, the need for auxiliary views may be somewhat diminished, and the difficulty in creating auxiliary views is greatly reduced. First of all, since the 3-D model is often sent directly to a CAM system for fabrication, it may not be necessary to create an auxiliary view to locate holes and other features accurately on an inclined surface. Because the 3-D model contains all of the necessary information for the creation of the part, an auxiliary view of an inclined surface might not provide any additional information and, therefore, is not needed for manufacturing the part.

Second, when an auxiliary view from a 3-D solid model is needed, creating it is a relatively easy task. Recall that an auxiliary view is created by "looking" perpendicular to the inclined surface. With 3-D modeling software, you usually can select a plane on the object to define the viewing plane. The software will then rotate the object in space so the selected plane is parallel to the computer screen, meaning the plane will appear in true size and shape. With some software, you will be able to show only the plane; with other software, you will be forced to show the entire object from this viewpoint. However, since this auxiliary view is so simple to create, showing the entire object is a small price to pay. Figure 4.29 illustrates a 3-D solid model and an auxiliary view showing the inclined surface in true shape and size.

FIGURE 14.29. The creation of auxiliary views of the AeroTec bow handle from its solid model.

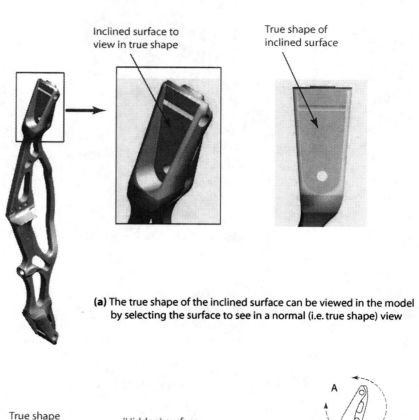

Inclined surface to view in true shape

True shape of inclined surface

(a) The true shape of the inclined surface can be viewed in the model by selecting the surface to see in a normal (i.e. true shape) view

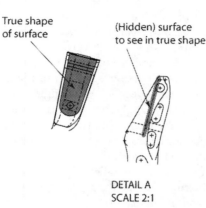

True shape of surface

(Hidden) surface to see in true shape

DETAIL A
SCALE 2:1

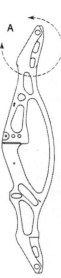

A

(b) The true shape of the inclined surface can be viewed in the drawing by selecting the surface to see in an auxilary view

Solid model of object with oblique surface

Top view

Normal (true shape)
view of oblique surface

Front view

Right-side view

FIGURE 14.30. An object with an oblique surface created by a solid model can easily be presented in any view orientation, including a normal (i.e., true shape) view of the oblique surface.

Also, note that the software can just as easily show the true size and shape of an oblique surface and that successive auxiliary views are not required in this application. Figure 14.30 shows a 3-D model of an object containing an oblique surface and the corresponding auxiliary view in true size and shape.

14.06 Sketching Techniques for Auxiliary Views

In creating auxiliary views as described in this chapter, you should realize by now that you will need to create parallel and perpendicular lines accurately. Many advanced drafting techniques allow you to create these lines; however, you can use a simple set of triangles to create parallel and perpendicular lines. To draw a line parallel or perpendicular to another line, align one leg of one of the triangles with the line. Place the hypotenuse of the second triangle (the base triangle) up against the hypotenuse of the first triangle and hold the base triangle firmly in place. Slide the first triangle up or down the paper, making sure its hypotenuse is always in contact with the hypotenuse of the base triangle. As you slide the triangle, one of its legs will remain parallel to the original line and the other leg will remain perpendicular to the line. You can use either of these straightedge surfaces to draw your parallel or perpendicular lines according to the type of line you need to construct. The method of using triangles to draw parallel or perpendicular lines is illustrated in Figure 14.31.

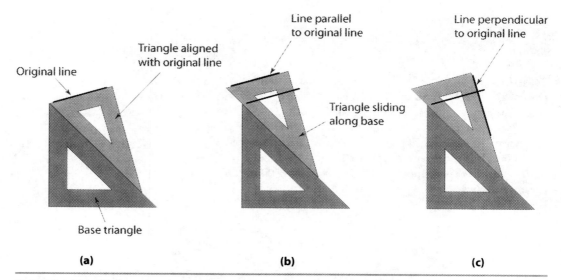

FIGURE 14.31. Sliding triangles used to construct parallel and perpendicular lines.

14.07 Chapter Summary

Auxiliary views allow you to look perpendicular to an inclined surface and see it in its true shape and size. When you are looking perpendicular to the surface, it is important to note that your viewing plane is parallel to the plane in question. Auxiliary views also are used to find information between two lines, a line and a plane, and two planes; however, these applications are left for your exploration in a supplementary chapter on descriptive geometry. The procedure you use to create an auxiliary view is based on the principles from orthographic projection described in detail in previous chapters of this text. In essence, when creating an auxiliary view, you are inserting a pane of glass into the imaginary glass cube that is parallel to the inclined surface. When the glass cube is unfolded, including the extra pane, the auxiliary view shows the inclined surface in true size and shape. In the age of 3-D solid modeling, the need for auxiliary views may be diminished; however, knowing the basics of creating this type of view is important for your understanding of graphic communication. Three-dimensional solid modeling software also enables you to easily create an auxiliary view of an inclined or an oblique surface using a few clicks of the mouse button.

14.08 glossary of key terms

adjacent views: Views that are aligned side by side to share a common dimension.

auxiliary views: Views on any projection plane other than a primary or principal projection plane.

edge view (of a plane): A view in which the given plane appears as a straight line.

foreshortened (line or plane): Appearing shorter than its actual length in one of the primary views.

inclined surface: A plane that appears as an edge view in one primary view but is not parallel to any of the principal views.

oblique surface: A plane that does not appear as an edge view in any of the six principal planes.

projection ray: A line perpendicular to the projection plane. It transfers the 2-D shape from the object to an adjacent view. Projection rays are drawn lightly or are not shown at all on a finished drawing.

14.08 glossary of key terms (continued)

reference line: Edges of the glass box or the intersection of the perpendicular planes. The reference line is drawn only when needed to aid in constructing additional views. The reference line should be labeled in constructing auxiliary views to show its association between the planes it is representing; for example, H/F for the hinged line between the frontal and horizontal planes. A reference line is also referred to as a fold line or a hinged line.

related views: Views adjacent to the same view that share a common dimension that must be transferred in creating auxiliary views.

true shape (of a plane): The actual shape and size of a plane surface as seen in a view that is parallel to the surface in question.

14.09 questions for review

1. What is a primary auxiliary view?
2. What is the purpose of an auxiliary view?
3. How is a full auxiliary view different from a partial auxiliary view?
4. List the five basic steps or procedure for drawing an auxiliary view.

5. Why might the creation of auxiliary views not be necessary with 3-D solid modeling software?
6. How does 3-D solid modeling software make the job of auxiliary view creation easier and less prone to errors?

14.10 problems

1. For each of the pictorials shown in Figure P14.1, create the top, front, and right-side views. Then, create an auxiliary view to present the **true shape** of the inclined surface.

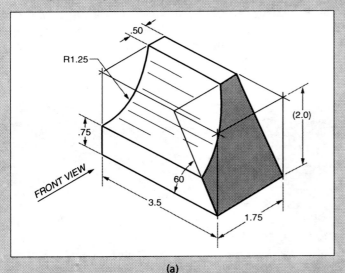

(a)

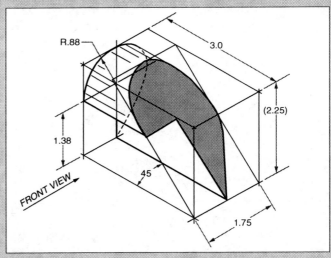

(b)

14.10 problems (continued)

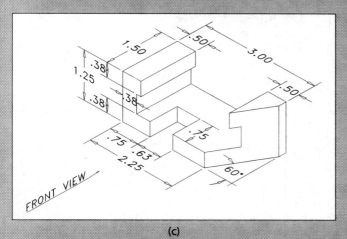

(c)

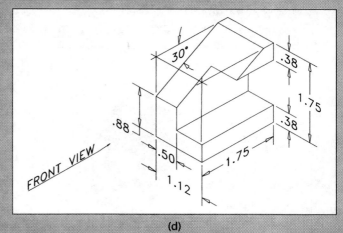

(d)

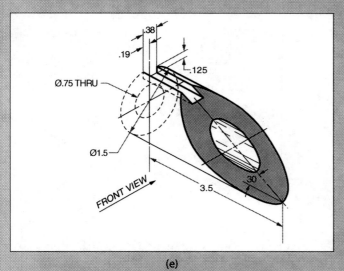

(e)

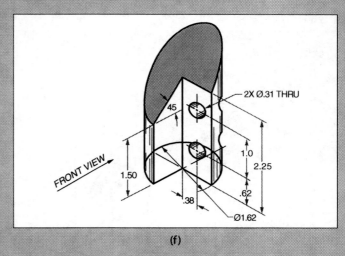

(f)

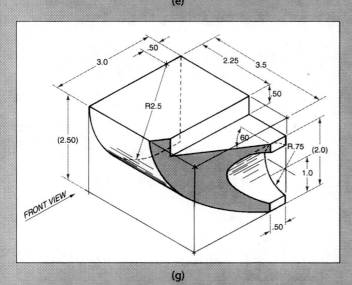

(g)

FIGURE P14.1.

14.10 problems (continued)

2. For each of the pictorials shown in Figure P14.2, create the top, front, and right-side views. Then, create an auxiliary view to present the entire object with the inclined surface shown in its true shape.

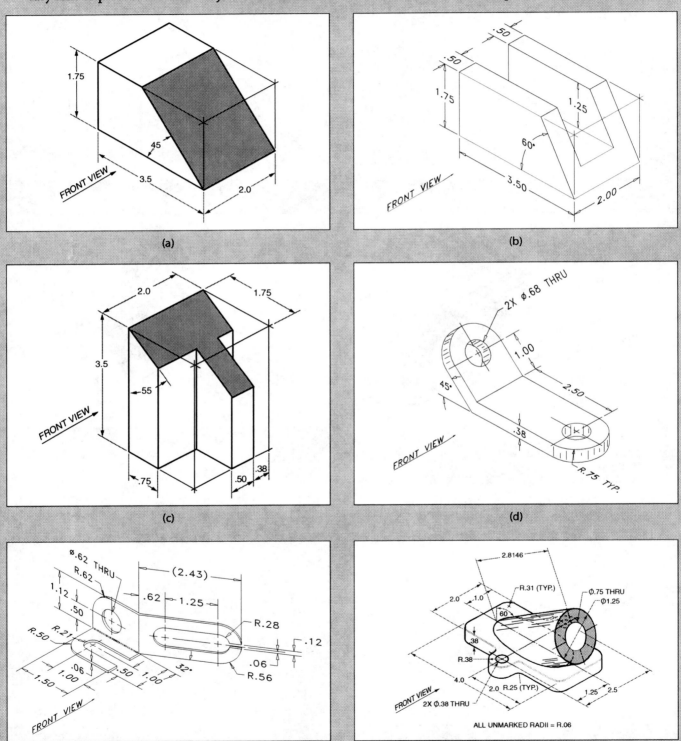

(a)

(b)

(c)

(d)

(e)

(f)

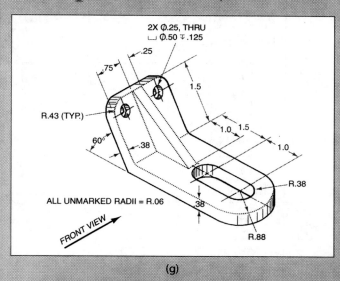

(g)

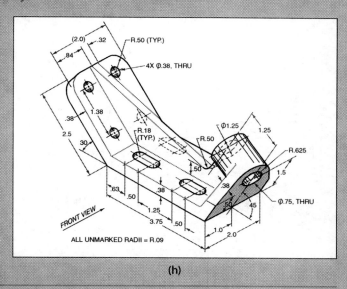

(h)

FIGURE P14.2.

3. For each of the multiview drawings shown in Figure P14.3, create an auxiliary view to present the entire object with the inclined surface shown in its true shape.

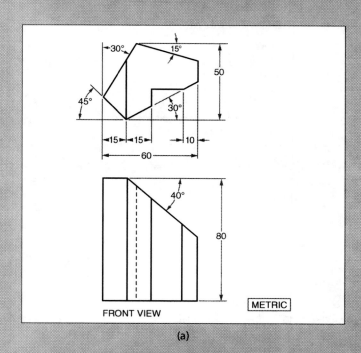

(a)

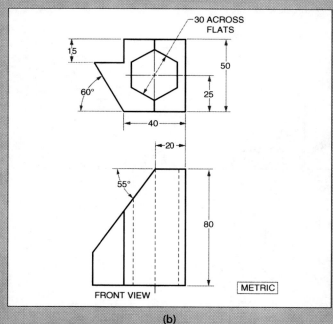

(b)

14.10 problems (continued)

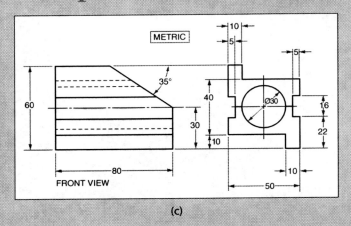

(c)

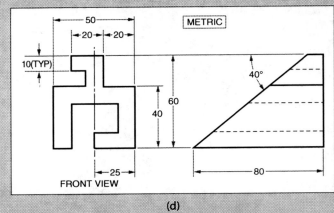

(d)

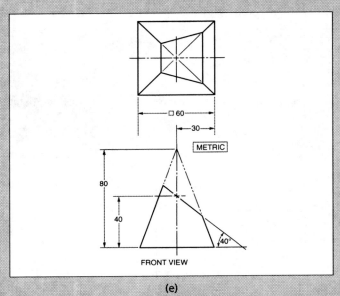

(e)

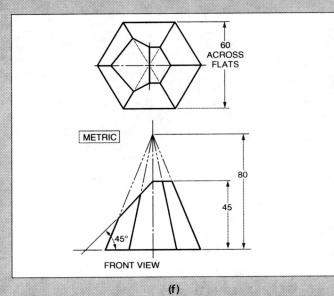

(f)

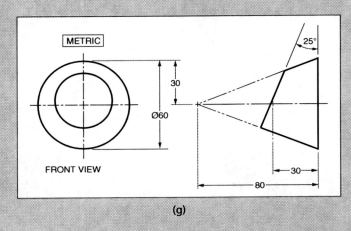

(g)

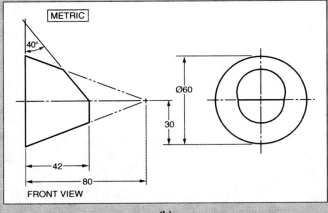

(h)

FIGURE P14.3.

Section Views

The precisely aligned images in a multiview drawing offer an excellent start in defining the exact geometry needed for a part that you want to build. However, this description alone may not be adequate to define all of the features in many types of parts. Some features may be partially or fully obscured in the standard views. The use of hidden lines can alleviate the problem, but too many hidden lines may cause confusion. In these cases, it is useful to have a means of revealing proposed interior detail. This is done by showing cross sections, or section views, at important locations. As with multiview drawings, to minimize ambiguity, you must follow certain guidelines when you want to present a section view.

13.02 A Look Inside

Pick up an everyday object (for example, a coffee mug) and look at it from all directions. If you cannot find a coffee mug, some images have been provided for your convenience in Figure 13.01. You will notice that you cannot view the mug from a direction where the inside depth of the cup or the thickness of the bottom can be directly measured (unless it is made of a clear material). If the mug has a handle on it, look at that as well. Are the edges of the handle rounded? Can you look at the handle from a direction where you get an undistorted view of the radius of the edge? These features are simple examples of measurements that cannot be made from looking at an object in a multiview drawing. Yet there must be some means of showing these types of features so a fabricator will know what to make and what sizes are required. A coffee mug is a very simple example.

Here is an industrial example. Consider the Hoyt AeroTec bow handle again. Its image and multiview engineering drawing are shown in Figure 13.02, with its cross brace highlighted. Note that the edges of the cross brace are rounded. Can these rounded edges be seen on the drawing? Assume the edges of the cross brace are not rounded, (i.e., the surfaces meet at a 90° angle). How would the drawing change? The answer is that in its current state, with all of the complexity and exquisite detail, the drawing cannot show the existence of rounded edges. Clearly, something must be added to the drawing to show that these edges are rounded and to what size they are rounded.

FIGURE 13.01. Two views of an object (a coffee mug) with interior detail.

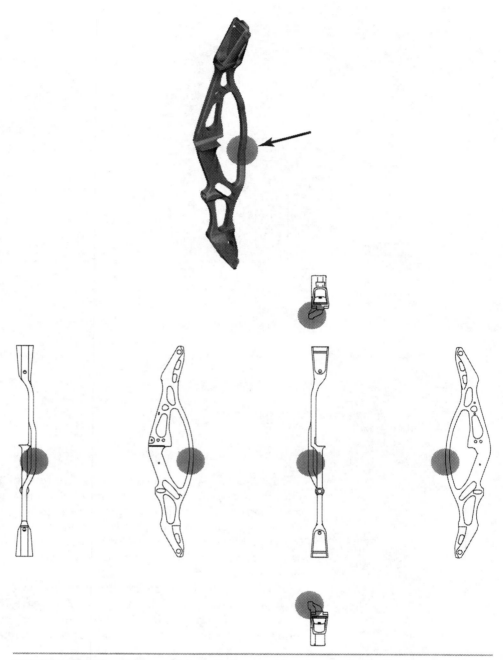

FIGURE 13.02. The geometry of the cross brace on the AeroTec riser cannot be seen in the multiview drawing.

Backing up a bit, look at the mug again to find out what is causing the problem. Figure 13.03 shows the multiview engineering drawing of the mug. Note that the depth of the mug and the radius of the edges of the handle cannot be seen on this drawing. The reason is because the object gets in the way of itself. Portions of the object obscure other portions of the same object. The outside of the mug hides the inside.

A possible solution to this problem is to use hidden lines, as shown in Figure 13.04. The hidden lines show the depth and geometry of the inside of the mug, as well as the geometry of the edges on the handle. However, the use of hidden lines is not always an ideal solution. As objects become more complicated, too many hidden lines make the views confusing, particularly when the images of different features start to fall atop one another.

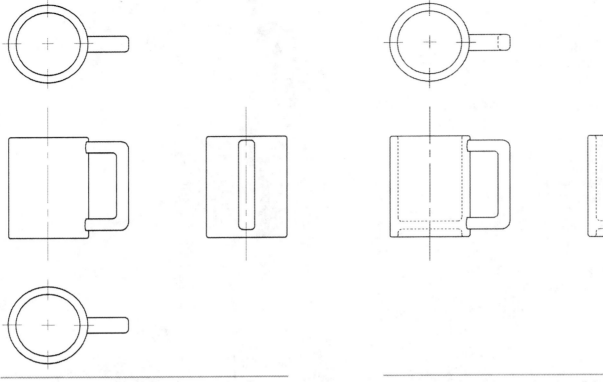

FIGURE 13.03. Orthographic views of the coffee mug fail to define interior detail.

FIGURE 13.04. A multiview drawing of the coffee mug using hidden lines to show interior detail.

In Chapter 3, you learned about cross sections of 3-D objects. If there were a way to cut the mug open, as shown in Figure 13.05, you could take the sliced part and turn it around until you were able to see the desired geometry. This hypothetical slicing is the essence of creating a cross section of the object, to create what is called a **section view**. The slicing, however, must be done following certain rules to ensure that the person who sees a section view on a drawing knows exactly where the slicing has occurred and how it was performed.

A drawing of the mug with three orthogonal views and two types of sections views is shown in Figure 13.06. Do not worry if you have difficulty understanding the extra views in this figure. The following sections discuss in detail how various types of section views are made and how they should be interpreted.

FIGURE 13.05. Hypothetical cutting of the object to reveal interior detail.

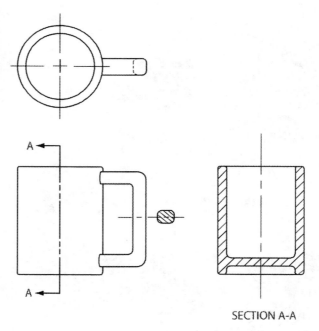

SECTION A-A

13.03 Full Sections

The simplest section view is the **full section**. In a full section, the object is cut completely apart by a **cutting plane** that is perpendicular to one of the standard viewing planes, such as the front, top, or side views. The image of the original whole object is made on the viewing plane using orthogonal projection, and the cutting plane is seen in edge view. A good way to think of a cutting plane is as a very thin knife with the blade held perpendicular to the viewing plane, which hypothetically splits the part into two pieces. This process is shown in Figure 13.07. Note that the cutting plane has an associated **viewing direction**, identified by a set of arrows pointing in the direction of the freshly cut surface that is to be viewed. To create the section view, the image of the split part is imprinted on the cutting plane. The cutting plane and the image are then rotated away from the split part until it is coplanar with the viewing plane. The hinge for this rotation of the cutting plane is its intersection with the viewing plane. With this definition of a section view and its location on the viewing plane, the alignment and orientation of the section view is the same as that used to create an orthogonal view. The section view is the image of the cut object as seen through the cutting plane, and this image is then placed on the viewing plane. In essence, a full section view is just another orthogonal view, but one that reveals the interior of the object.

On an engineering drawing, the original images of the object are not cut apart, as shown in Figure 13.08. A heavy line that extends across the entire part, with alternating short-short-long dashes, represents the edge view of the cutting plane. This line is called a **cutting plane line**. The orientation of the section view relative to the original view of the object is the same as if the viewing plane and the cutting plane were orthogonal viewing plans that had been unfolded. **Section lines**, which are a form of shading, are used to identify areas on the section view that are solid on the original whole object.

There are some important things to note in a full section on an engineering drawing. First, the cutting of the part is imaginary. The part is not to be split into separate pieces. The use of a full section is similar to saying, "If we imagine that the part was cut here, this is what we would see." The cutting plane is flat and goes all the way through the object. Notice the pairs of large, bold capital letters on the cutting plane line next to the arrows. These are used for unique identification of cutting plane lines and their associated section views on a drawing. If the letter A is used beside both arrows on a cutting plane line, there must be a note immediately below the corresponding section view that identifies it as "SECTION A-A." The arrows on the cutting plane line point in

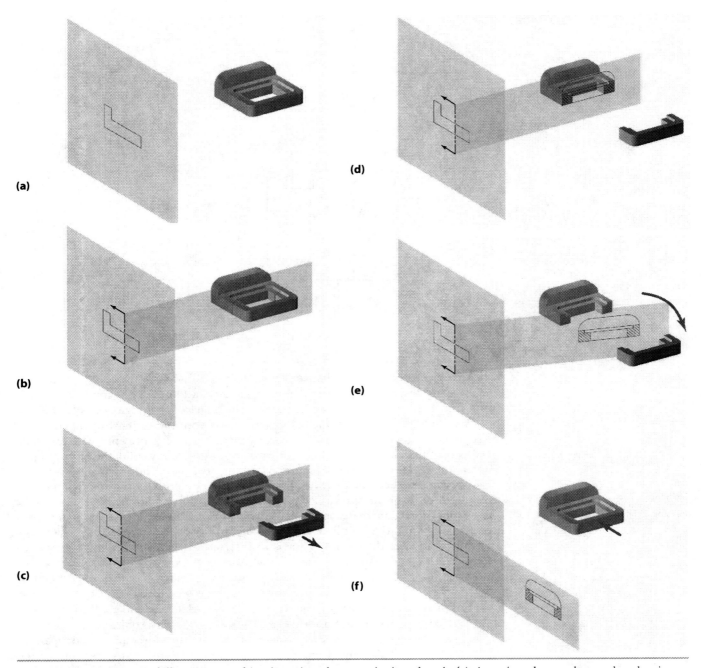

(a)

(b)

(c)

(d)

(e)

(f)

FIGURE 13.07. Creating a full section. An object is projected onto a viewing plane in (a). A cutting plane orthogonal to the viewing plane slices the object in (b). The piece to be viewed remains, while the other piece is removed in (c). The projection of the sliced object is made on the cutting plane in (d). The cutting plane and image are rotated about the section line in (e). The section view is coplanar with the viewing plane in (e).

the direction of viewing. This last point is important because the viewing direction and the orientation of the section view are not arbitrary. An error in either may cause confusion for the reader. Try to visualize the cutting process by comparing Figure 13.07 with Figure 13.08. Correlate the 3-D cutting process in Figure 13.07 with what is shown on the 2-D representation in Figure 13.08. The arrows on the cutting plane point are in the same direction as the arrows on the cutting plane line.

If the arrows on the cutting plane and its corresponding cutting plane line were reversed, as shown in Figure 13.09, the section view would be slightly different. Although the surface that is created by the cutting operation would be the same, the background image of the part would be different. This change is due to the fact that you would be retaining and looking at the other piece that was created when the part was hypothetically split compared to the case in Figure 13.08. When working with multiview drawings, you can remember the proper orientation of the section view by noting that it has the same orientation as the orthogonal view opposite to which the cutting plane line arrows point. For example, if the cutting plane line was located on the front view (and its arrows pointed away from the right-side view), the associated section view would have the same orientation and alignment as the right side view.

FIGURE 13.08. An engineering drawing with a section view to reveal interior detail.

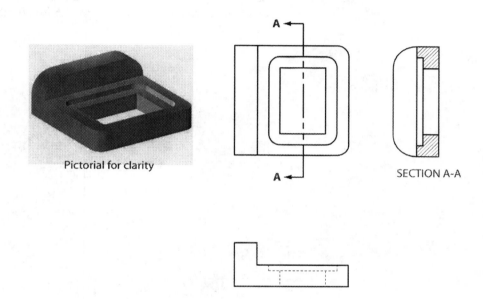

FIGURE 13.09. An engineering drawing with a section view to reveal interior detail.

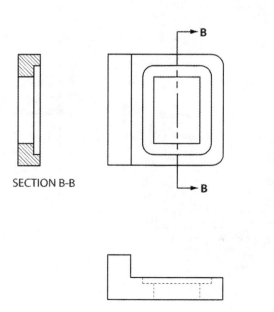

The drawing in Figure 13.10 shows a part with multiple section views. If a drawing has multiple section views, a pair of letters must uniquely identify each set of cutting plane lines and corresponding section views. So if there is a second cutting plane line and corresponding section view on the drawing, it may be identified as "SECTION B-B" if "SECTION A-A" already exists. The third set may be called "SECTION C-C," and so on. These identification labels are customarily used even when a drawing has only one section view. The hypothetical interpretation of the multiple sections on the object in Figure 13.10 is shown in Figure 13.11.

One way section views differ from conventional orthogonal views is that, in practice, section views are not required to remain aligned with their adjacent orthogonal views. Although breaking this alignment may violate the rules of orthogonal projection used to create a section view, it is allowed for convenience. Figure 13.12, for example, shows multiple section views of the part. One section is aligned with the view in which it was created. The other section views are nonaligned, but this is permitted in engineering drawing. However, note that even when the section views are nonaligned, they still are required to maintain the same rotational orientation as if they were aligned.

FIGURE 13.10. Multiple section views on a single object.

Pictorial for clarity

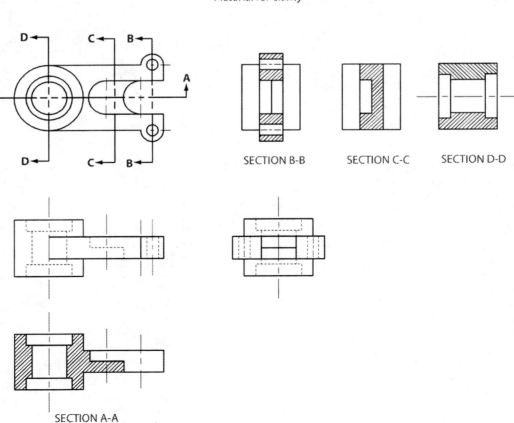

SECTION B-B   SECTION C-C   SECTION D-D

SECTION A-A

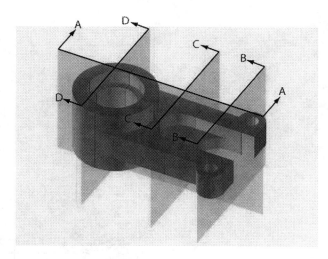

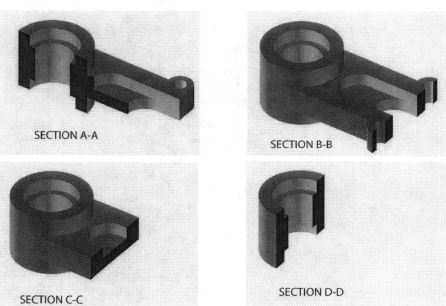

Another difference between a section view and a conventional orthogonal view is that a section view is permitted to have a different scale, or magnification, than the view in which it was created. An example of this property is shown in Figure 13.12, where three of the section views are magnified to reveal detail inside the part that would otherwise be difficult to see. When a section view uses a scale that is different from that of the principal views, the new scale must be clearly marked below the note used to identify the section view, as shown in Figure 13.12.

When a section view is created, even though the cutting plane is perpendicular to the viewing plane, there is no requirement that the cutting plane be parallel or perpendicular to any of the other orthogonal views. This property of section views makes it convenient to view features that may be placed at odd angles with respect to the principal views, as with the part shown in Figure 13.13.

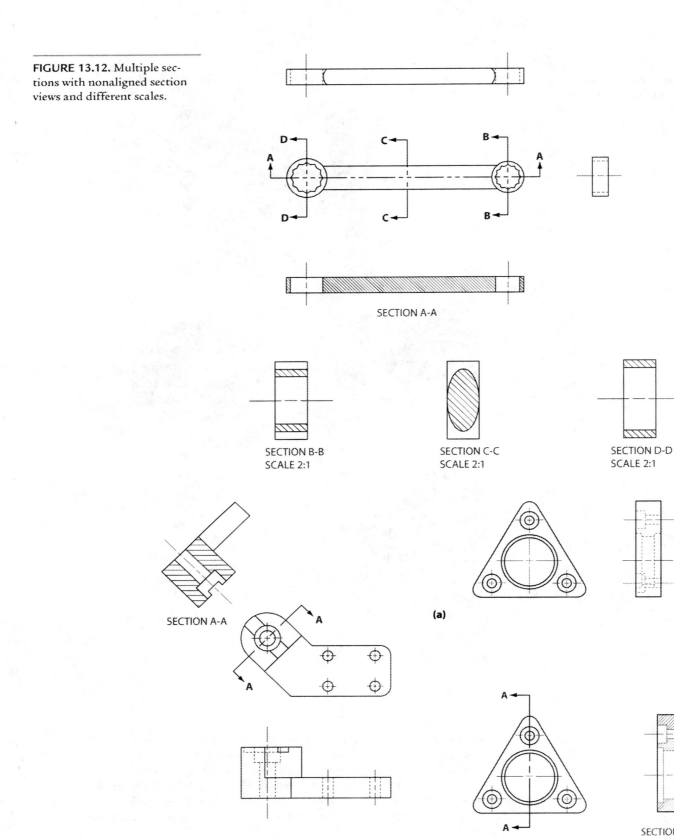

FIGURE 13.12. Multiple sections with nonaligned section views and different scales.

SECTION A-A

SECTION B-B
SCALE 2:1

SECTION C-C
SCALE 2:1

SECTION D-D
SCALE 2:1

SECTION A-A

(a)

(b)

SECTION A-A

FIGURE 13.13. A full section through a feature placed at an angle.

FIGURE 13.14. The need for many hidden lines in the original drawing (a) is reduced by the use of a section view (b).

13.04   What Happens to the Hidden Lines?

One of the main incentives for using section views is to reduce the use of hidden lines, which until now has been the only method available for revealing the interior and hidden features of many types of objects. When there are too many hidden lines on the view of an object, the drawing becomes confusing. Replacing those hidden lines with one or more section views greatly clarifies the drawing. When section views are used in this manner, there is no longer any need to retain the hidden lines; and they can be removed from the drawing. Hidden lines are typically not shown on the section-line-filled portions of a section view except to indicate the presence of screw threads. Figure 13.14 compares an example of a drawing that originally contained many hidden lines with a revised drawing that replaces one of the orthogonal views with a section view. The improvement in clarity is substantial.

13.05   The Finer Points of Section Lines

Section lines are used to improve the clarity of a section view by indicating the portions of the part that had been solid at the location it was hypothetically cut. However, indiscriminate section line patterns may cause more confusion than clarification. The most basic pattern is a set of lines with a common inclination angle, thickness, and spacing, as shown in Figure 13.15. The line thickness for the pattern is usually no thicker than that used for the part edges. Even with this simple set of variables, the pattern requires some thought. The pattern must be discernible as being section lines when the drawing is read, and the pattern must be reproducible without significant distortion occurring when the drawing is copied. For example, optical copiers, scanners, and fax machines can greatly distort a high-density pattern. A low-density pattern may not appear as section line patterns at all, and the section lines may be misinterpreted as edges on the part.

The pattern should not be parallel or perpendicular to any of the major feature edges of the part; otherwise, there may be some confusion about which lines are part edges and which are section lines. Vertical and horizontal lines are rarely used for section lines.

Different section line patterns can be used to represent different materials. Sample patterns are shown in Figure 13.16. For some materials used in construction, such as concrete or earth, section line patterns are more of a texture than a simple geometric pattern.

POOR!

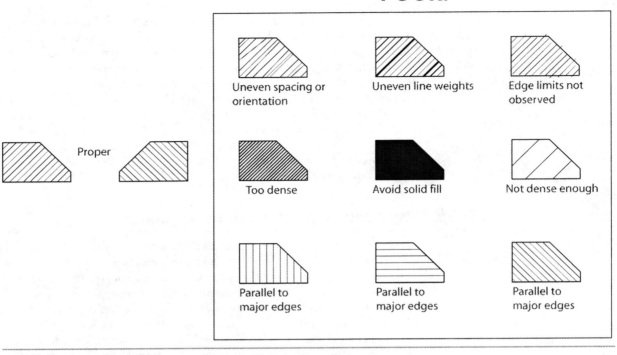

FIGURE 13.15. Examples of proper and poor cross-hatching techniques.

FIGURE 13.16. ANSI standard cross-hatch patterns for various materials.

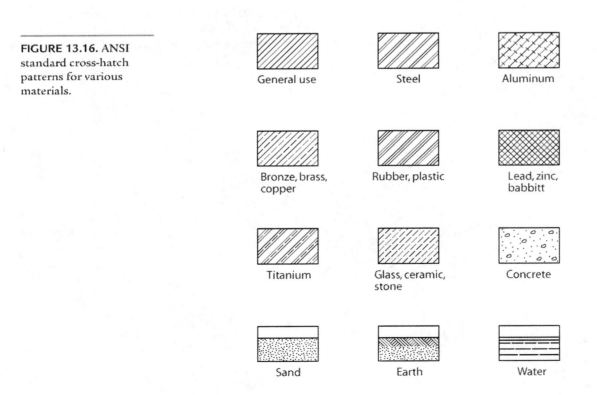

13.06 Offset Sections

Offset sections can be considered modifications of full sections. An offset section allows multiple features, which normally require multiple section views, to be captured on a single view. As with a full section, an external surface hypothetically cuts through an entire part. However, instead of the part being divided with a single flat cutting plane, the cutting surface is stepped. The size and location of each step is chosen to best capture the features to be displayed. Also, as with a full section, an offset section has its viewing direction indicated by arrows that point at the cut surface to be seen. When the offset cutting surface is rotated onto the viewing plane, the cross sections of multiple features, which could not be shown otherwise with a single cutting plane, can be displayed on a single view. This process is shown in Figure 13.17.

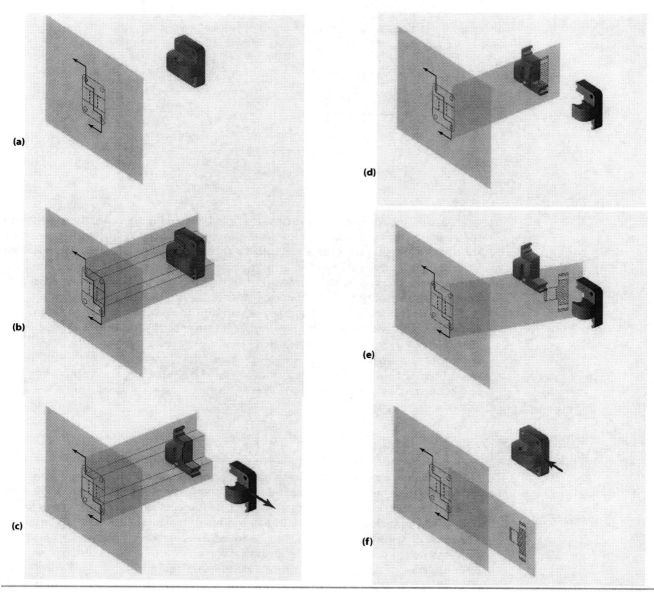

(a)

(b)

(c)

(d)

(e)

(f)

FIGURE 13.17. Creating an offset section. An object is projected onto a viewing plane in (a). A stepped cutting plane orthogonal to the viewing plane slices the object in (b). The piece to be viewed remains, while the other piece is removed in (c). The projection of the sliced part is made on the outermost segment of the stepped cutting plane in (d). The cutting plane and image are rotated about the section line in (e). The section view is coplanar with the viewing plane in (f).

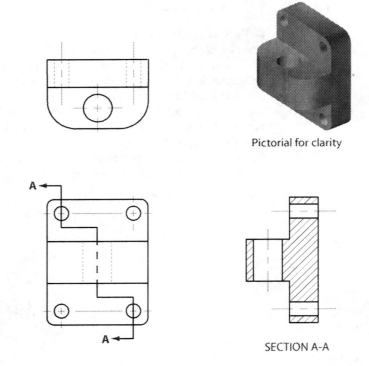

FIGURE 13.18. An engineering drawing using an offset section view to reveal multiple interior detail.

Pictorial for clarity

SECTION A-A

On an engineering drawing such as the one shown in Figure 13.18, the edge view of the stepped cutting surface is represented by a heavy stepped line with alternating short-short-long dashes. This is still called a cutting plane line, although technically it is no longer a straight line. The arrows point in the direction of viewing, and the cutting plane line and its associated offset section view are uniquely identified in each drawing with a pair of capital letters, as before.

As with full sections, the rotation orientation of an offset section view must be consistent with the creation of an orthogonal view; but the location and scale of the view is left to the discretion of the person creating the drawing. Note that in an offset section view, it is customary not to show the locations of the steps on the view. The reason is because this information is already available by inspecting the cutting plane line and because adding step lines may cause confusion by showing edges that do not actually exist on the part.

13.07 Half Sections

Half sections are used to save space and labor on an engineering drawing, especially for symmetrical parts. Recall what you learned about symmetry in Chapter 3. When an object is symmetrical about a plane or an axis, it is acceptable to present the object partially in its original state and partially in a sectioned state on the same orthogonal view. The plane of symmetry separates the two states. Another way of visualizing a half section is to imagine a part that is cut such that one-quarter of it is removed to reveal the interior detail. This hypothetical process is shown in Figure 13.19.

In the engineering drawing for this half section, the cutting plane line extends across the object only to the plane of symmetry. The cutting plane line extends partway across the object. A single arrow on the cutting plane line points in the direction of viewing. The absence of a second arrow is an indication that the cutting plane line is for a half section. There is no separate section view. Instead, the orthogonal view and the section view are combined such that the exterior of the part is shown on one half and the interior of the part is shown on the other half. In Figure 13.20, the view types change at the plane of symmetry, which is shown as a centerline. Note that hidden lines are not shown on the unsectioned half of the part.

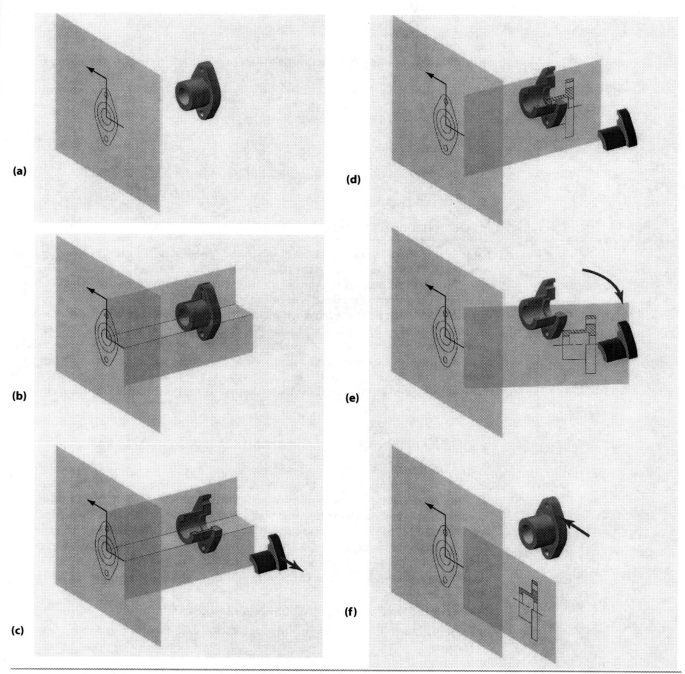

(a)

(b)

(c)

(d)

(e)

(f)

FIGURE 13.19. Creating a half section. An object is projected onto a viewing plane in (a). A stepped cutting plane slices through the object to the plane of symmetry in (b). The piece to be viewed remains, while the other piece is removed in (c). The image of the sliced object is projected onto an orthogonal viewing plane in (d). The viewing plane and image are rotated about the intersection line in (e). The section view is coplanar with the original viewing plane in (f).

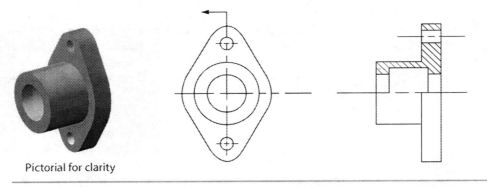

Pictorial for clarity

FIGURE 13.20. An engineering drawing shows the use of a half section to reveal interior as well as exterior detail.

13.08   Procedures for the Creation of Section Views

Later in this chapter, you will learn about some special types of section views; but for now, you will focus on creating the three types you have learned about so far: the full, offset, and half section views. A problem that many new engineers have when they are creating an engineering drawing is deciding whether to include section views. The basic question that must be answered when making this decision is this: Will the section view improve the clarity of the presentation? When the answer is clearly "yes," include section views. When the answer is "probably not," section views may not be necessary. Since section views are used to show interior or hidden details, objects that do not have such features usually fall into the latter category. Objects with such details must reveal them with hidden lines or section views. The question then becomes, which technique is better?

13.08.01 Deciding When to use Section Views

The decision to use section views is somewhat subjective. If the hidden features are relatively few and simple in geometry, such as a few simple holes or slots that go all the way through the part, the use of hidden lines would probably be best. Such features are so common that standard orthogonal views with hidden lines are quickly interpreted, and the addition of section views may actually contribute to unnecessary clutter on the drawing. However, as the hidden features become more numerous or complex in geometry, section views should be used to clearly define their geometries. As a guide, consider using section views when the answer to any of the following questions is yes if only hidden lines will be used.

▫ Are any hidden lines composed of multiple segments?

▫ Do any hidden lines of a feature intrude into the area occupied by another hidden feature?

■ Do any hidden lines of a feature share or come close to sharing any hidden lines with another feature unless the lines are exactly common?

Examples of these types of features are shown in Figure 13.21. An overall rule of thumb is that whenever the shear number or the geometric complexity of hidden lines makes the presentation of the object confusing, consider using section views.

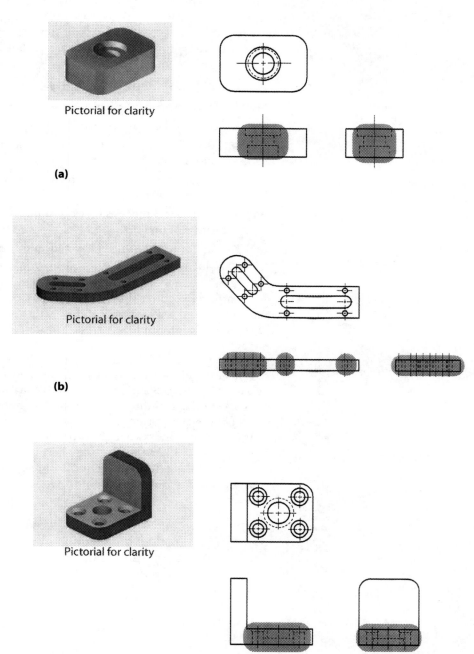

FIGURE 13.21. Internal features with hidden lines that have multiple segments (a) or overlap (b and c) are good candidates for using section views.

13.08.02 Creating a Full Section View

When the decision has been made to add section views to a drawing, the next step is to create them. When you are the original designer of the part, this task may be simple since you probably already visualize the internal geometry you want to feature. If the part is someone else's design, the process is trickier because you may need to interpret a rather messy drawing that needs the section views to improve the drawing's presentation. If this is the case, you will need to correctly align, identify, and visualize internal features that have been outlined with hidden lines in adjacent views. This task becomes difficult when some hidden lines are missing or have been removed for clarity. The steps to creating a full section view are outlined below and then explained in more detail using an example.

Step 1: Identify the feature(s) to be revealed and the desired viewing direction.

Step 2: Draw the cutting plane line that represents the edge of the cutting plane.

Step 3: Outline the modified part in an adjacent orthogonal view.

Step 4: Identify the intersection points of the part's exterior and interior edges with the cutting plane.

Step 5: Outline the internal features associated with the intersection points on the cutting plane.

Step 6: Find the boundaries between solid and empty space and fill the solid areas with section lines.

Step 7: Add or remove background edges in space and remove edges in solid areas.

When the section view is completed, it may be moved to a more convenient location on the drawing as long as its rotational orientation remains the same.

Consider the object shown in Figure 13.22, which has a pair of grooves inside its main bore. When the geometry of this feature is defined using hidden lines, these lines are composed of multiple segments. Thus, a section view would probably present this feature more clearly.

First (step 1), the bore with its grooves is identified as the feature to be shown in a section view. This feature can be presented best by using a cutting plane that contains the axis of the bore. Slicing the part in this manner would reveal the width and depth of the grooves. In this case, as in most cases, choosing a cutting plane that is parallel to one of the preferred principal views will make section view creation simpler. A cutting plane line (step 2) is drawn in the top view to represent the edge of the cutting plane, as shown in Figure 13.23. The cutting plane is a vertical plane seen as an edge in the top view. Because the cutting plane line is horizontal on the top view of the drawing, the cutting plane also is parallel to the front view; and outlining the part for the next step becomes easier.

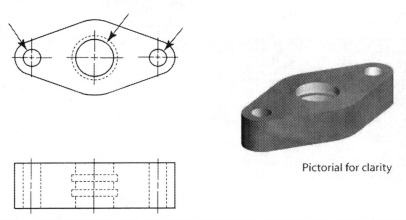

Pictorial for clarity

FIGURE 13.22. Construct a full section view of this part. It is desired to reveal the indicated features (step 1).

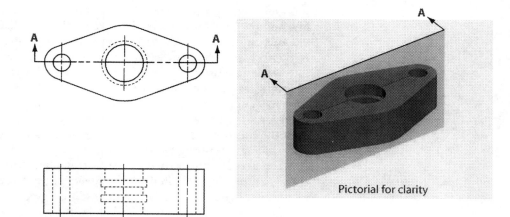

Pictorial for clarity

The direction of the arrows on the cutting plane line shows that the direction of viewing is from front to back. Since the cutting plane is parallel to the front viewing plane, the outline of the part in the section view is likely to be a significant portion of the outline as seen in the front view. This outline (step 3) is shown in Figure 13.24. Note that the size of the outline and its orientation are the same as in the front view from which it was derived. This outline is temporarily placed below the front view for convenience in feature alignment.

Next (step 4), examine the intersections of the cutting plane line with each visible and hidden edge inside the part, as shown in Figure 13.25. Note that some hidden edges may be obscured by visible edges. At every such intersection, a corresponding point will exist in the section view where the edge direction of an internal feature will change. The edges of the internal features appear as hidden lines in the front view but become visible edges in the section view. By tracking the internal edges, the outline of each sectioned internal feature on the cutting plane can be created.

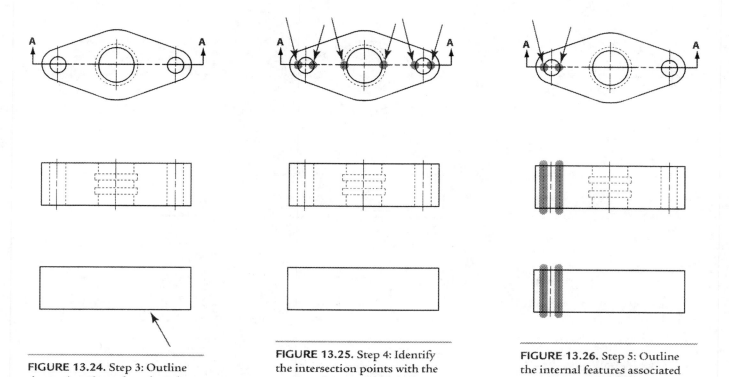

FIGURE 13.24. Step 3: Outline the sectioned part based on the adjacent view.

FIGURE 13.25. Step 4: Identify the intersection points with the cutting plane and see what is happening on the adjacent view.

FIGURE 13.26. Step 5: Outline the internal features associated with the intersection points on the cutting plane.

One way to proceed (step 5) is to examine sets of intersections on the cutting plane line and try to associate and visualize the internal features that created those intersections on the adjacent view. For example, from left to right on the cutting plane line in the top view, the first feature crossed is the visible edge of a circle. When the two intersection points of the cutting plane line on the circle are aligned with their corresponding features on the adjacent view, as shown in Figure 13.26, a pair of hidden lines is seen. The internal feature capable of generating such 2-D geometries on adjacent views is a simple hole that extends all the way through the part. In the section view, the optical limits (or "sides") of the hole become visible edges when the part is hypothetically split at the cutting plane.

The next feature crossed by the cutting plane line is a bit more complicated. It is composed of a visible circular edge inside a hidden circular edge. When these elements are aligned with their corresponding elements in the adjacent view, as shown in Figure 13.27, the feature described is a hole with two internal grooves. In the section view, the hidden edges of this feature seen in the front view become visible edges in the split part.

The final feature crossed by the cutting plane line is another hole. The section view showing all of the edges of the interior features revealed by the cutting plane is shown in Figure 13.28.

The next question that must be asked is, which of the interior areas of the section view were formerly solid, and which were formerly space? The ability to visualize the interior features is important here. The insides of holes, slots, and grooves, for example, contain space. Their edges in the section view separate space from former solid. In Figure 13.29, the portions of the section that are solid have been filled with section lines for easier visualization (step 6). Since the sectioned part also reveals the edges of the slots in the interior surface of the bore, these must be added to the section view (step 7), as shown in Figure 13.30. Note that in the final presentation, the original front

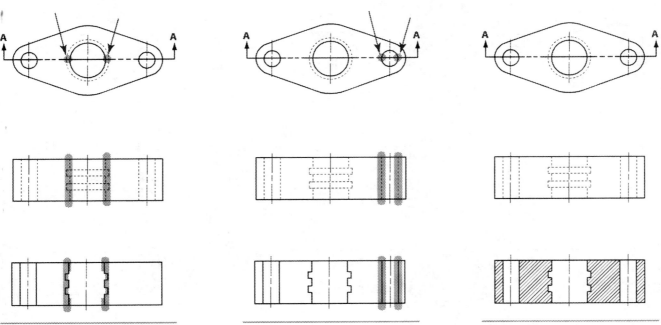

FIGURE 13.27. Continue and outline the next internal feature associated with the intersection points on the cutting plane.

FIGURE 13.28. Continue and outline the last internal feature associated with the intersection points on the cutting plane.

FIGURE 13.29. Step 6: Find the boundaries of air and solid and cross-hatch the solid areas.

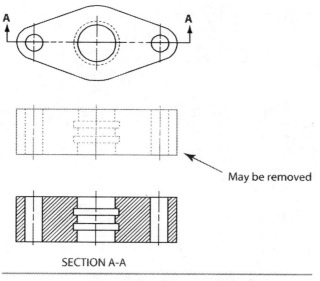

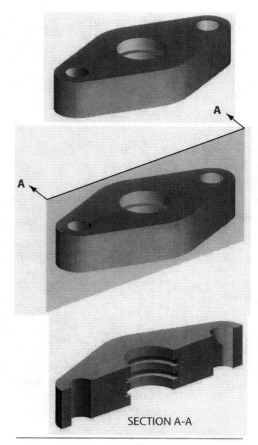

FIGURE 13.31. The whole part and the sectioned part.

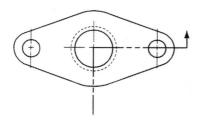

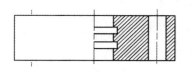

SECTION A-A

FIGURE 13.30. Step 7: Add any new edges that are revealed. Label the view. Note that the former front view may be removed since it adds no additional information.

view may be removed because it adds no additional information after the completed section view has been added. A pictorial of the part before and after sectioning is shown in Figure 13.31.

13.08.03 Creating a Half Section

The steps for creating a half section view are identical to those for creating a full section view except that only half the interior of the object needs to be revealed. A drawing with a half section view of the object in Figure 13.31 is shown in Figure 13.32. Note that this object is symmetrical about the centerline of the bore on its left and right sides.

In this case, the cutting plane line is created on the top view and extends only to the plane of symmetry (located at the axis of the bore). The single arrow on the cutting plane line points in the direction that the object is to be viewed. The half section view completely replaces the front view and shows the object in its unsectioned state without hidden lines on one side of the symmetry axis and the interior of the object on the other side of the axis.

FIGURE 13.32. Presentation as a half section view.

13.08.04 Multiple Section Views

When an object is particularly complex, multiple section views should be used to reveal all of its internal details. The object shown in Figure 13.33, for example, has multiple holes and slots that extend from different directions and that intersect. The plethora of hidden lines that result from the internal features make the multiview drawing difficult to interpret.

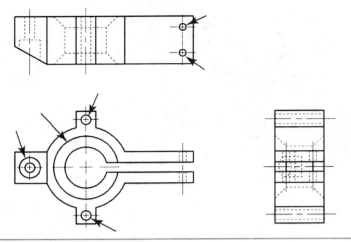

FIGURE 13.33. A complex object requiring multiple sections. It is desired to reveal the interior of the indicated features (step 1).

To reveal the interior details of the part (step 1) and remove the necessity of the hidden lines, three section views are needed. The cutting plane lines are labeled as A-A, B-B, and C-C on Figure 13.34. Note that each section has been chosen to reveal something unique about the interior detail (step 2), although different sections may share the same details. The seven-step process will be used to create Section A-A. The creation of Section B-B and Section C-C are left as a reader exercise, and only the results are shown.

Cutting plane line A-A extends across the length of the part at the keyhole-shaped slot in the front view. Since the arrows of the cutting plane line point away from the top view, an outline of the section view can be begun with a copy of the outline of the top view (step 3), as shown in Figure 13.35. Note that if the arrows of the cutting plane line had been pointing in the other direction (i.e., in the direction away from the (nonexistent) bottom view), the section view would need to have the same alignment and rotational orientation as the bottom view.

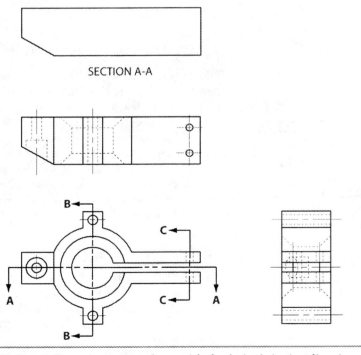

FIGURE 13.34. Step 2: Draw the cutting planes with the desired viewing directions.

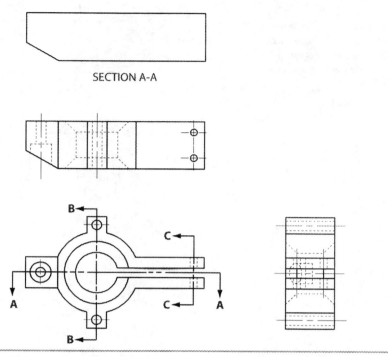

FIGURE 13.35. Step 3: Outline the sectioned part based on the adjacent view.

From left to right, the cutting plane line enters the part; crosses a set of concentric circles, then a set of concentric partial circles; and exits the part. The top view shows that the interior line is created by the edge of the inclined surface. When the intersection between the cutting plane line and concentric circles is aligned to their corresponding hidden edges in the adjacent views (step 4), as shown in Figure 13.36, it can be seen

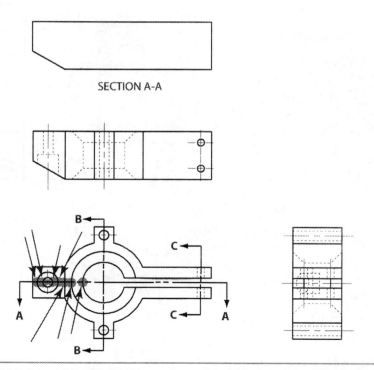

FIGURE 13.36. Step 4: Identify the intersection points with the cutting plane and see what is happening on the adjacent view.

FIGURE 13.37. Step 5: Outline the first internal feature associated with the intersection points on the cutting plane.

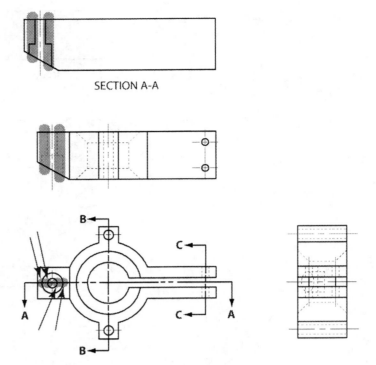

that the concentric circles represent the edges of a counterbored hole. On the section view, the hidden edges of the hole become visible (step 5), as shown in Figure 13.37.

By aligning the intersection between the cutting plane line and circles to their corresponding hidden edges in the adjacent views, it can be seen that the semicircles represent the edges of a countersunk-keyhole-shaped slot. On the section view, the hidden edges of the slot become visible (more of step 5), as shown in Figure 13.38.

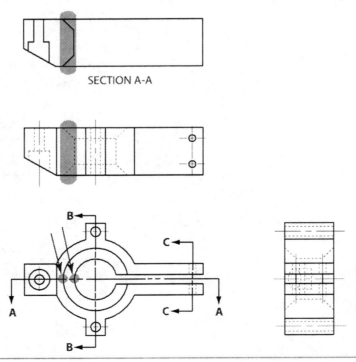

FIGURE 13.38. Step 5 cont: Outline the next internal feature associated with the intersection points on the cutting plane.

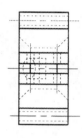

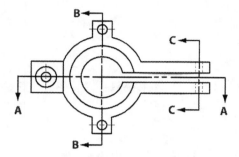

FIGURE 13.39. Step 6: Find the boundaries of air and solid and cross-hatch the solid areas.

Notice that as you continue to move from left to right along the cutting plane line, it does not intersect any other object feature. This means that the object behind the cutting plane is still visible, but there will not be any section lines to worry about because the cutting plane is not "cutting" through any more solid areas. The insides of the hole, slot, and counterbores contain space. Their edges in the section view separate space from former solid. In Figure 13.39, the portions of the section that were formerly solid have been filled with section lines for visualization (step 6). Note that in this case, the section view reveals the back "uncut" part of the object along with two edges in the keyhole slot that were previously hidden in the regular orthogonal view (step 7), as shown in Figure 13.40.

FIGURE 13.40. Step 7: Add background edges in the air. Label the view.

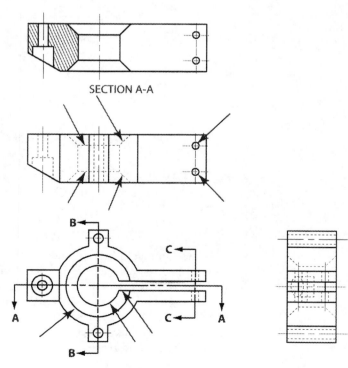

SECTION A-A

FIGURE 13.41. Add the other two sections using the same method of construction. Note that many of the hidden lines can be removed.

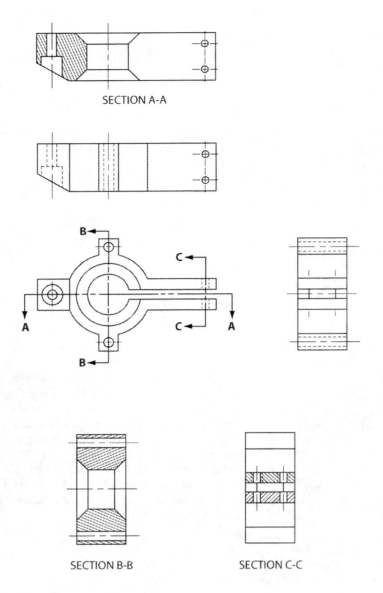

SECTION A-A

SECTION B-B   SECTION C-C

The completed Sections B-B and C-C are shown in Figure 13.41. The addition of Section B-B reveals the interior detail of the two holes beside the countersunk hole, which eliminates the confusion of the multiplicity of hidden lines in the multiview drawing. The addition of Section C-C reveals the interior detail of the cross hole that goes through the keyhole-shaped slot. Note that this view gives the appearance of two disjointed pieces because of the direction in which the section is viewed. A pictorial of the part before and after sectioning is shown in Figure 13.42.

FIGURE 13.42. The whole part and the part split at three different locations.

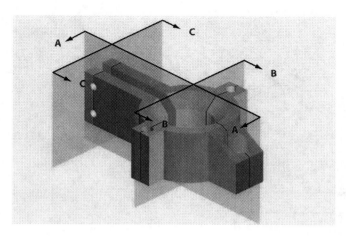

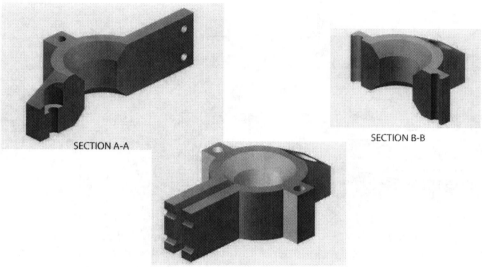

SECTION A-A

SECTION B-B

SECTION C-C

13.08.05 Creating an Offset Section

As mentioned previously, when the multiple internal features do not line up along a single cutting plane, it may be possible to capture most or all of them with an offset cutting plane, which is not a true plane but rather a stepped planar surface. The procedure for creating an offset section is similar to creating a full section, with a few modifications to step 2.

Step 1: Identify the features to be revealed and the desired viewing direction.

Step 2: Draw the stepped cutting plane line to reveal the desired features.

Step 3: Outline the modified part in an adjacent orthogonal view.

Step 4: Identify the intersection points of the part's exterior and interior edges with each segment of the cutting plane.

Step 5: Outline the internal features associated with the intersection points on the cutting plane.

Step 6: Find the boundaries between solid and empty space and fill solid areas with section lines.

Step 7: Add or remove background edges in space and remove edges in solid areas.

In particular, for step 2, it is desired to create a stepped cutting surface that reveals the true dimensions of the features to be revealed with no overlap of these features in the section view.

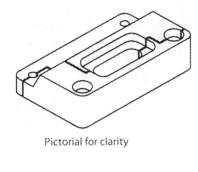

Pictorial for clarity

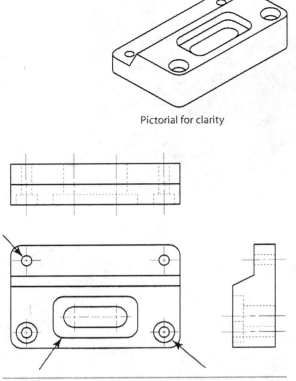

FIGURE 13.43. The indicated features (step 1) of this part can be revealed with an offset section.

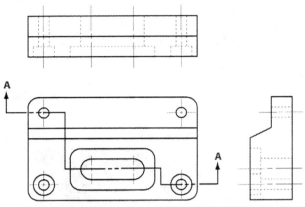

FIGURE 13.44. Step 2: Draw the cutting plane and select the desired viewing direction.

Consider, for example, the part shown in Figure 13.43, which contains two counterbored holes, a stepped slot, and two simple holes. It is desired to reveal the interior detail of the slot and each type of hole (step 1).

When creating the cutting plane line for an offset, it is important to select a good viewing direction as well as a good line configuration. The hidden lines in the right-side view show that the projections of these features overlap in this view. In the top view, however, the hidden lines show that the projection of these features do not overlap in this view. An offset cutting plane line can be imagined as being composed of two types of segments. The **cutting segments** are the portions that cut through the internal features to be viewed. Each of these segments should pass through entire features if they are to be revealed in their entirety. The **step segments** are transitions between the various cutting segments and are perpendicular to them. The step segments should not pass through any features on the object. A section view that shows all of the desired internal features without interference is desirable; so in this case, the cutting segments are chosen to be parallel to the top view. The precise lengths of the cutting segments are not important as long as they pass through the entire feature. A good offset cutting plane line (step 2) is shown in Figure 13.44.

Since the arrows of the cutting plane line point away from the (nonexistent) bottom view, an outline of the section view can be begun with the outline of the bottom view (step 3). Since a bottom view does not exist, this view or its outline needs to be created with the proper alignment and orientation of a regular orthogonal view, as shown in Figure 13.45. If only the outline of this view is created, the projections of the internal features must then be inferred from the top view.

In this example, each cutting sample passes through only one feature, although in general, a cutting segment can pass through multiple features. From left to right on the cutting plane line in Figure 13.45, the first feature crossed is a circle that represents the edge of a simple hole. The next cutting segment passes through the stepped

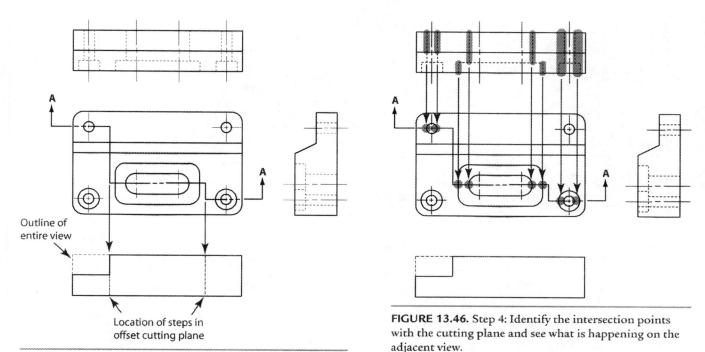

FIGURE 13.45. Step 3: Outline the part based on adjacent views. Temporarily note locations of steps in the offset line to use as reference marks.

FIGURE 13.46. Step 4: Identify the intersection points with the cutting plane and see what is happening on the adjacent view.

slot, and the final cutting segment passes through a set of concentric circles that represent the edges of a counterbored hole. The intersections of the cutting plane line with the edges of these features (step 4), shown in Figure 13.46, indicate the aligned locations on the section view where something should be happening (namely, a change in depth of the feature) to create those edges.

When the part is hypothetically cut, the edges of the counterbored hole, the slot, and the simple hole would be exposed (step 5), as shown in Figure 13.47. Note that if

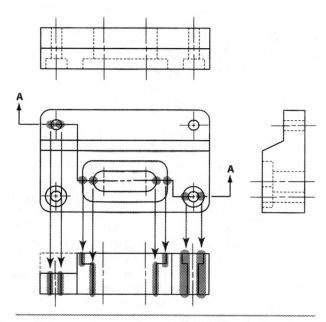

FIGURE 13.47. Step 5: Transfer the features into the section view and form the feature edges.

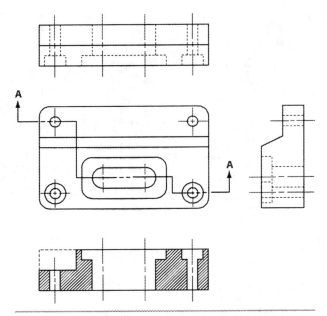

FIGURE 13.48. Step 6: Find the boundaries of air and solid and cross-hatch the solid areas.

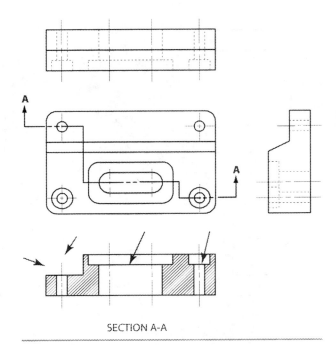

SECTION A-A

FIGURE 13.49. Step 7: Add newly revealed background edges and remove the step edges of the cutting plane. Label the section view.

the cutting implement had actually been a stepped plane, new edges also would have been created at the locations of the step segments. These edges are temporarily shown in Figure 13.47 merely to illustrate the location of the steps. In engineering drawing practice, these edges are removed.

The inside of the hole, slot, and counterbores contain space. Their edges in the section view separate space from solid. In Figure 13.48, the portions of the section that are supposed to be solid have been filled with section lines for visualization (step 6). Note that in this case, the section view reveals edges in the counterbored hole and slot that were previously hidden in the regular orthogonal view (step 7), as shown in Figure 13.49. The boundary edges in the upper left corner of the section view must be deleted because those edges were formed by a portion of the object that would not be seen on the sectioned object. Finally, you must delete any edges formed by the stepped cutting plane that you may have included for reference.

13.08.06 Creating a Sectioned Pictorial

An excellent aid for visualizing sectioned objects is to present pictorials of them. Creating this type of view is also an excellent academic exercise for the development of visualization skills. The process involves removing the portion of the object that is not viewed, creating a multiview drawing of the remaining portion, and creating a pictorial of the remaining portion from the modified drawing. Constructing such a pictorial continues the previous example. The construction of a section pictorial should not be done on the original drawing; rather, it should be done on a copy of the drawing on a separate worksheet to avoid confusion between the real part that is to be built and the model that is for visualization purposes only.

In the drawing in Figure 13.49, the cutting plane line arrows in the front view point toward the portion of the object to be retained and viewed, while the other portion is to be discarded. The modified front view is shown in Figure 13.50.

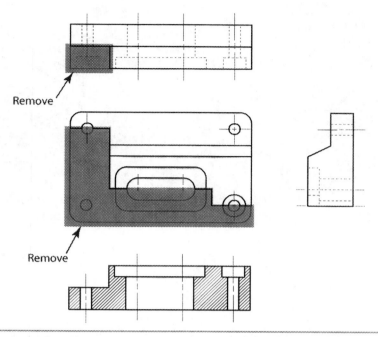

FIGURE 13.50. To visualize the sectioned part, remove the portion that is not seen from the existing orthogonal views.

Once a portion of the part has been removed in the front view, the remaining views also must be modified to be consistent with the modified part. In this case, there will be no changes to the top view. The right-side view must be modified to show that material has been removed. The section view can be used for the bottom view if the section lines are removed and the edges formed by the step segments are once again included. Note that if a left-side view was created, that view also would need to include the new edges formed by the stepped cutting plane. These modified views are shown in Figure 13.51.

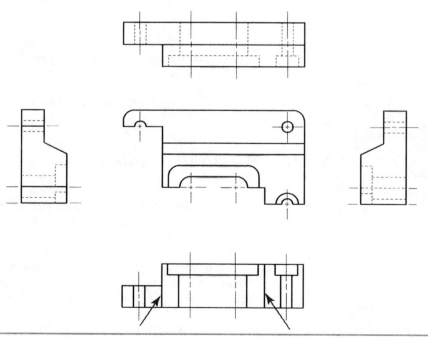

FIGURE 13.51. For ease of visualization, turn the former section view into the bottom view by removing cross-hatching and adding a section step line. Add a left view.

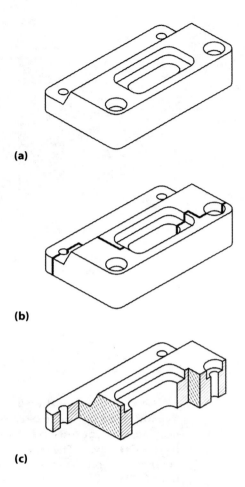

(a)

(b)

(c)

With the completed modified views of the object actually cut, the pictorial can be created by using the point, edge, or surface tracking techniques detailed in Chapter 11. The complete pictorial of the sectioned object is shown in Figure 13.52. Note that the freshly created surfaces from the cutting operation should be shaded or filled with section lines to show that these surfaces were artificially created and do not exist on the real part.

13.09 Removed Sections

In certain cases, it is convenient to use a removed section instead of a full section. A **removed section** offers the convenience of showing only the new surfaces created by a cutting plane, without the complexity of showing the remaining surfaces on an object. A hypothetical procedure for creating a removed section image is shown in Figure 13.53.

In this figure, a cutting plane intersects the object in the area of interest in (a). The cutting plane should be parallel to one of the principal views or perpendicular to the major surfaces of the part where the cut is made in order to reveal its true sizes. In (b), the cutting plane is removed from the part with the image of the intersection imprinted on the plane. The cutting plane and image are then rotated by 90 degrees in (c) such that the arrows point into the page on a drawing (d). The complete removed section view, as would be seen in an engineering drawing, is shown in Figure 13.54.

There is no need for view alignment for the removed section, although its orientation must still follow the rules of multiview presentation and the section view should be located near the cutting plane line. If the scale of the section view is different from that used on the multiview projections, the new scale must be included with the labeling of the section view.

For views where the surfaces created by a hypothetical cut are relatively small compared to the remaining surfaces of the view or where full sections may create unnecessarily large or confusing views, removed sections are a good option for improving clarity while reducing effort and complexity in a drawing. Figure 13.55 shows how removed sections were used for defining various parts of the Hoyt AeroTec bow handle. In this case, full sections or offset sections would have created unnecessary complexity in the drawing.

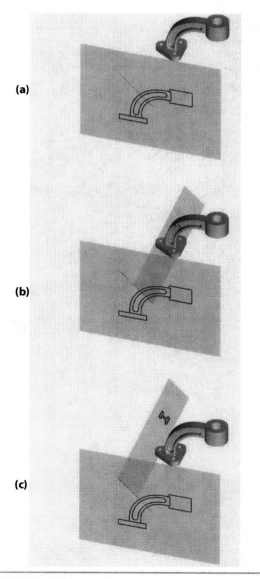

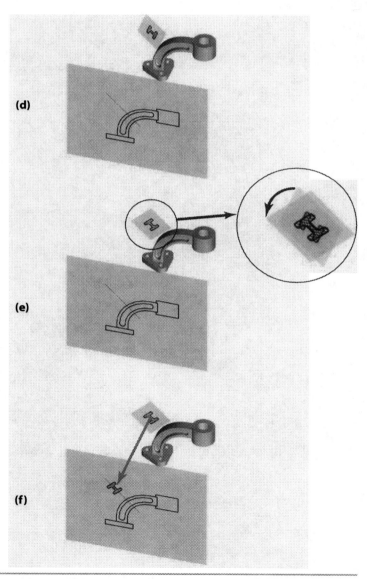

FIGURE 13.53. Creating a removed section. An object is projected into a viewing plane in (a). The cutting plane slices the object in (b). The image of the intersection is removed from the object in (c). The removed image is initially perpendicular to the viewing plane in (d) but is then rotated to be parallel to the viewing plane in (e). The removed image is finally projected onto the viewing plane in (f).

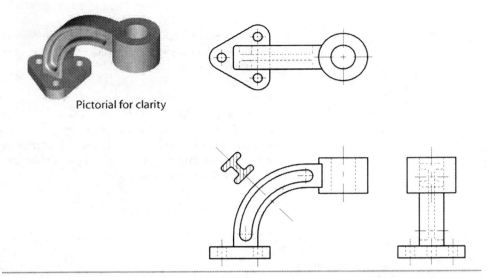

FIGURE 13.54. A removed section as it would be placed on an engineering drawing.

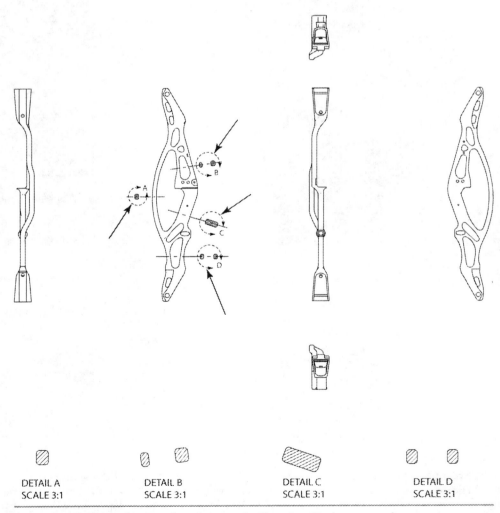

DETAIL A	DETAIL B	DETAIL C	DETAIL D
SCALE 3:1	SCALE 3:1	SCALE 3:1	SCALE 3:1

FIGURE 13.55. Use of removed sections on the Hoyt AeroTec bow example.

13.10 Revolved Sections

Revolved sections are created in a manner similar to that of removed sections. A hypothetical procedure for creating a revolved section image is shown in Figure 13.56.

In this figure, a cutting plane intersects the object in the area of interest and the image of the intersection is imprinted on the plane. The cutting plane should be parallel to one of the principal views or perpendicular to the major surfaces of the part where the cut is made in order to reveal its true sizes. The cutting plane is rotated by 90 degrees such that the arrows point into the page on a drawing. The axis of rotation of the intersection image is on the cutting plane, parallel to the cutting plane line, and through the geometric center of the image. Unlike the removed section, the cutting

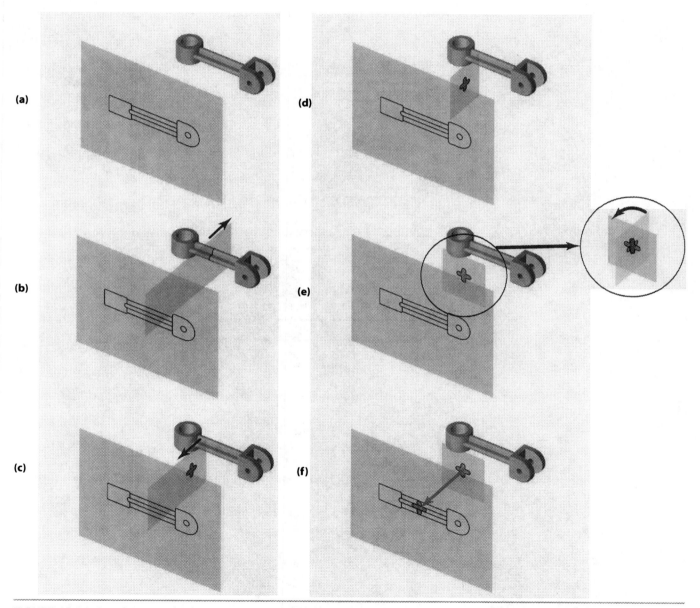

(a)

(b)

(c)

(d)

(e)

(f)

FIGURE 13.56. Creating a revolved section. An object is projected onto a viewing plane in (a). The cutting plane slices the object in (b). An image of the intersection is removed in (c). The intersection image is initially perpendicular to the viewing plane in (d) and then rotated to be parallel to the viewing plane in (e). The image is projected onto the viewing plane in (f).

plane is not removed from the object. Thus, the image of the intersection is superimposed on the orthogonal view. The complete revolved section view, as would be seen in an engineering drawing, is shown in Figure 13.57. Since a revolved section view is constructed at the location of the cutting plane line, there is no need to label the view.

The scale of the revolved section must be the same as for the principal views, and its orientation must follow the rules of multiview presentation. For views where the surfaces created by a hypothetical cut are relatively small compared to the remaining surfaces of the view, revolved sections are another good option for improving clarity while reducing effort and complexity in a drawing. Revolved sections should not be used when the section image interferes significantly with other features in the principal view. Figure 13.58 shows another example where the use of revolved sections is convenient.

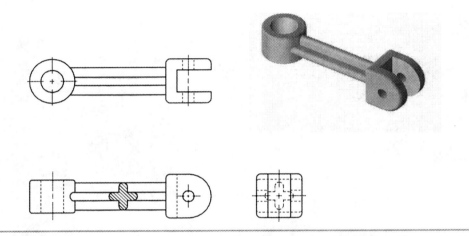

FIGURE 13.57. A revolved section as it would be placed on an engineering drawing.

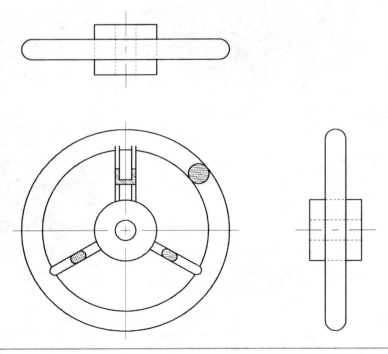

FIGURE 13.58. An example of a part with multiple revolved sections.

13.11 Broken-Out Sections

A **broken-out section** can be used when the internal feature to be revealed is a small portion of the entire object and a full section would not reveal additional details of interest. Use of a broken-out section in this manner would decrease the size and complexity of a drawing, as well as reduce the effort required to make it.

A broken-out section, as with the revolved and removed sections, offers the convenience of slicing only a fraction of the entire object when only a small slice is needed to define an internal geometry. However, a broken-out section offers the added convenience of not requiring the cutting plane to go all the way through the part. With all of the other sections you have studied so far, cutting plane lines start in space, go through the part, and end in space. With a broken-out section, the ends of the cutting plane line can be wholly or partially embedded in the part, as shown in Figure 13.59, where a cutting plane that has its extent limited to the area immediately surrounding a feature is

(a)

(b)

(c)

(d)

(e)

(f)

FIGURE 13.59. Creating a broken-out section. The object is projected onto a viewing plane on (a). A cutting plane slices through the feature of interest (but not the entire part) in (b). The portion in front of the cutting is broken out and removed in (c). The interior details of the feature are shown in (d). The image of these features is projected forward in (e) and placed directly on the part image in (f).

imbedded into the part. A piece of the object that is opposite the viewing direction is then hypothetically broken off to reveal the interior details of the feature.

The portion of the cutting plane that is embedded in the part is shown on the section view as an irregular edge to emphasize that the part would hypothetically be broken to reveal the interior details shown at that location. The broken-out-section view may be shown on the corresponding orthogonal view, as shown in Figure 13.60, or in a separate detail view, as shown in another example in Figure 13.61.

FIGURE 13.60. A broken-out section as it would be placed on an engineering drawing.

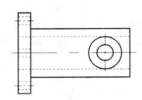
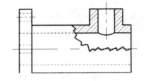
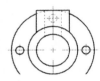

FIGURE 13.61. A broken-out section used to reveal some pocket details of the Hoyt AeroTec bow.

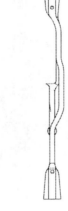
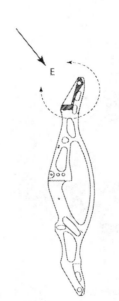

DETAIL E
SCALE 2:1

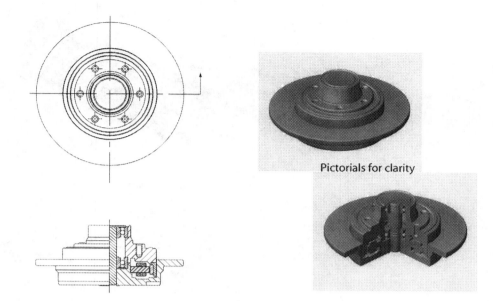

FIGURE 13.62. The method for showing the assembly of many parts.

Pictorials for clarity

13.12 Sections of Assemblies

Section views are commonly used in drawings that show multiple parts in their intended mating configuration to illustrate proper alignment of different features between the parts. When multiple parts are sectioned, as in Figure 13.62, it is advisable to use a different section line pattern for each part in order to distinguish the different parts easily. In everyday practice, assemblies that include pins, keys, shafts, or bolts usually do not show these items sectioned even though the cutting plane line may pass through them. These items usually have standardized geometries and sizes; thus, their sections add little information to a drawing and may even detract from the information presented by parts of greater interest.

13.13 A Few Shortcuts to Simplify Your Life

As with many other engineering drawing practices, acceptable shortcuts for creating section views can be used to reduce the time it takes to create a drawing and/or to minimize possible misinterpretation of a drawing. With all of the shortcuts presented next, the main question you need to ask yourself before using any of them is, "Will this approximation or shortcut increase or decrease the speed and accuracy of interpretation of the drawing?" If the speed or accuracy of interpretation decreases, the shortcuts should not be used.

13.13.01 Small Cutouts on Curved Surfaces

A shortcut is allowed when there is a small hole or another cutout on a curved surface. Figure 13.63, for example, shows a small hole and slot on a tube compared to larger cutouts. If a true projection of these features were made, the orthogonal views would show a curved depression on the surface of the tube. The shape of this curve is complex and would take some time to create. Since in most applications the size of the depression on the surface is unimportant, the depression is not shown on the orthogonal views. The true projection of these features and the accepted shortcut are shown in Figure 13.63. This approximation makes the drawing easier to create, with very little loss of information. However, when the cutouts are large or the size of the depression cannot be ignored in the function of the part, the true projection should be used. What is considered "small" is rather subjective.

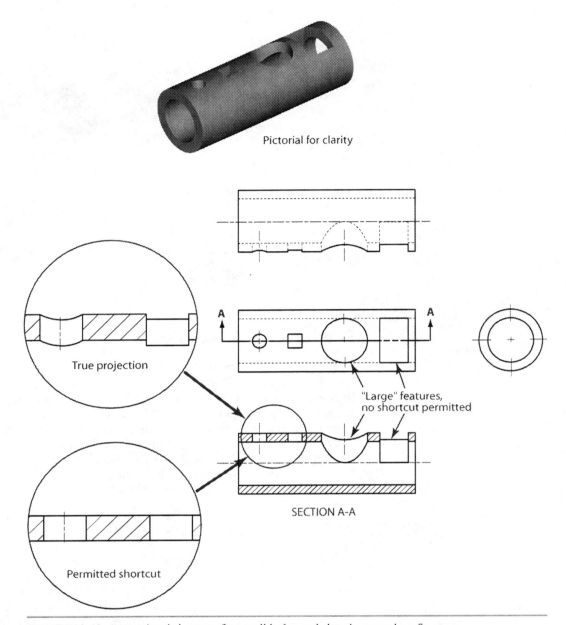

Pictorial for clarity

True projection

Permitted shortcut

"Large" features,
no shortcut permitted

SECTION A-A

FIGURE 13.63. A permitted shortcut for small holes and slots in curved surfaces.

13.13.02 Threaded Parts

Another shortcut is in the representation of a threaded part, such as the pneumatic fitting shown in Figure 13.64. A thread on the outside of a bolt or screw or the inside of a nut has many complex curved surfaces that would result in a very complicated drawing, especially if it were created with manual instruments or 2-D CAD. Much simpler representations of internal and external threads are included in Figure 13.62. These schematic representations are easier to construct, with very little loss of information, especially since thread sizes are mostly standardized based on the diameter of the part. A note and arrow are required to specify the precise thread sizes. Methods for the complete specification of thread sizes can be found in most machinists' or engineers' handbooks.

FIGURE 13.64. A section of a threaded part.

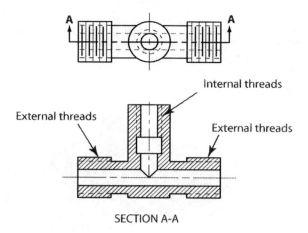

13.13.03 Thin Features

For sectioned features that have relatively small thickness when compared to the remainder of a sectioned part, it is acceptable not to fill these features with section lines even when cutting plane lines pass directly through them. As an example, consider the objects in Figure 13.65. These two objects are composed of the same main body but

FIGURE 13.65. The conventional section (a) and recommended variation for a thin feature (b).

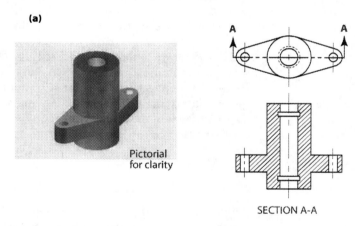

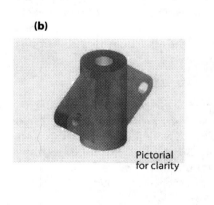

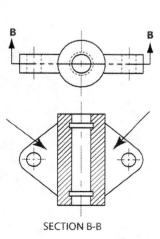

FIGURE 13.66. The recommended presentation of thin webs.

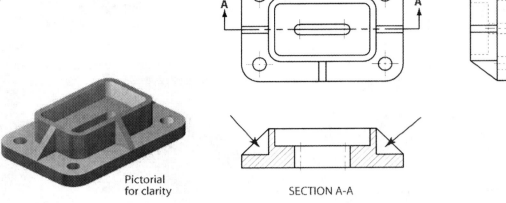

Pictorial for clarity

SECTION A-A

with mounting flanges turned differently. In both cases, the cutting plane line goes through both the main body and the flanges. For the part in (a), the thickness of the two flanges in the section view is about the same as the depth of the main body. In this case, the flanges are filled with section lines, as normal. For the part in (b), the thickness of the two flanges in the section view is a fraction of the depth of the main body. In this latter case, it is acceptable not to fill the flanges with section lines because doing so may give an immediate false impression that the flanges are about the same thickness as the main body. As an alternative to not filling thin features with section lines, it is permissible to use a different section line pattern for spokes and vanes than is used for the main body of the object. Note that for this shortcut, an extra edge must exist to separate the thin feature from the main body in the section view. Webs and fins, such as those shown in Figure 13.66, are generally treated in this manner.

13.13.04 Vanes, Fins, Spokes, and the Like

Objects with axially symmetric features such as vanes and spokes, as shown in the two parts in Figure 13.67, also are not filled with section lines even when cutting plane lines pass directly through them. Filling such features with section lines may give the false impression that the features are solid throughout the part. It also is permissible to use a different section line pattern for spokes and vanes than is used for the main body of the object. Note that for this shortcut, an extra edge must exist to separate spokes and vanes from the main body in the section view.

13.13.05 Symmetry

An interesting exception to the rules of true projection occurs when parts with rotational symmetry, which means that the part can be divided into identical wedges along an axis, are sectioned. Note that rotational symmetry is different from the planar symmetry discussed in Chapter 3, where the image of an entire object can be created by reflecting a portion of it on a plane. For example, examine the part shown in Figure 13.68. This part has one-third rotational symmetry, with three thin support ribs and three holes about the center tube.

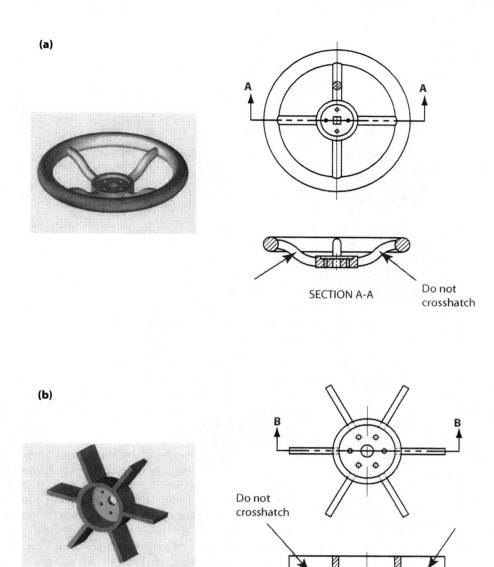

(a)

A
A

SECTION A-A

Do not
crosshatch

(b)

B
B

Do not
crosshatch

SECTION B-B

FIGURE 13.67. Two examples of the recommended presentation of spoke, vanes, and fins.

A multiview drawing created using true projection would be like that shown in Figure 13.68. Using a true projection for the front view in this case has some problems. First, using instruments or 2-D CAD, the projection is rather difficult to create. Also, the true projection of the side view may have the negative effect of representing the part as being nonsymmetrical.

An acceptable shortcut for this drawing also is included in Figure 13.68. This drawing is easier to create and gives the impression that the part is symmetrical. The top view clarifies any possible misinterpretation about the number and locations of the support ribs. Interestingly, if the part had one-quarter (or higher) symmetry, for example, four (or more) support ribs instead of three, the front view would be exactly the same as the part with one-third symmetry.

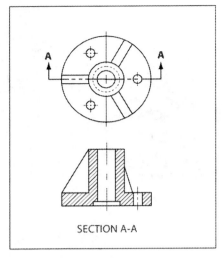
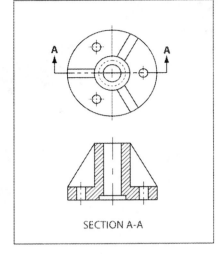

SECTION A-A

SECTION A-A

True projection

Preferred presentation

FIGURE 13.68. The preferred presentation of symmetrical features.

CAUTION

Creating section views is still part science and part art. Even though the rules of orthographic projection generally must be followed (except for the shortcuts mentioned), engineers, designers, and drafters are allowed considerable freedom in choosing when and where section views should be used, what type of section to use, and what presentation method to use. However, experienced people who are required to read and interpret drawings expect certain rules to be followed when the drawings are created; and deviation from these rules may cause confusion. Beginners are sometimes prone to poor choices and errors. In the best case, the person reading the drawing can interpret it because the necessary information is still contained on the remaining views. Still, errors can cause confusion and slow down the process of interpreting the drawing. In a more serious case, errors cause ambiguity that makes the drawing impossible to interpret correctly. In a worst-case scenario, the errors may cause the part to be interpreted as an entirely different part than originally desired. The following sections of this text are a compilation of the most common beginners' errors and ways to avoid them.

Cutting Through Only a Piece of an Internal Feature

Section views should be constructed to reveal true sizes. For example, consider the object shown in Figure 13.67. The full section cuts through the center of the large bore, revealing the true measurable sizes of the diameters inside. The cutting plane line goes through two holes, but not at their centers. The resulting section shows the two holes not at their true diameters. This section may be easily misinterpreted as having hole diameters that are smaller than they really are. A better way to section the object is to use an offset section in which the cutting plane line goes through the center of all of the internal features revealed, also shown in Figure 13.69.

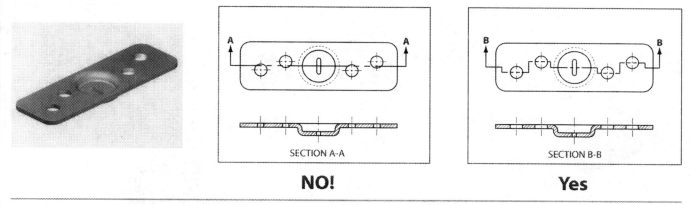

NO! **Yes**

FIGURE 13.69. A common error: Cutting through a feature such that its true size is not shown.

Forgetting the Rest of the Object

A proper full or offset section shows the object as if it had been cut, including any background edges that still may appear outside the cut surfaces. Sometimes it is easy to forget these background edges because the cut surfaces are usually of prime importance. Nevertheless, for a full or offset section to be correct, the background edges must be included, mostly for use as reference locations for the cut surfaces, as shown in Figure 13.70.

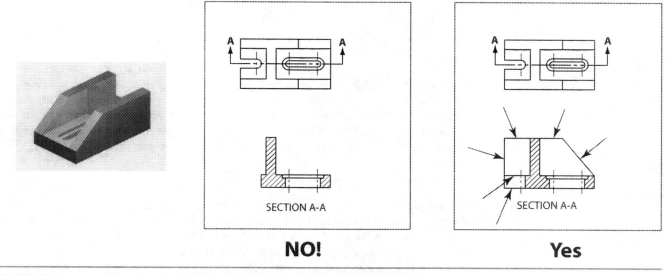

NO! **Yes**

FIGURE 13.70. A common error: Forgetting the rest of the object on a full or offset section.

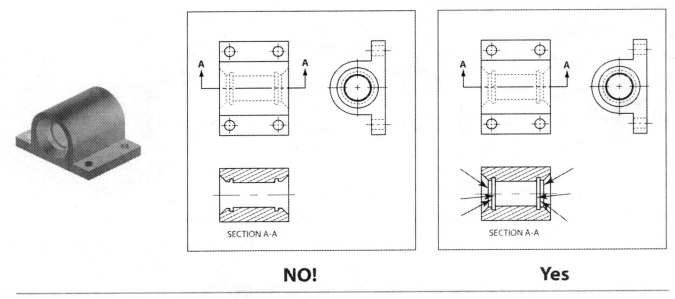

FIGURE 13.71. Forgetting internal edges made visible.

Forgetting Back Edges That Are Made Visible

Newly revealed internal edges also are often carelessly omitted. Edges of grooves, counterbores, cross holes, and other similar features have edges that become visible once the object is cut, as shown in Figure 13.71. Neglecting to include these edges may cause confusion about the true geometry of the features.

Incorrect Rotation Orientation

Sometimes in a hastily created section view, the rotational orientation of the view is incorrect, as shown in Figure 13.72. Section views are created and presented using the rules of orthogonal projection and multiview presentation. Even though a section view is forgiven the requirement of proper position alignment with the other orthogonal views (for purposes of drawing convenience), the requirement for proper rotational orientation still exists. Recall that a cutting plane line on an orthogonal view is the edge view of a cutting plane that is perpendicular to that view. Incorrect rotational orientation of the section view may cause confusion with its interpretation.

Viewing the Object from the Wrong Side

The arrows of a cutting plane line point in the viewing direction. A common error, as shown in Figure 13.73, is to show the section view looking at the piece of the object that should have been removed, rather than the piece that is to remain. The areas that have been cut (i.e., the areas that are filled with section lines) are the same for both pieces. However, the background edges and the rotational orientation of the object may be incorrect.

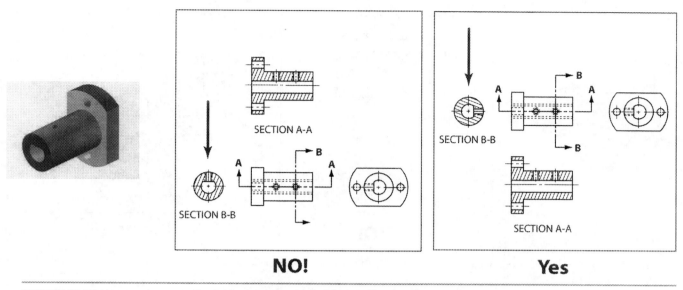

FIGURE 13.72. A common error: Rotational orientation of the section view is incorrect.

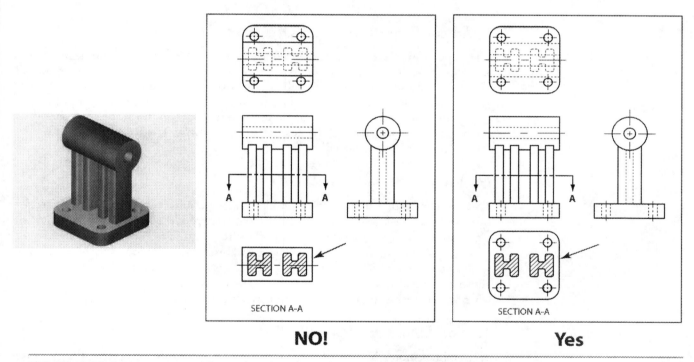

FIGURE 13.73. A common error: The section view shows the wrong side of the object.

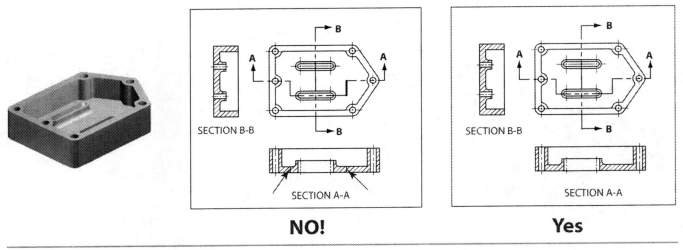

NO! **Yes**

FIGURE 13.74. A common error: Step lines are not removed from the offset section.

Including Step Lines on an Offset Section

The steps in an offset section, as shown in Figure 13.74, create edges; but leaving these edges on a section view is considered improper. Therefore, they should be removed. Actually, if you were to follow the rules of orthogonal projection strictly, the edges created by the changes in direction of the cutting plane should be shown. However, someone in the past thought a nicer-looking drawing would result from their removal; thus, the practice remains today. Until this practice is formally changed, the edges in an offset section should be removed.

No View Label or View Scale

To avoid confusion with parts that have multiple section views, every full or offset section view must be labeled with the same letters used to identify their respective cutting plane line, as shown in Figure 13.75. This labeling is practiced even when only one section view is on the drawing. Half, revolved, and broken-out section views have the same scale as the view on which it was created. Full, offset, and removed section views are allowed to be a different scale than the view on which they were created. However, whenever there is a change in scale, the new scale must be clearly labeled on the view.

Section Lines with Poor Spacing or Angle

Section lines should be created in such a manner that they are easily recognizable as section lines. Section lines should be easily distinguishable from edges on the part. If the section line density is too low or if the angle of the section lines matches the angle of some of the edges of the part, as shown in Figure 13.76, there may be confusion between the section lines and the edges of the part. On the other hand, too dense a section line pattern is difficult to reproduce cleanly when the drawing is printed, copied, or transmitted.

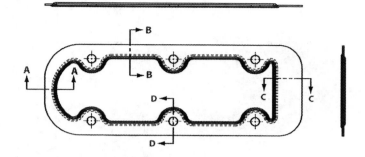

FIGURE 13.75. A common error: No scale or view is missing labels.

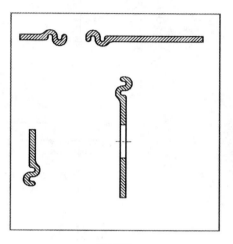

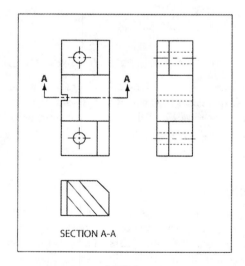

SECTION A-A
SCALE 4:1

SECTION C-C
SCALE 4:1

SECTION B-B
SCALE 4:1

SECTION D-D
SCALE 4:1?

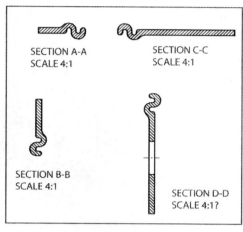

NO!

Yes

FIGURE 13.76. A common error: Poor choice of cross-hatching.

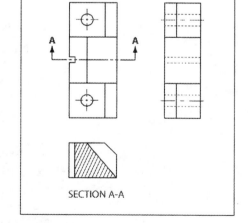

SECTION A-A

SECTION A-A

NO!

Yes

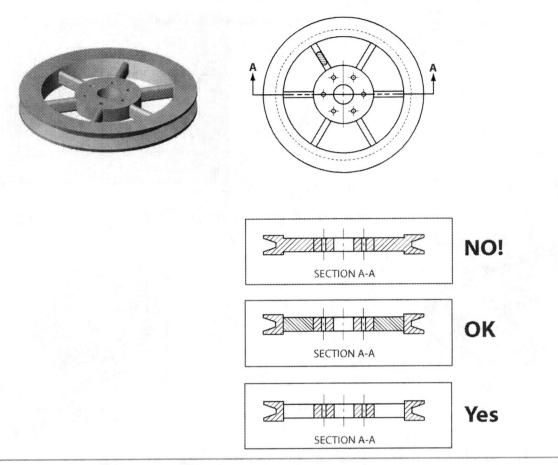

FIGURE 13.77. A common error: Cross-hatching in vanes or spokes.

Filling Vanes or Spokes with Section Lines

Filling spokes or vanes with section lines, as shown in Figure 13.77, gives an immediate but false impression that the object is solid throughout the spoke or vane area. Spokes and vanes should not be filled at all or should be filled with a different section line pattern than is used for the rest of the sectioned object.

Common Section Line Pattern on Different Parts in an Assembly

A common section line pattern used for different parts in a sectioned assembly, as shown in Figure 13.78, gives the immediate but false impression that the separate parts are a single part. Different parts in a sectioned assembly, even when they are made of the same material, should be filled with section lines that are of different patterns.

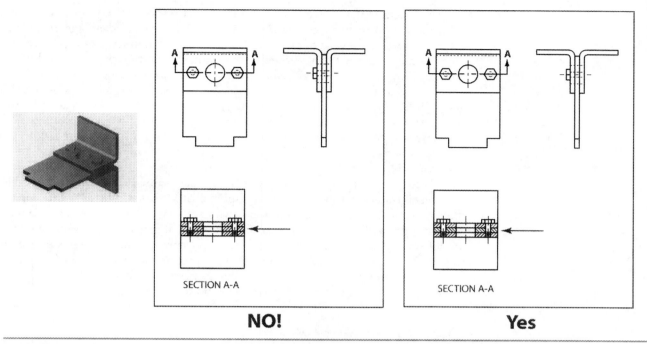

FIGURE 13.78. A common error: The same cross-hatch pattern for different parts in an assembly.

13.14 Considerations for 3-D Modeling

With solids modeling software, parts are initially modeled as a series of protrusions and cuts to create a 3-D graphical model of a part. The solids modeling software creates a mathematical model of the geometry from which the projections of the object are used to create drawings. Once the solids model is created, it is usually a simple matter to extract a front view, side view, or any of the other orthogonal views from the model. A section view is created merely as another orthogonal view, but with a portion of the object removed. The ease with which section views can be created from a solids model has many advantages, but also some disadvantages. The greatest advantage is the speed and accuracy with which section views can be created. With most software, creating additional views is simply a matter of specifying the cutting plane and viewing direction and then picking a location on the drawing where the new view is to appear. Cutting planes can be specified as existing or newly created reference planes. Creating stepped cutting plane lines in the views of interest usually specifies offset cutting planes. The process is often a matter of a few strokes on a keyboard or a few clicks with a mouse or another pointing device. The time required is usually only a few seconds. Also, accurate orthogonal projection of features that were previously represented by shortcut practices, such as small cutouts in curved surfaces or thin symmetrical features, are very easy to create. In fact, with most software, it would be difficult to create a view that is *not* an accurate projection. Using section lines to fill areas that were formerly solid is also a rather simple matter. The software identifies the newly cut surfaces and automatically fills them. All the software user needs to do is specify the section line pattern to be used and modify it if necessary.

The selection of where to section an object to view its interior or the type of section to use is still up to the person making the drawing. One disadvantage of the nearly automatic section creation offered by 3-D modeling is that in some cases, the modeling becomes too accurate. Many of the shortcuts and clarification practices used in traditional drafting are no longer available in some software. For example, a section through a spoke or vane used in a 3-D model would show the spoke or vane filled with section lines, not blank as would be preferred. Also, all projections would be true projections. With an object of odd rotational symmetry, there would be no opportunity to modify the projection to create a symmetrical presentation, as would be preferred. With some software, the step edges of an offset section may be visible in the section view, and not removed as is practiced.

Another disadvantage of 3-D modeling is that manual creation of section views has been a traditional method of developing spatial reasoning and mental imaging skills. When the process is too automatic with software, a person may not adequately develop these skills in the absence of the software and may become too dependent on the software. When faced with multiple section views in a shop drawing, that person may not be able to create a mental image of the part or may not develop the skills necessary to interpret the drawings. Eventually, the person will develop these skills, but it may require exposure to many solids models and their drawings.

13.15 Chapter Summary

With many complex objects, looking only at the exterior may not fully reveal all of their features. The use of section views is a method of looking at the internal details of such objects. The section process involves using a hypothetical cutting plane to hypothetically cut an object into pieces so the interior details one or more features. These features can then be examined more closely, specified in such a manner that the details can be fabricated and inspected to ensure that they meet the desired specifications. On an engineering drawing, the cutting plane appears in an edge view called a cutting plane line. Several types of section views are available for use at the discretion of the drafter, depending on the desired presentation. Whichever type is used, certain rules and practices must be followed to ensure that these views can be interpreted easily and quickly without ambiguity. Of primary importance is that the rules of orthogonal projection and multiview presentation be used.

13.16 glossary of key terms

broken-out section: The section view produced when the cutting plane is partially imbedded into the object, requiring an irregular portion of the object to be removed before the hypothetically cut surface can be seen.

cutting plane: A theoretical plane used to hypothetically cut and remove a portion of an object to reveal its interior details.

cutting plane line: On an orthographic view of an object, the presentation of the edge view of a cutting plane used to hypothetically cut and remove a portion of that object for viewing.

cutting segment: On a stepped cutting plane for an offset section view, that portion of the plane that hypothetically cuts and reveals the interior detail of a feature of interest.

full section: The section view produced when a single cutting plane is used to hypothetically cut an object completely into two pieces.

half section: The section view produced when a single cutting plane is used to hypothetically cut an object up to a plane or axis of symmetry, leaving that portion beyond the plane or axis intact.

offset section: The section view produced by a stepped cutting plane that is used to hypothetically cut an object completely into two pieces. Different portions of the plane are used to reveal the interior details of different features of interest.

removed section: The section view produced when a cutting plane is used to hypothetically remove an infinitesimally thin slice of an object for viewing.

13.16 glossary of key terms

revolved section: The section view produced when a cutting plane is used to hypothetically create an infinitesimally thin slice, which is rotated 90 degrees for viewing, on an object.

section lines: Shading used to indicate newly formed or cut surfaces that result when an object is hypothetically cut.

section view: A general term for any view that presents an object that has been hypothetically cut to reveal the interior details of its features, with the cut surfaces perpendicular to the viewing direction and filled with section lines for improved presentation.

step segment: On a stepped cutting plane for an offset section view, that portion of the plane that connects the cutting segments and is usually perpendicular to them but does not intersect any interior features.

viewing direction: The direction indicated by arrows on the cutting plane line from the eye to the object of interest that corresponds to the tail and point of the arrow, respectively.

13.17 questions for review

1. When should a section view be used?

2. What does a cutting plane line represent?

3. What does the area filled with section lines on a section view represent?

4. What are some guidelines concerning good drafting practice in creating section line patterns?

5. What is the significance of the direction of the arrow on a cutting plane line?

6. Why is it important that the rotational orientation of a section view, even if it is moved, be maintained as if it were an orthogonal view?

7. When should an offset section be used instead of a full section?

8. When should revolved or removed sections be used instead of full or offset sections?

9. Under what conditions should certain areas on a section view not be filled with section lines even though the cut is through solid material?

13.18 problems

1. In the problem shown in Figure P13.1, the views indicated by the balloons are to be changed to full section views taken along the centerline in the direction indicated by the arrows in the remaining view. For each set of views, select the correct section view from the twenty-four proposed views shown at the right. A section view choice may be used more than once. A correct answer may not be available as a choice.

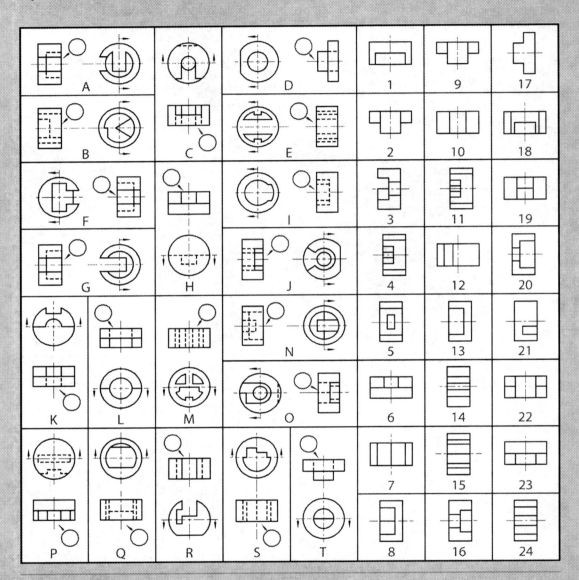

FIGURE P13.1.

13.18 problems (continued)

2. In the problem shown in Figure P13.2, the views indicated by the balloons are to be changed to half section views as indicated by the letters A-A taken along the centerline in the direction in the remaining view. For each set of views, select the correct section view from the twenty-four proposed views shown at the right. A section view choice may be used more than once. A correct answer may not be available as a choice.

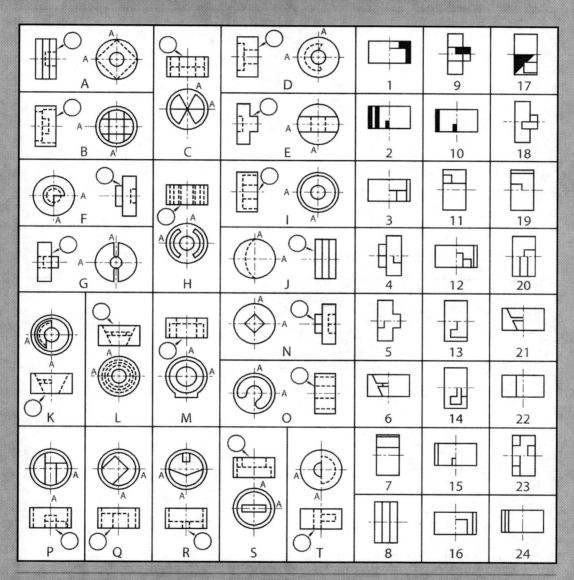

FIGURE P13.2.

13.18 problems (continued)

3. In the problem shown in Figure P13.3, the views indicated by the circles are to be the location of section views. Select the correct section view to complete each problem from the thirty proposed views shown. A section view choice may be used more than once. A correct answer may not be available as a choice.

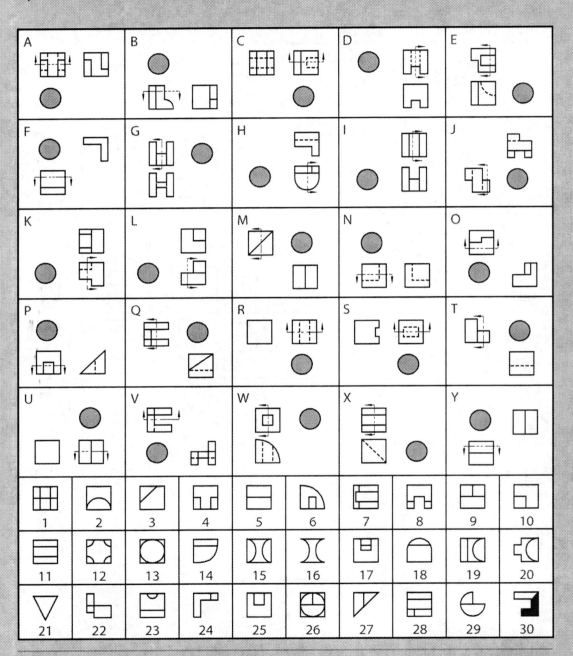

FIGURE P13.3.

13.18 problems (continued)

4. In the problem shown in Figure P13.4, the views indicated by the circles are to be the location of offset section views. Select the correct section view to complete each problem from the thirty proposed views shown. A section view choice may be used more than once. A correct answer may not be available as a choice.

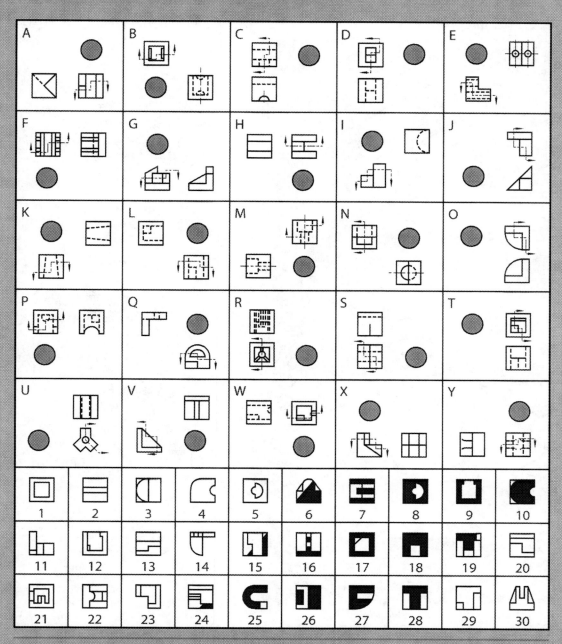

FIGURE P13.4.

13.18 problems (continued)

5. For each object represented in Figure P13.5, create a multiview drawing to fully describe the object, including the indicated full section views to reveal interior detail. When the precise location of the cutting plane line for the full section is not specified, choose the location to best reveal the interior detail.

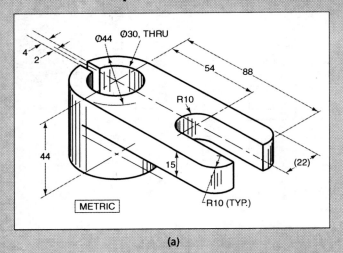

(a)

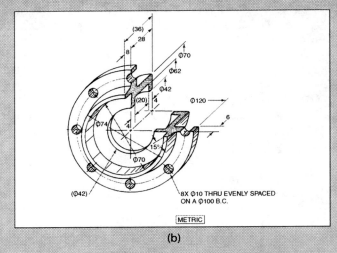

(b)

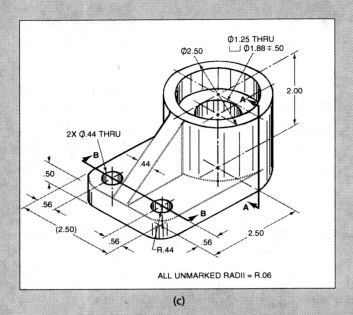

(c)

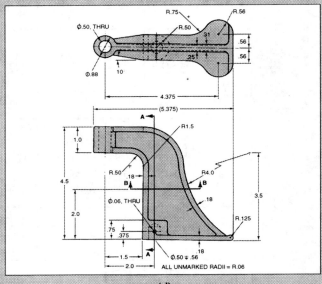

(d)

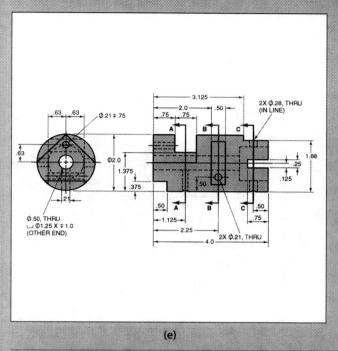

(e)

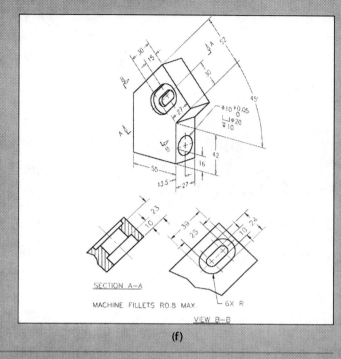

(f)

FIGURE P13.5.

6. For each object represented in Figure P13.6, create a multiview drawing to fully describe the object, including the indicated half section views to reveal interior detail. When the precise location of the cutting plane line for the half section is not specified, choose the location to best reveal the interior detail.

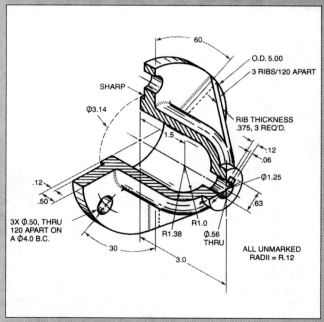

(a)

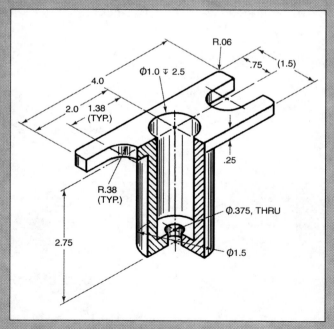

(b)

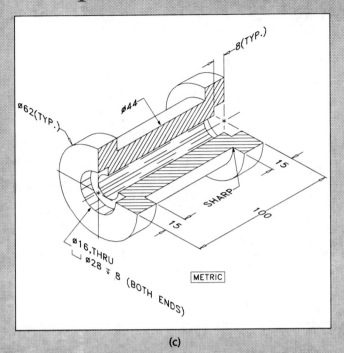

(c)

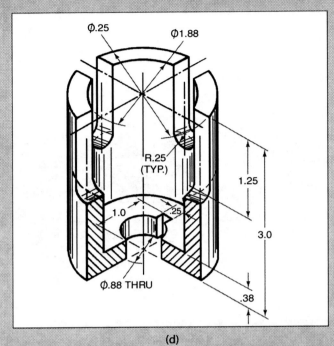

(d)

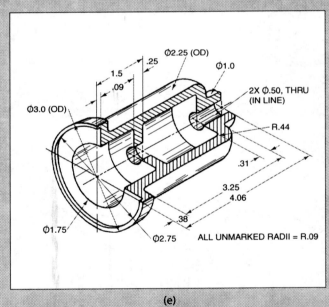

(e)

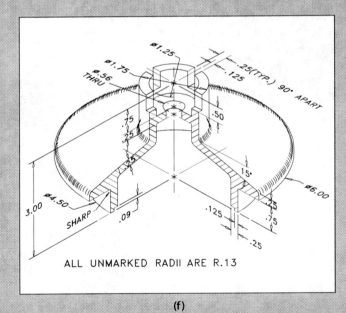

(f)

FIGURE P13.6.

13.18 problems (continued)

7. For each object represented in Figure P13.7, create a multiview drawing to fully describe the object, including the indicated offset section views to reveal interior detail. When the precise location of the cutting plane lines for the offset sections are not specified, choose the locations to best reveal the interior detail.

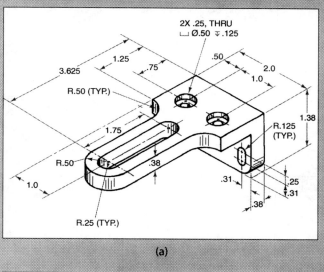

(a)

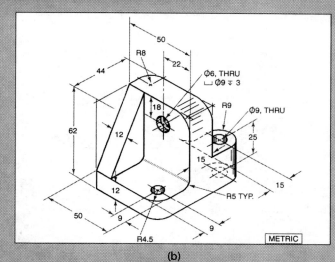

(b)

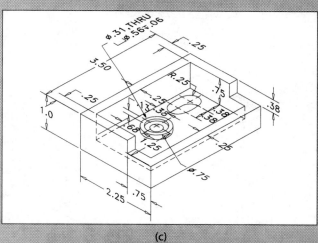

(c)

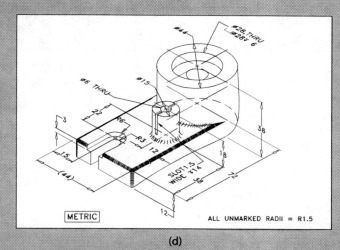

(d)

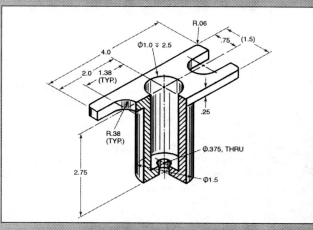

(e)

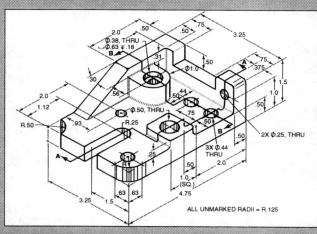

(f)

13.18 problems (continued)

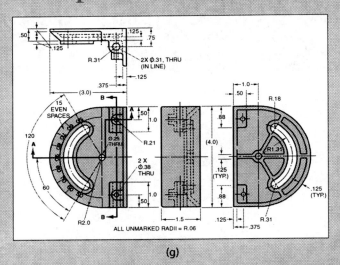

(g)

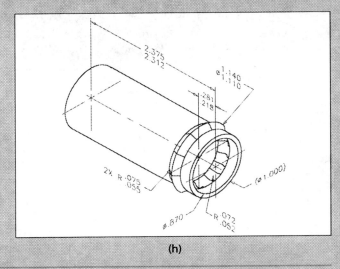

(h)

FIGURE P13.7.

8. For each object represented in Figure P13.8, create a multiview drawing to fully describe the object, including the indicated removed or revolved section views to reveal interior detail. When the precise location of the cutting plane line for the removed or revolved section is not specified, choose the location to best reveal the interior detail.

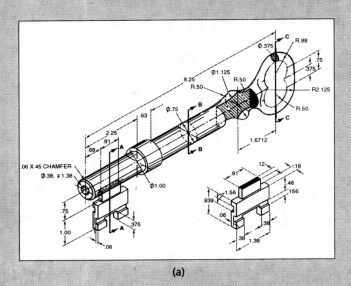

(a)

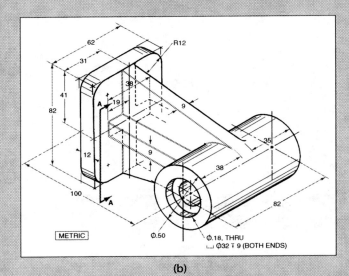

(b)

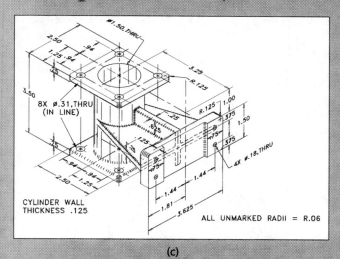

(c)

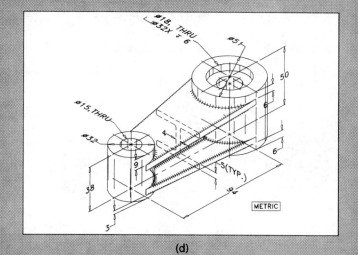

(d)

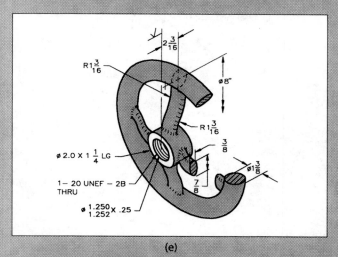

(e)

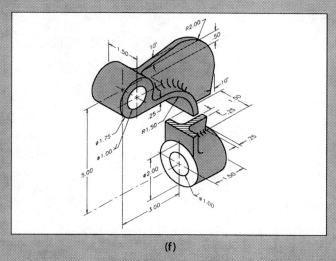

(f)

FIGURE P13.8.

13.18 problems (continued)

9. For each object represented in Figure P13.9, create a multiview drawing to fully describe the object, including the indicated broken-out-section view to reveal interior detail. When the precise location of the broken-out section is not specified, choose the location to best reveal the interior detail.

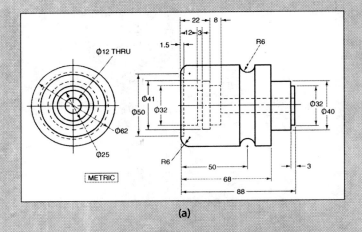

(a)

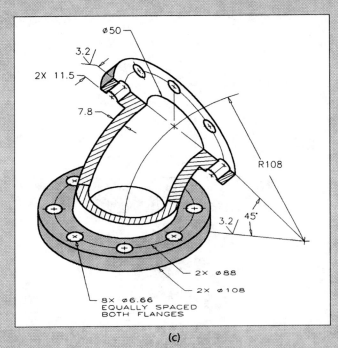

(c)

FIGURE P13.9.

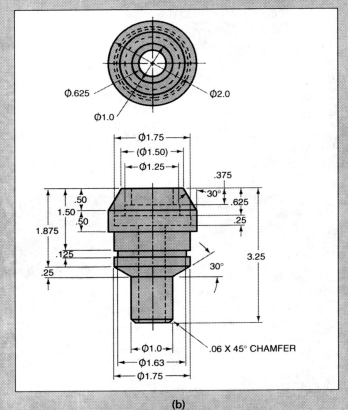

(b)

13.18 problems (continued)

10. For the three objects represented in Figure P13.10, create a multiview drawing to fully describe objects in their assembled state, including a removed section view to reveal the interior detail of how the separate parts are mated.

11. For each object presented in a multiview format in Figures P13.1–P13.10, create an isometric pictorial of the remaining object after it has been sectioned.

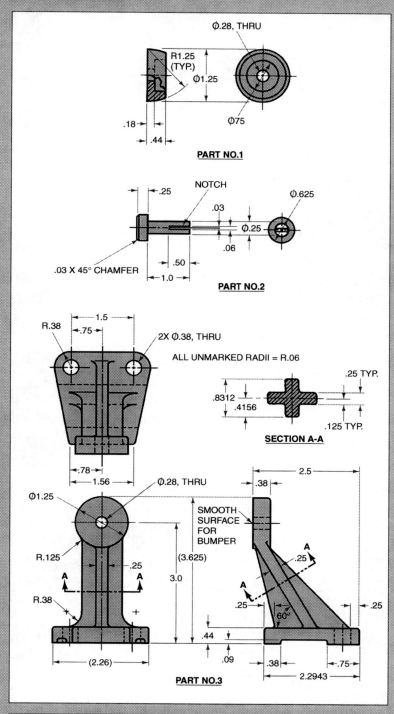

FIGURE P13.10.

Dimensioning

objectives

After completing this chapter, you should be able to

- Use the concept of dimensioning
- Explain the idea of tolerance in dimensioning
- Recall the fundamental rules and apply the techniques for dimensioning
- Select appropriate dimensions for a moderately complex part and correctly apply them to a drawing of that part

15.01

introduction

In the previous chapters, you learned how to represent the shape of objects in various ways. You learned about standard ways of representing objects with orthogonal projection techniques, pictorials, sectional views, and auxiliary views. You learned about different techniques for creating solid models and the way parametric, feature-based modeling is used to create 3-D representations of objects. All of this information is great for representing the shape of objects; but at some point, you will want to communicate size information to someone who will construct or manufacture your design. Until your designs are built, you will not be making any money. As with orthogonal projection, there are standard ways of displaying this size information, or dimensions, on drawings. In this chapter, you will examine some of these standards as well as look at some reasons for dimensioning objects in certain ways.

To begin, it is critical that you understand something about how dimensions are formally presented in a design. As you learned in your work with 3-D solid modeling, objects are a combination of features such as rectangular prisms, cylinders, holes, fillets, and chamfers. Recall from solid modeling that most of these features require that they be defined by their **sizes** and their **locations**. For example, the hole in the object shown in Figure 15.01 is considered a feature. The size (.500 diameter) must be given so the person manufacturing the part can select the correct drill bit or cutting tool to machine the hole to the proper size. For engineering drawings, diameters (such as the .500 for this hole) are preceded with the Ø symbol. Location dimensions (1.250 from the right and .750 from the top) are given from the sides of the part to the center of the hole so the machinist can accurately locate the center of the drill bit on that point.

Similarly, the slot in the top of the object shown in Figure 15.02 must also be defined by its size and location. The size of the slot feature is defined by its width (.500) and its height (.250). A location dimension is given from the left side (1.000).

Dimensioning is much like creating constraint-based solid models—you define the size and location of the features within the software, and the part is created "virtually" to your size and location specifications. Figure 15.03 illustrates how the size and location dimensions for a rectangle are used to define an extruded cut in a constraint-based solid modeling program for the object shown in Figure 15.02.

One of the key points you should learn from this chapter is a strategy for determining the types of dimensions required to define a part. You already have a head start through your experiences with 3-D solid modeling software. Following the correct standards for representing dimensions on a drawing is important, but being able to apply the best dimensions to a drawing will impress your boss more than your knowing the standards and applying bad dimensions. For example, imagine you work for a company that manufactures hardware for household doors. Your current project involves the deadbolt lock assembly shown in Figure 15.04. Your boss asks you to design a cover plate where the door meets the doorjamb. You are familiar with the standard ways to represent the shape of the part. One or two views will be enough to describe the shape of the plate, but what are the dimensions needed to manufacture the plate? What are the critical dimensions that must be given? What are some of the standard dimensions that exist on other parts or previous parts? Think about the assembly and these questions because you will return to this example later in the chapter.

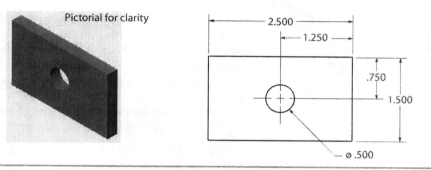

FIGURE 15.01. The size and location of a hole feature.

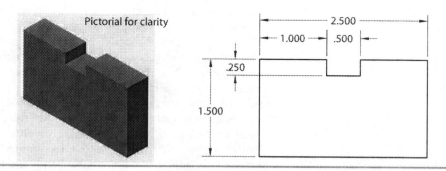

FIGURE 15.02. The size and location of a slot feature.

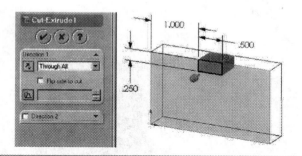

FIGURE 15.03. Defining features in a constraint-based modeling program.

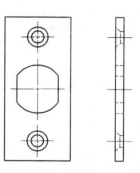

FIGURE 15.04. A deadbolt lock plate.

15.02 Is the Dimension I See on a Drawing Exact?

People are not perfect. When they fabricate metal objects, mold plastic parts, and build houses, some room must be made to account for their imperfection. Even when robots are used to machine parts, there may be some slight imperfection in the resulting object. For machined parts, the amount of variation, or **tolerance**, might be relatively small. There are various ways of including allowable tolerances for a part on a drawing. An example of a note appearing on an engineering drawing might be this:

ALL LINEAR DIMENSIONS ± .010 UNLESS OTHERWISE SPECIFIED.

In the construction industry, tolerances for laying brick or pouring a concrete foundation are typically larger than tolerances on hand-held sized machined parts.

Tolerance dimensions also help with effective size control of finished parts. Examine the assembly of parts in Figure 15.05. For this design, the BUSHING is not supposed to spin inside the WHEEL, but the SHAFT is designed to spin inside the BUSHING. Therefore, the largest diameter of the SHAFT must be just a little smaller than the diameter of the hole in the BUSHING, and the outside diameter of the BUSHING must be just a little larger than the hole in the WHEEL. Dimensioning the hole in the BUSHING and the diameter of the SHAFT as .750 would not communicate the intended type of fit between the two parts. The person putting the parts together would not know whether you wanted the parts to spin freely or be jammed together.

Detail drawings of the BUSHING and the SHAFT are shown in Figure 15.06 and Figure 15.07, respectively. Notice that tolerance dimensions (specifically, limit dimensions) are given to ensure effective size control between the parts. The hole in the BUSHING is dimensioned as .7500–.7512, and the diameter of the SHAFT is given as .7484–.7492. If the parts are manufactured within these specifications, the SHAFT will spin freely within the BUSHING.

FIGURE 15.05. Parts requiring effective size control.

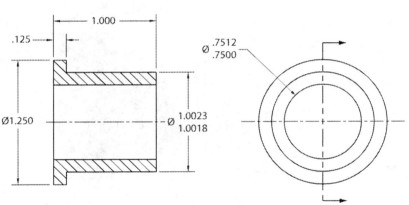

FIGURE 15.06. The detail drawing of the BUSHING.

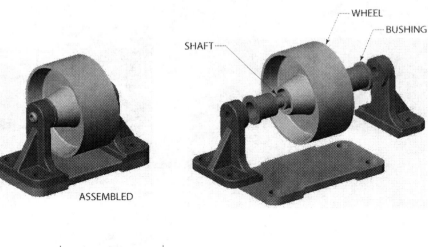

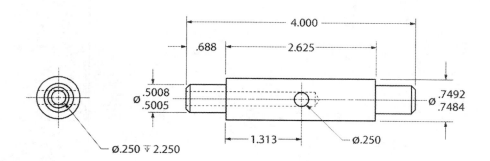

FIGURE 15.07. The detail drawing of the SHAFT.

15.03 What Are the Rules for Dimensioning?

As with most topics in engineering graphics, dimensions conform to national, international, and individual company standards. The accepted national standard in the United States for Dimensioning and Tolerancing is **ANSI Y14.5** (currently referenced as *ASME Y14.5M-1994*), which is published by the American Society of Mechanical Engineers (ASME). This standard outlines uniform practices for displaying and interpreting dimensions and related information on drawings and other forms of engineering documentation. The information in *ASME Y14.5M-1994* is important, but do not be too concerned with it right now. Remember, keep trying to figure out what the critical dimensions are, and you will worry about standard dimensioning technique later.

15.03.01 Millimeters, Inches, or Angstroms?

"The 200 meter dash." "First down and 10 yards to go." "Hand me that 2 × 4." These are all examples of length measurements that are familiar to most people. For most track and field events, lengths are defined in meters. In baseball and football, lengths are measured in feet and yards. In the construction industry, decimal or fractional inch measurements are the standard way lengths are defined. Engineering drawings also have standard units of measure. Most drawings conform to the International System of Units (SI), which is metric and uses the millimeter as the standard unit; or they conform to U.S. customary units with a standard unit of the decimal inch. Throughout this chapter, you will see examples using both millimeter and inch dimensions. The next section will discuss how to recognize the differences between the two. Since both standards are used thoughout the United States, it is important that you be able to work with each type. You should be familiar with both standards by the end of the chapter.

15.03.02 Types of Dimensioning

At this point in your class, you may have noticed that your instructor or professor is fairly picky about the way things look on sketches or drawings, mostly because, as was mentioned earlier, engineering drawings do follow standards. Well, here is the first really picky thing about dimensioning that will help you recognize the differences between metric- and inch-based drawings. For metric drawings where millimeters are the standard unit (see Figure 15.08), the following rules apply (*ASME Y14.5M-1994*, p. 5):

1. Where the dimension is less than one millimeter, a zero precedes the decimal point.

2. Where the dimension is a whole number, neither the decimal point nor the zero is shown.

3. Where the dimension exceeds a whole number by a decimal fraction of one millimeter, the last digit to the right of the decimal point is not followed by a zero.

4. Neither commas nor spaces shall be used to separate digits into groups in specifying millimeter dimensions on drawings (e.g., 1000 not 1,000).

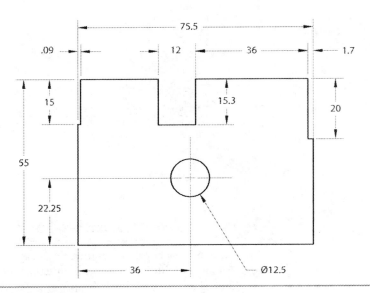

FIGURE 15.08. Millimeter dimensions.

To help distinguish between the two systems, the following rules have been established for decimal inches (*ASME Y14.5M-1994*, pp. 5–6) (see Figure 15.09):

1. A zero is not used before the decimal point for values less than one inch.
2. A dimension is expressed to the same number of decimal places as its tolerance. Zeros are added to the right of the decimal point where necessary.

What does this mean? When dimensioning in millimeters, show leading zeros for values less than 1, but do not show trailing zeros. When using inches, do not show leading zeros for values less than 1, but do show trailing zeros equal to the precision on the drawing.

15.03.03 Fundamental Rules for Dimensioning

As you can imagine, making sure that a drawing created by a designer in Raleigh, North Carolina, can be read by a manufacturer in Detroit, Michigan, or Taipei, Taiwan, requires that some standards be established. The main reason for having standards is

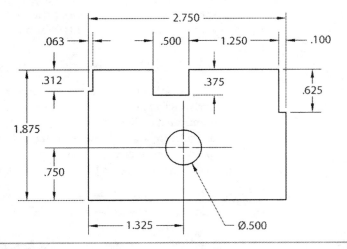

FIGURE 15.09. Dimensioning in inches.

to ensure consistency in the way things are done. Over the last 100 years, individuals in the automotive, aircraft, and military industries and in other industries have refined the standards for dimensioning objects. As mentioned previously, fundamental rules and standards for dimensioning and tolerancing are published in *ASME Y14.5M*. These rules define engineering and design intent clearly. Some of the rules are listed here. (A complete list of the fundamental rules is given at the end of the chapter.)

1. *Each dimension shall have a tolerance.* As was mentioned earlier in the chapter, tolerance dimensioning is necessary to account for human imperfection and to allow for effective size control. If a dimension does not appear as a limit dimension, the tolerance is usually covered by a general note on the drawing or in the title block.

2. *Dimensioning and tolerancing shall be complete so there is full understanding of the characteristic of each feature.* Drawings need to be dimensioned so the manufacturer or construction worker does not have to guess at anything. It is your responsibility to provide all necessary information to produce, manufacture, or build the design.

3. *Each necessary dimension of an end product shall be shown. No more dimensions than those necessary for complete definition shall be given.* As you will see later in the chapter, you do not want to give more dimensions than necessary to describe your design. Show only the dimensions that the person producing the design will need. Taking rule 3 together with rule 2 means you need "just enough" dimensions to define the part—not too many and not too few.

4. *The drawing should define a part <u>without</u> specifying manufacturing methods.* Do not specify that a hole is to be drilled, reamed, punched, or made by any other operation. The person manufacturing your design is responsible for determining the best method for producing the hole.

5. *Dimensions should be arranged to provide required information for optimum readability. Dimensions should be shown in true profile views and refer to visible outlines.* Show the size and location of a hole in the view where the hole shows up as a circle. When the hole is created in the part, it will be located and drilled from that same view. This ensures consistency between the design and the manufacturing of the part. Also, do not dimension hidden features on a part. Find a view where the feature is visible, and dimension in that view.

15.04 Definitions

The following terms are used in the remainder of this chapter. Studying them now will help you better understand the dimensioning concepts that follow. (*Definitions are from *ASME Y14.5M-1994*.)

- **Dimension**—*A numerical value expressed in appropriate units of measure and used to define the size, location, geometric characteristic, or surface texture of a part or part feature.

- **Arrowhead**—A small triangle at the end of dimension lines and leaders to indicate the direction and extent of a dimension (see Figure 15.10).

- **Dimension Line**—A thin, dark, solid line that terminates at each end with arrowheads. The value of a dimension typically is shown in the center of the dimension line. *A dimension line, along with its arrowheads, shows the direction and extent of a dimension (see Figure 15.10).

- **Extension Line**—A thin, dark, solid line extending from a point on an object, perpendicular to a dimension line. *Extension lines are used to indicate the extension of a surface or point to a location preferably outside the part outline (see Figure 15.10). There should be a visible gap between extension lines and

FIGURE 15.10. Dimensioning terminology.

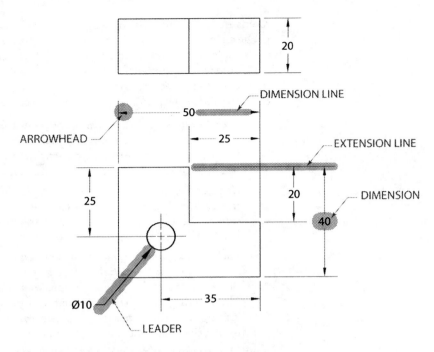

visible lines so the person reading the drawing can distinguish between the part and the dimensions describing the part.

- **Leader**—A thin, dark, solid line terminating with an arrowhead at one end and a dimension, note, or symbol at the other end. *Leaders are used to direct a dimension, note, or symbol to the intended place on a drawing.

15.05 Redundancy is Dumb

As you learn more about dimensioning parts, you will discover that clarity is very important and that a certain amount of economy goes a long way. The machinist is not going to be too happy if you dimension every point in every view on a drawing. He or she is expecting to see only the dimensions that are necessary to manufacture the part. Dimensions should appear only once on a drawing. In addition, each dimension should be placed in the view where the contour shape is best shown. This is known as the **contour rule** or **contour dimensioning**. Examine the part and dimensions shown in Figure 15.11. In (a), too many dimensions are given. It is not necessary to give dimensions to every point in each view. Notice the dimensions in (b). Each dimension is shown only once in the view where the contour or shape for that particular dimension shows up the best. For example, the hole shows up the best in the top view; therefore, it is best to show the size and location of the hole in that view rather than in the front view.

Another example of redundancy that should be avoided is shown in Figure 15.12. This is a very simple example, but notice that one of the horizontal dimensions can be omitted since 20 + 15 + 20 = 55. The same is true for the vertical dimensions since 10 + 20 = 30. The task here is to determine which dimensions are needed most and include just those.

To help you determine which dimensions are most critical, imagine a similar part in a couple of situations. In Figure 15.13(a), notice that the spacer must fit correctly with respect to a couple of different features within the larger part. The tab in the larger part fits into the slot, and the left side of the spacer fits against the right side of the larger part. For the drawing in (b), there is no need to include the dimension of 23 on

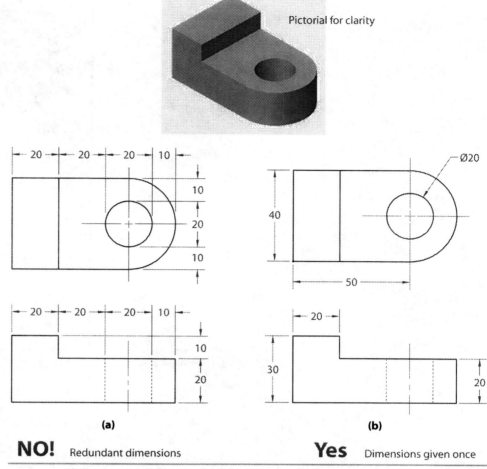

Pictorial for clarity

(a)

(b)

NO! Redundant dimensions   **Yes** Dimensions given once

FIGURE 15.11. Redundant dimensions in (a) are poor practice. Dimensions in (b) are shown once in the view best suited for viewing.

the right of the part since it is not really critical. The overall dimension is more important in this context. Overall dimensions help to define outer boundaries of parts quickly. Figure 15.13(c) is not appropriate in this situation. The critical dimension of 20 is omitted, and the noncritical dimension of 23 is included. It is being left to chance

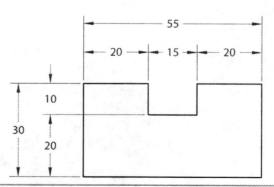

FIGURE 15.12. Redundant dimensions.

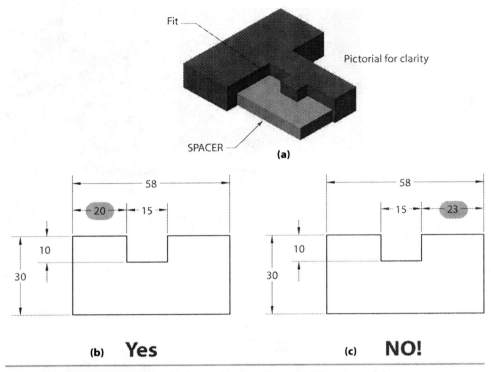

(a)

(b) **Yes** **(c)** **NO!**

FIGURE 15.13. Dimensions applied, considering the fit and function of the part named SPACER.

that the feature whose size is 20 will be correct based on the other three dimensions being manufactured to their exact correct sizes.

When the "inside" dimensions are more important or more critical than the overall dimension, the overall dimension should be identified as a reference dimension. In Figure 15.14 (a), the two tabs on the spacer fit into two holes in the larger part. In this case, the sizes of the tabs *and* the space between them are critical for the parts to fit together. In this case, the overall dimension is given as a reference dimension so the person making the part does not have to add the three dimensions to figure out the overall size. Reference dimensions, like the overall dimension in (b), are identified by enclosing them in parentheses. Here the person inspecting the parts can use the overall dimension as a quick check.

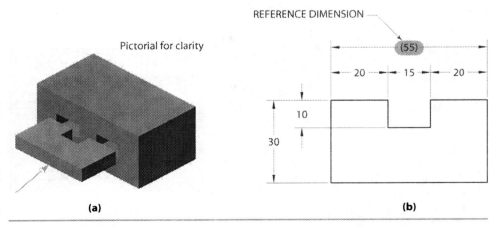

(a) **(b)**

FIGURE 15.14. Reference dimensions.

15.06 Geometrically Correct, but Still Wrong!

Why does it matter what dimensions are given if all of the geometry is defined? It may not matter if you are converting 3-D CAD data *directly* to produce molds for plastic parts, STL (stereolithography) file data for rapid prototyping, or tool paths for CNC machining. However, when drawings are being used to document parts for manufacture, accepted rules and practices must be followed to ensure acceptable results.

15.06.01 Different Ways of Specifying the Same Geometry

One of the first things to recognize when dimensioning objects is that there are standards for specifying particular types of geometry. For example, circles are typically dimensioned as diameters (Ø), and arcs are dimensioned as radii (see Figure 15.15). Circles are dimensioned with diameters since they typically represent machined holes, and machined holes are produced with standard tools that are defined by diameter dimensions. If the part in Figure 15.15 is a gasket, the three holes must line up with three holes on mating parts. Therefore, the 35 and the 70 dimensions are important dimensions to include since they identify the centers of the holes. Although the 94 dimension might be of interest to someone knowing the overall width of the object, it is not critical for defining the geometry. For the part shown in (a), the overall width can be determined by adding the 70 to the radii on the ends if necessary.

15.06.02 Identifying and Specifying the Critical Dimensions for Part Function

As you get more experience in engineering and design, one skill you will acquire is the ability to identify the critical dimensions on parts. In fact, by carefully planning the way a part is dimensioned, you may be able to eliminate potential errors in assembly. Examine the SPACER shown in Figure 15.16. The purpose of this part is to make sure the vise assembly stays together when the vise is opened to its maximum width. What are the critical dimensions on the SPACER? Are the overall height and width dimensions critical? To some extent yes, but the most important dimensions are the size of the machined holes and the distance between the two holes. The size of the holes is critical because the cylindrical bars must fit correctly in the holes. The location dimension between the holes is important because it ensures that both bars line up with both holes. For this example, you are going to concentrate on dimensioning the location of the holes.

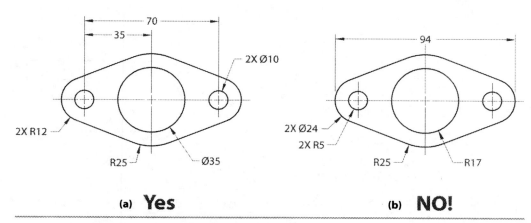

FIGURE 15.15. Proper dimensioning of circles and arcs.

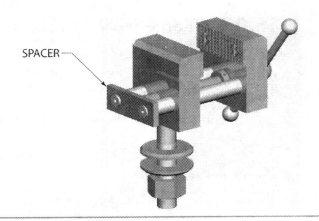

FIGURE 15.16. The vise assembly SPACER.

Figure 15.17 includes two examples of dimensioning the location of the holes on the spacer from the assembly shown in Figure 15.16. You might be asking yourself, why does it matter whether you dimension the holes from the ends of the part (b) or give the dimension between the centers (a)?

Imagine the parts are manufactured according to the fixture shown in Figure 15.18. A jig has been set up such that the SPACER stock material is slid into the jig, held down, and then cut to its overall length of 70 mm. Next, a machinist uses the dimensions on the drawing you prepared to locate and drill the two holes. What happens if during the day of manufacturing parts, the jig begins to slip? By the end of the day, the overall length of the parts are coming out to be 72 mm instead of 70 mm. If the machinist used

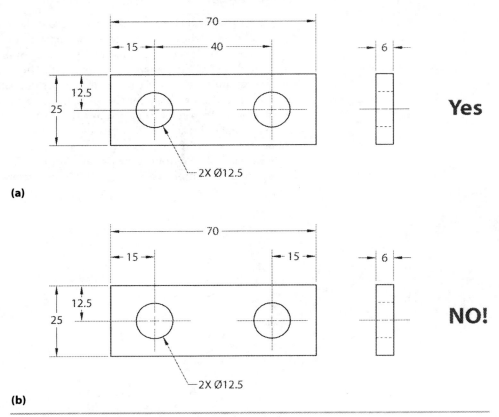

(a)

(b)

FIGURE 15.17. Two possible dimensioned drawings of the SPACER.

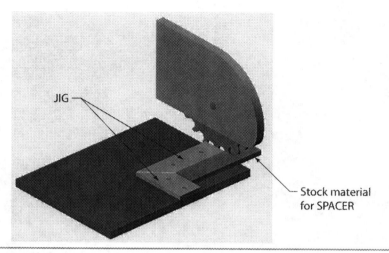

FIGURE 15.18. Cutting the SPACER.

the drawing in Figure 15.17(a) to locate and drill the holes, the parts would not function since the distance between the holes is probably 42 mm instead of 40 mm (72 – 30 = 42). If the drawing in Figure 15.17(b) was used to machine the parts, the overall length would still be incorrect, but the distance between the holes would be right. The SPACER would still function, and the additional material could be removed if necessary.

15.06.03 Baseline versus Chain Dimensioning

There are many different ways to locate features. As mentioned already, starting with an examination of how the part will function within the assembly is the best way to begin determining which dimensions are most important. Two of the main types of dimensioning techniques are baseline and chain.

Baseline dimensioning is illustrated in Figure 15.19. Notice how all of the dimensions in a given direction originate from a base or datum. This type of dimensioning is frequently used for CNC machines that work from a rectangular coordinate system.

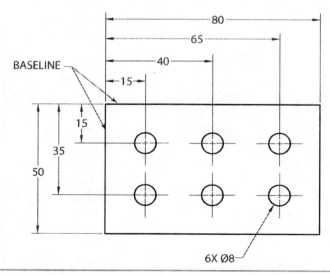

FIGURE 15.19. Baseline dimensioning.

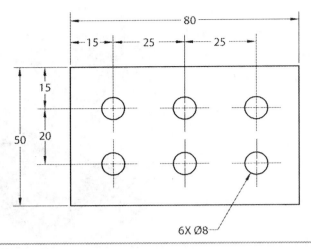

FIGURE 15.20. Chain dimensioning.

Chain dimensioning is shown in Figure 15.20. In this system, features are dimensioned relative to one another. This is appropriate when part function requires that features be related to one another, as discussed previously for the part in Figure 15.17(b). As you will see in the next chapter, chain dimensioning can cause problems with tolerance accumulation; so baseline dimensioning is often preferred, However, there are times when chain dimensioning is appropriate.

15.06.04 What Types of Dimensions Can Be Measured and Checked?

As was discussed earlier, it is important that you give dimensions that make sense to the person who is manufacturing or constructing the object you are designing. When dimensioning holes, you dimension to their centers because the machinist will locate the same points and center the drill bit at that location. When dimensioning parts, you also should select dimensions that can be measured. The object in Figure 15.21(a) is dimensioned to locate the center of the R50 arc. It would be very difficult for the person inspecting the part to locate the center of the arc since it is not on the object. In Figure 15.21(b), the ends of the arc are dimensioned, as well as the radius. This is better practice because the linear dimensions on the final part can be easily checked with standard measuring tools.

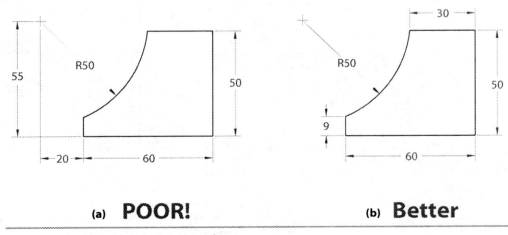

(a) **POOR!**   (b) **Better**

FIGURE 15.21. Checking the location of an arc center.

As you dimension more parts, you will get a better idea about where to place particular dimensions. As mentioned earlier in the chapter, showing dimensions in the view where the contour or shape of the object shows up the best is a good global rule to follow. There are some exceptions; but for most parts, following this contour rule is good practice. Figure 15.22(a) shows an example of poor dimensioning. Notice that the contour of the slot shows up the best in the right-side view; but the depth dimension of 16 is given in the top view, and the height dimension of 5 is given in the front. The size and location dimensions for the hole also are not clear in Figure 15.22(a). The diameter of 8 and the location dimension of 30 from the left side should both be in the top view, not the front view. Figure (b) shows the hole correctly dimensioned in the view where its size, location, and shape show up the best (top view).

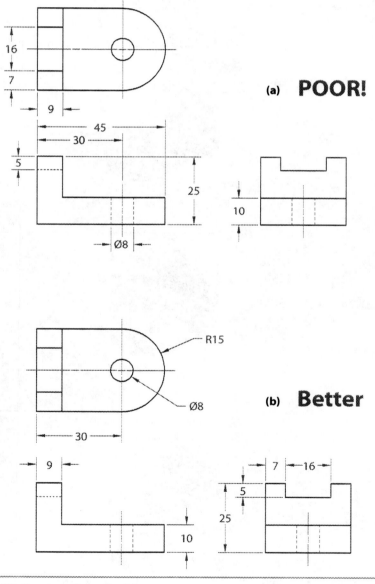

FIGURE 15.22. Contour dimensioning.

As an illustration of the process used in picking the correct view for dimensions, this example can be broken down into smaller steps. Figure 15.23 illustrates a step-by-step feature breakdown of the CONTOUR BLOCK. A solid model of the first feature is shown in Figure 15.23(a). This feature is defined by three dimensions shown in (b): the radius of the arc (R15), the distance from the left side of the part to the center of the arc (30), and the height of the feature (10). Based on following contour dimensioning, the

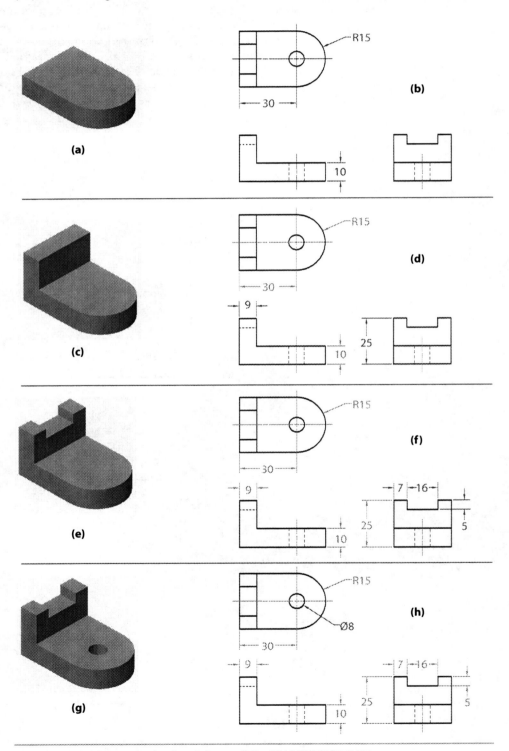

FIGURE 15.23. Dimensioning breakdown of the CONTOUR BLOCK.

R15 and 30 dimensions show up best in the top view; but the 10 dimension is best placed in the front view. The next feature is the extruded piece on the left side of the part shown in Figure 15.22(c). This feature is defined by the two dimensions in (d): the height of the feature from the bottom of the part (25) and the width of the part (9). The front view is the only view where the 9 dimension clearly shows the width of the extrusion. The height of the extrusion (25) can be shown in either the front or right-side views; but since you will be putting other dimensions in the right-side view, it is better to group them. The rectangular cut feature is shown in Figure 15.23(e). This feature is defined by three dimensions in (f): the height of the cut (5), the depth of the cut (16), and a location dimension for the cut (7). The contour of this feature is best seen in the side view, so that is where these three dimensions should be located. The last feature of this part is the hole shown in Figure 15.23(g). Since the hole has the same center as the arc, there is no need for a location dimension. The only dimension necessary for the hole feature is the diameter. Figure 15.23(h) illustrates how this dimension shows up best in the top view, where the hole's contour is most clearly seen.

15.07.01 Solid Lines Only

Another good rule of thumb to follow when dimensioning is to dimension only to visible or solid lines. This is related to the contour rule. In Figure 15.24(a), notice how the extension line of the 10 dimension is related to the hidden line. The dimension is much clearer in figure (b) where the extension line extends from a visible or solid line. Also notice the illustration of this rule on the drawing shown in Figure 15.22.

15.07.02 Placement and Spacing

As you place dimensions on drawings, you should follow established guidelines for the distance that dimensions should be located from views, gaps between extension lines and visible lines, lengths of arrowheads, etc. Figure 15.25 shows the standard practice related to dimension placement and spacing. When someone is looking at your drawing, the first thing that will be noticed will be the object itself. Several conventions and standards help distinguish dimensions from object geometry. As mentioned earlier in the book, visible lines are thick and dark to make the outline and visible edges of the object stand out. Dimension lines, extension lines, and leader lines should be thin and dark. Dimension lines also should be at least 10 mm (.375 inches) from any view, helping to avoid clutter. When dimensions are placed outside other dimensions, there should be at least 6 mm (.25 inches) between dimension lines. The standards for dimensioning also require a visible gap between extension lines and object geometry. Typically, 1 mm (.0625 inches) is a good rule of thumb. Also, extension lines should extend just past their corresponding dimension line (2–3 mm or .125 inches).

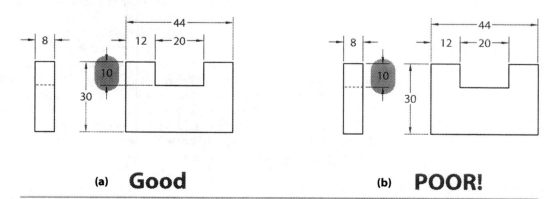

FIGURE 15.24. Dimensioning to solid lines.

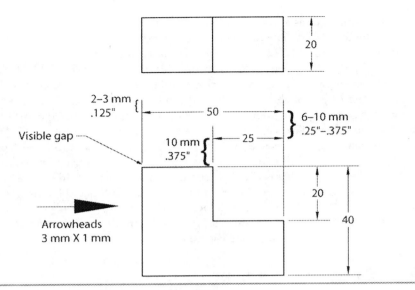

FIGURE 15.25. Dimension placement and spacing.

FIGURE 15.26. Fonts for dimensioning.

15.07.03 Font

Engineering drawings require the use of single-stroke gothic lettering. In addition, letters should be uppercase since few languages worldwide have an upper- and a lowercase. Typical fonts used in CAD software are Century Gothic and Romans.shx (see Figure 15.26).

15.08 Shortcuts

The last 20 years have seen a shift toward the use of symbols to define features on drawings rather than notes written in English. Since many companies have adopted international standards for design and production and they must be able to communicate in a universal language that everyone understands, symbols often lend themselves to clarity of design intent. Some of these symbols are used in the shortcuts representing dimensions for diameters, radii, chamfers, machined holes, threads, and standard features as described in the following sections.

15.08.01 Diameters and Radii

As shown earlier in the chapter in Figure 15.15, circles are dimensioned as diameters using the Ø symbol and arcs are dimensioned as radii using the R symbol. Both symbols are shown preceding the dimension value. For holes, diameter dimensions are usually shown in the view where the hole appears as a circle since that is the view of the part a machinist will see when the hole is being produced. When the diameter of a cylinder is dimensioned, however, the dimension should be placed in the rectangular view of the feature (see Figure 15.27). This helps distinguish holes from positive space cylinders.

Figure 15.28 illustrates several options for dimensioning arcs. When the arc is large enough, as in (a), the leader line and text can be placed on the inside of the arc. In (b), the arc is not large enough to place the text on the inside. In this case, the leader line should extend through the arc with the text on the outside. With small arcs such as (c) and (d), the leader line and the text should be placed on the outside.

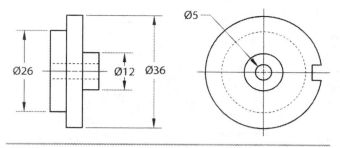

FIGURE 15.27. Dimensioning cylinders and holes.

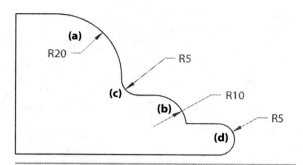

FIGURE 15.28. Dimensioning arcs.

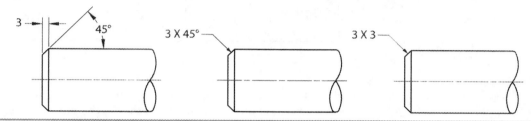

FIGURE 15.29. Dimensioning chamfers.

15.08.02 Chamfers

Chamfers are beveled or angled edges that typically appear on the ends of shafts or fasteners to aid in assembling parts or to smooth out rough edges. They are dimensioned by giving a length from the end of the part and an angle or by specifying two distances. Figure 15.29 illustrates the different options for dimensioning a chamfer.

15.08.03 Standard Machined Holes: Countersinks and Counterbores

The use of symbols also is very important when you are dimensioning the sizes of machined holes such as counterbores, countersinks, spotfaced holes, and blind holes. Take a look at Figure 15.30. Symbols used in the top view represent the different types of machined holes. In these examples, ⌴ represents a counterbore, ⌵ represents a countersink, and ⤓ is the symbol used for specifying depth. Note that according to standard practice, no manufacturing processes are specified (e.g., drill, ream, or bore).

- Figure 15.30(a) illustrates a standard *drill* hole with a diameter of 8 mm.

- Figure 15.30(b) illustrates a *blind* hole with the same diameter. The depth of 15 is measured from the top surface to the horizontal line at the bottom of the cylindrical portion of the hole, not the point.

- A *counterbore* hole is shown in (c). The 8 diameter indicates the original drill size, the 15 diameter is the size of the counterbore, and the 7 is the depth of the counterbore. Counterbore holes are used to accept fillister head and hex socket head screws.

- Figure 15.30(d) illustrates a *countersink*. The 8 indicates the original drill diameter, the 14 is the diameter of the countersink, and the 82° is the angle of the countersink bit. Countersunk holes are used for applications with flat head and oval head screws.

FIGURE 15.30. Dimensioning
the sizes of machined holes.

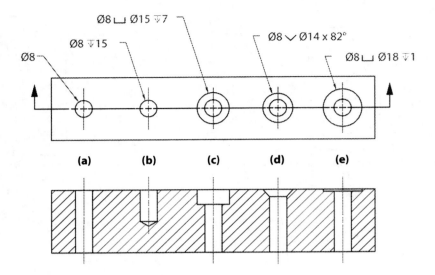

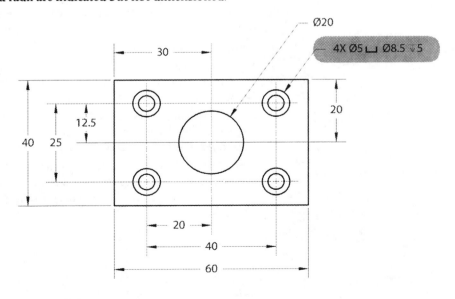

A *spotface* hole is shown in (e). Spotfacing is used to clean off the rough surface of a cast part typically to accept a hexagon head type screw. The format of the dimension is the same as the counterbore; however, the depth dimension may be left off if a company uses a standard spotface depth.

It should be noted that you string the symbols together in the order that a machinist would perform the operations. For example, in Figure 15.30(c), the diameter of the through hole is given first, followed by the diameter and depth of the counterbore. These symbols are included in that order because a machinist would first drill the hole and then make the counterbore at that location.

When multiple holes with the same size are present, only dimension one of the holes. The X symbol is used to indicate how many times that particular hole is machined. In Figure 15.31, 4X is placed before the counterbored hole dimension to indicate that four holes require that size dimension.

15.08.04 Slots

Slots are produced with standard tools such as milling bits. Since these tools are specified by their diameters, slots also should be dimensioned by their diameters. Figure 15.32 shows several acceptable ways that slots can be dimensioned. Notice that in each case, the end radii are indicated but not dimensioned.

FIGURE 15.31. Dimensioning
multiple holes.

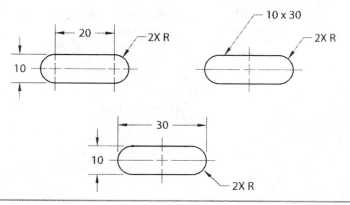

FIGURE 15.32. Dimensioning slots.

15.09 Notes

Most drawings require some type of note or notes in addition to the dimensions on the drawing in order to fully define the part. Since the purpose of your drawing is to give all of the information necessary to manufacture the part, some pieces of information cannot easily be shown in typical dimensions. No matter what type of notes are being shown, all of them should be placed so they are read from the bottom of the sheet of paper.

15.09.01 General Notes

General notes typically appear in the lower right-hand corner of a drawing and apply to the whole drawing. Some may be located in the titleblock. Examples of general notes are as follows:

> **MATERIAL: CAST IRON**
> **FAO (***finish all over***)**
> **ALL DIMENSIONS ARE IN MILLIMETERS**
> **ALL DIMENSIONS `0.1 UNLESS OTHERWISE SPECIFIED**
> **BREAK ALL SHARP EDGES**

15.09.02 Local Notes

Local notes appear on the drawing views and are usually specified with a leader line. Like general notes, local notes are used to specify information that cannot be shown with regular dimensions. Figure 15.33 includes examples of local notes.

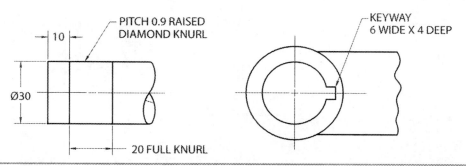

FIGURE 15.33. Using local notes.

15.10 Considerations for 3-D Modeling

Now that you have covered all of the rules and guidelines for dimensioning, take some time to think about what all of this means as you are creating parts using a 3-D modeler. If you have already been creating solid models, you probably noticed that drawings sometimes require more dimensions than what you would use when modeling. This happens because you can imbed certain geometric relations or constraints within a 3-D model that must be explicitly pointed out on a drawing. Figure 15.34 illustrates this idea. Notice that the drawing includes dimensions from the center of the hole to the ends of the part, but the 3-D model sketch does not. A machinist would need to know this information to locate the hole in the center of the part. The sketch incorporates symmetric constraints between the outside lines and their corresponding center line.

Since these differences between the dimensions are required in 3-D models and the drawings are required for documenting the parts, drawings with dimensions for manufacturing are typically done at the end of the design process instead of at the beginning. As you model parts, you want to add geometric and dimensional constraints that capture the design intent for each part. Documentation drawings can then be completed with dimensions for manufacture when the design is complete.

One of the nice features of constraint-based modelers is the ability of the software to let you know when geometry has been underdimensioned or overdimensioned. Your goal should be to fully define the geometry with geometric and dimensional constraints. If a constraint or constraints are missing, the software usually has some type of indicator that the geometry is underdefined. When geometry is underdefined, you should be able to grab entities and move them. When too many dimensions or geometric constraints are present, the software lets you know that the geometry is overdefined or overconstrained. To correct this problem, you must delete a dimension or geometric constraint that is in conflict with other constraints.

15.11 Dimensions for the Plate Example

Return to the senario where you work for the company that manufactures hardware for household doors. You were asked to think about several questions. What are the dimensions needed to manufacture the plate in Figure 15.35? What are the critical dimensions that must be given? What are some of the standard dimensions that exist on other parts or previous parts?

Figure 15.36 shows an example of how the part might be dimensioned. The critical dimensions on the plate are the distances between the countersunk holes and the center hole, the sizes of the holes, and the overall size of the plate (since it must fit in the door properly).

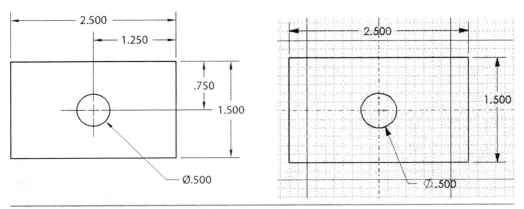

FIGURE 15.34. Differences between dimensioning drawings and 3-D models.

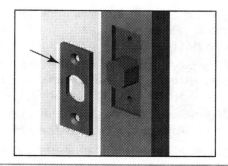
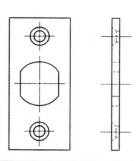

FIGURE 15.35. A deadbolt lock plate.

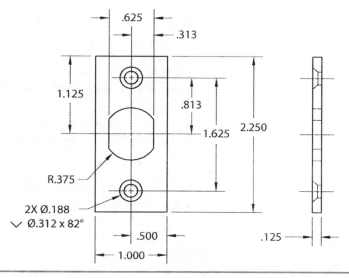

FIGURE 15.36. Plate dimensions.

The plate drawing includes dimensions that may not be present in the constraint-based solid model. Since symmetric geometric constraints may have been incorporated into the model, the highlighted dimensions may not exist in the 3-D solid model database. These dimensions will need to be specified on the drawing to ensure that the part is manufactured properly.

15.12 Fundamental Rules for Dimensioning

This chapter contains best practice suggestions for dimensioning a part; however, as stated previously, *ASME Y14.5M-1994* is the accepted standard for dimensioning practice. The following fundamental rules are quoted from the *ASME Y14.5M-1994* standards for Dimensioning and Tolerancing. For a complete listing of the standards, see *ASME Y14.5M-1994*.

    a. Each dimension shall have a tolerance, except for those dimensions specifically identified as reference, maximum, minimum, or stock (commercial stock size). The tolerance may be applied directly to a dimension (or indirectly in the case of basic dimensions), indicated by a general note, or located in a supplementary block of the drawing format.

    b. Dimensioning and tolerancing shall be complete so there is full understanding of the characteristic of each feature. Neither scaling (measuring the size of a feature directly from an engineering drawing) nor assumption of a distance of size is permitted, except as follows: Undimensioned drawings, such as loft, printed wiring, templates, and master layouts prepared on stable material, are excluded provided the necessary control dimensions are specified.

c. Each necessary dimension of an end product shall be shown. No more dimensions than those necessary for complete definition shall be given. The use of reference dimensions on a drawing should be minimized.

d. Dimensions shall be selected and arranged to suit the function and mating relationship of a part and shall not be subject to more than one interpretation.

e. The drawing should define a part <u>without</u> specifying manufacturing methods. Thus, only the diameter of a hole is given without indicating whether it is to be drilled, reamed, punched, or made by any other operation. However, in those instances where manufacturing, processing, quality assurance, or environmental information is essential to the definition of engineering requirements, it shall be specified on the drawing or in a document referenced on the drawing.

f. It is permissible to identify as nonmandatory certain processing dimensions that provide for finish allowance, shrink allowance, and other requirements, provided the final dimensions are given on the drawing. Nonmandatory processing dimensions shall be identified by an appropriate note, such as NON-MANDATORY (MFG DATA).

g. Dimensions should be arranged to provide required information for optimum readability. Dimensions should be shown in true profile views and refer to visible outlines.

h. Wires, cables, sheets, rods, and other materials manufactured to gage or code numbers shall be specified by linear dimensions indicating the diameter or thickness. Gage or code numbers may be shown in parentheses following the dimension.

i. A 90° angle applies where center lines and lines depicting features are shown on a drawing at right angles and no angle is specified.

j. A 90° basic angle applies where centerlines of features in a pattern or surfaces shown at right angles on the drawing are located or defined by basic dimensions and no angle is specified.

k. Unless otherwise specified, all dimensions are applicable at 20°C (68°F). Compensation may be made for measurements made at other temperatures.

l. All dimensions and tolerances apply in a free state condition. This principle does not apply to non-rigid parts.

m. Unless otherwise specified, all geometric tolerances apply for full depth, length, and width of the feature.

n. Dimensions and tolerances apply only at the drawing level where they are specified. A dimension specified for a given feature on one level of drawing (for example, a detail drawing) is not mandatory for that feature at any other level (for example, an assembly drawing).

15.13 Chapter Summary

This chapter provided an introduction to dimensioning. The chapter discussed how all dimensions have a tolerance and how tolerances are important for the function of designs. Dimensioning, like other drawing topics, follows fairly specific standards or rules. Whether dimensioning in inches or millimeters, you must follow these standards. This chapter also covered techniques for dimensioning different features, such as standard parts, machined holes, and notes.

The next chapter will discuss tolerance dimensioning in more detail, as well as introduce the topic of geometric dimensioning and tolerancing. These topics are key to the production of parts that are based on the specific intent of the designer.

15.14 glossary of key terms

ANSI Y14.5 *(ASME Y14.5M-1994)*: Industry standard document that outlines uniform practices for displaying and interpreting dimensions and related information on drawings and other forms of engineering documentation.

arrowhead: A small triangle at the end of dimension lines and leaders to indicate the direction and extent of a dimension.

baseline dimensioning: A system of dimensioning where each feature is dimensioned from the same origin.

chain dimensioning: A system of dimensioning where features are dimensioned from one another instead of from an origin.

contour dimensioning: Placing each dimension in the view where the contour or shape of the feature shows up best.

contour rule: A drawing practice where each dimension should be placed in the view where the contour shape is best shown.

dimension: A numerical value expressed in appropriate units of measure and used to define the size, location,

geometric characteristic, or surface texture of a part or part feature.

dimension line: A thin, dark, solid line that terminates at each end with arrowheads. The value of a dimension typically is shown in the center of the dimension line.

extension line: A thin, dark, solid line extending from a point on an object, perpendicular to a dimension line used to indicate the extension of a surface or point to a location preferably outside the part outline.

leader: A thin, dark, solid line terminating with an arrowhead at one end and a dimension, note, or symbol at the other end.

location: A dimension associated with the position of a feature on a part.

size: The general term for the size of a feature, such as a hole, cylinder, or set of opposed parallel surfaces.

tolerance: The total amount a specific dimension is permitted to vary. It is the difference between the upper and lower limits of the dimension.

15.15 questions for review

1. What is the current standard for dimensioning and tolerancing in the United States?

2. Explain the difference between dimensioning standards for inches and the standards for millimeters.

3. List at least four fundamental rules for dimensioning.

4. What are the correct line types and darkness for dimension lines, extension lines, and leaders?

5. When a two-view drawing of a simple rectangular block is given, what dimensions are necessary?

6. Explain the difference between baseline and chain dimensioning.

7. What is contour dimensioning?

8. What are the standard symbols for diameter, radius, counterbore, countersink, and depth?

9. Explain why the dimensions for a constraint-based solid model of a design may be different from the dimensions that appear on a detail drawing of the part.

15.16 problems

1. Sketch the necessary dimensions to fully define each object shown in Figure P15.1. Do not use redundant or reference dimensions.

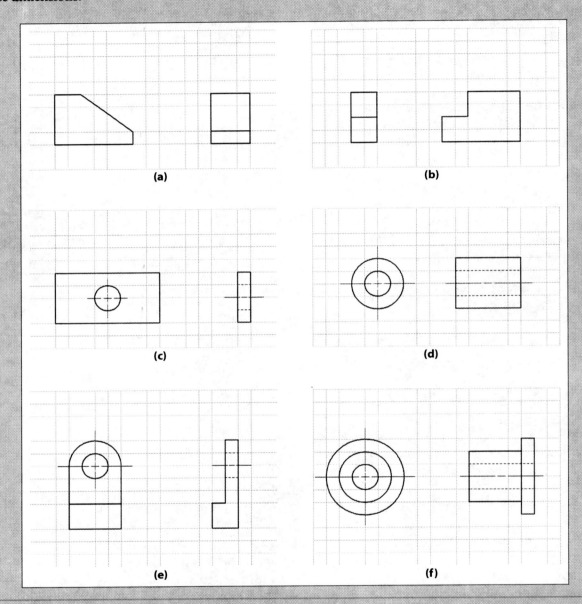

FIGURE P15.1.

15.16 problems (continued)

2. Scale and copy the drawings shown in Figure P15.2, leaving sufficient space between the views to add dimensions. Add the necessary dimensions to fully define each object. Add additional views as necessary to conform to the dimensioning guidelines in this chapter. Do not use redundant or reference dimensions.

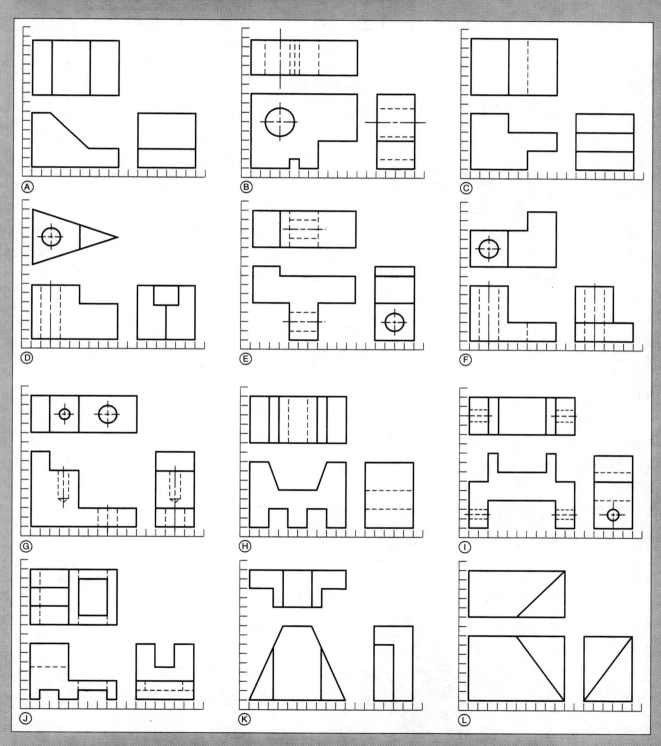

15.16 problems (continued)

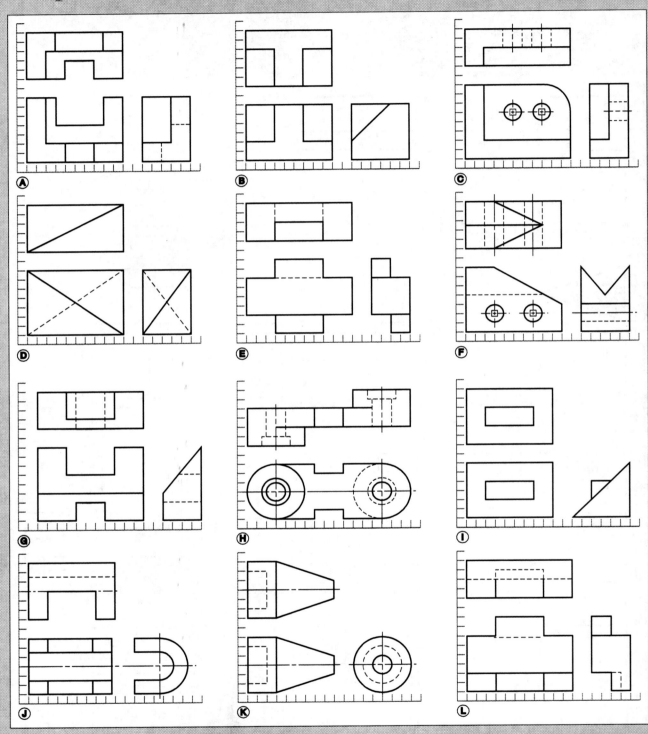

FIGURE P15.2.

15.16 problems (continued)

3. Scale and copy the drawings shown in Figure P15.3, leaving sufficient space between the views to add dimensions. Add the necessary dimensions to fully define each object. Add additional views and section views as necessary to conform to the dimensioning guidelines in this chapter. Whenever possible, apply accepted shortcut practices to describe appropriate features. Do not use redundant or reference dimensions.

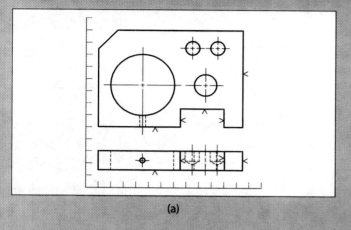

(a)

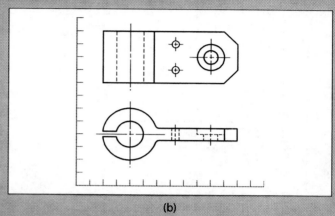

(b)

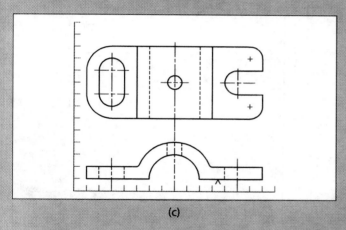

(c)

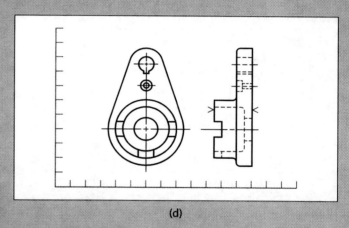

(d)

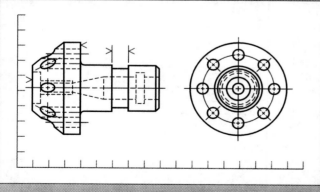

(e)

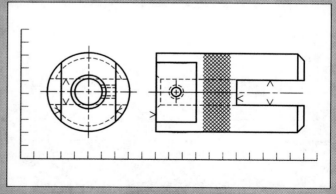

(f)

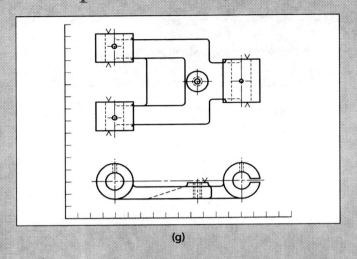

(g)

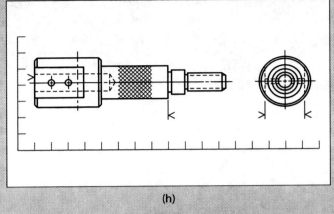

(h)

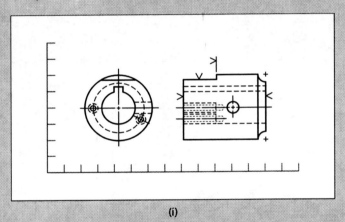

(i)

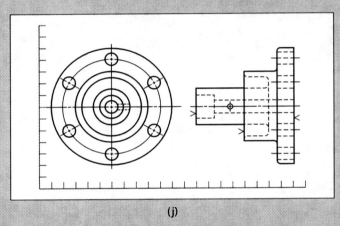

(j)

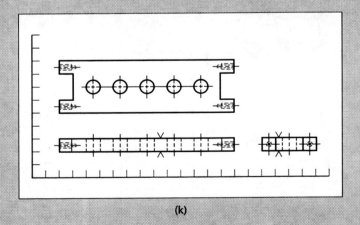

(k)

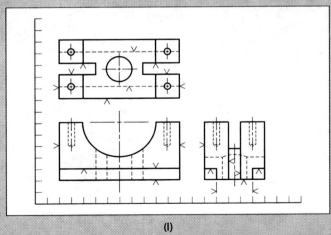

(l)

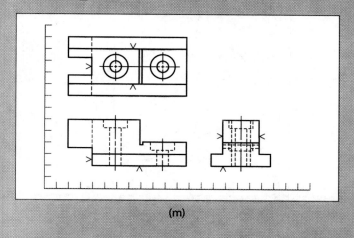

(m)

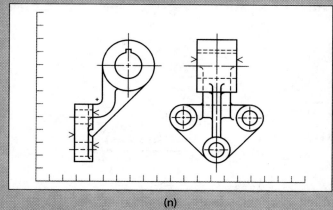

(n)

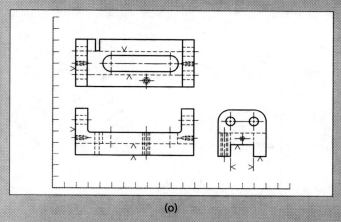

(o)

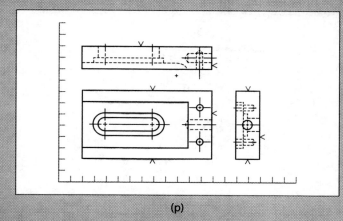

(p)

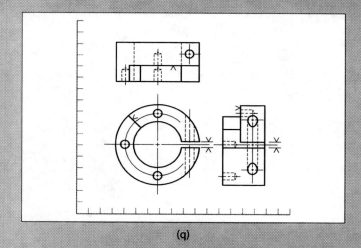

(q)

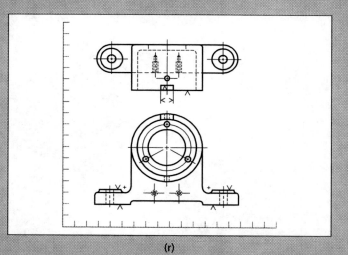

(r)

15.16 problems (continued)

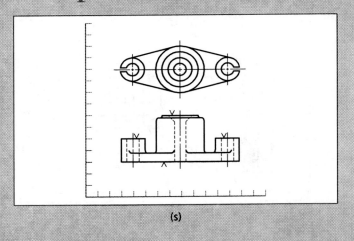

(s)

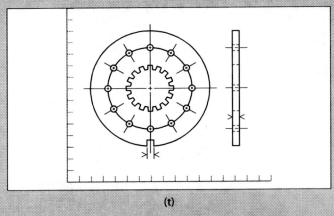

(t)

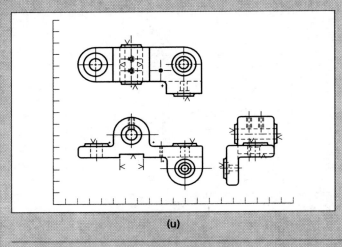

(u)

FIGURE P15.3.

15.16 problems (continued)

4. In Figure P15.4, consider the function of the indicated parts shown in their intended assemblies. For each drawing, add the necessary dimensions to fully define the object, giving consideration to the critical dimensions necessary for each part to fit and function in its intended assembly.

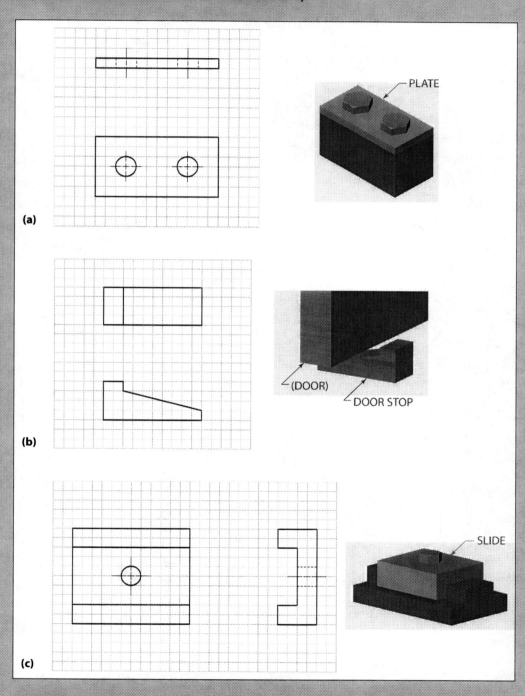

(a)

(b)

(c)

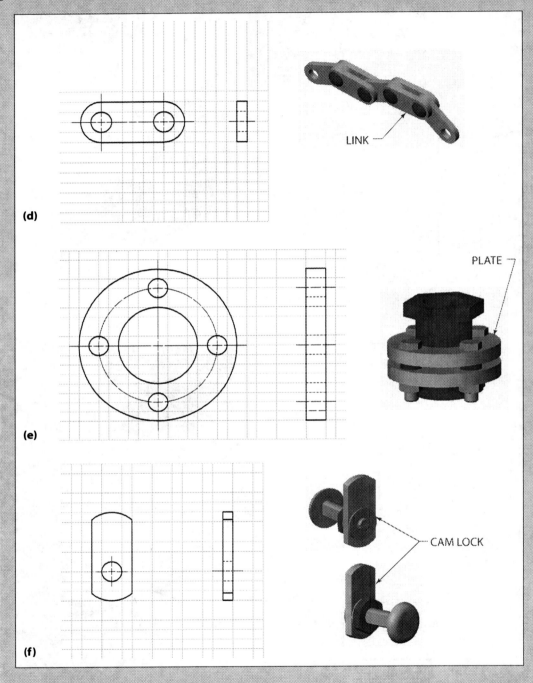

(d)

LINK

(e)

PLATE

(f)

CAM LOCK

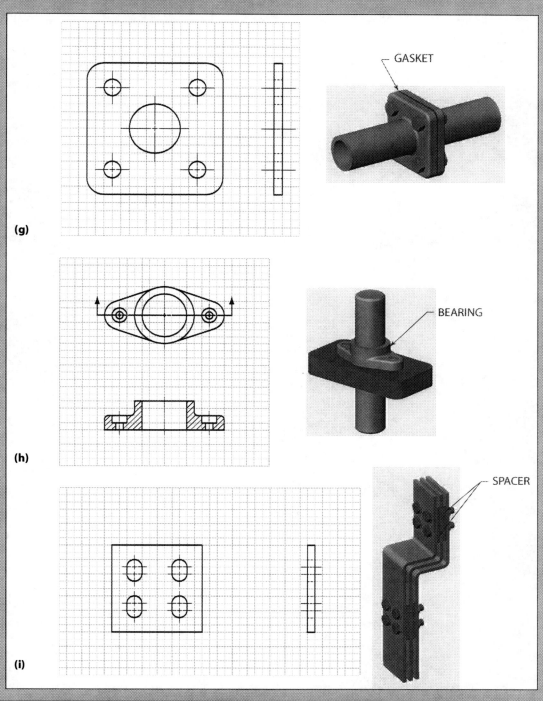

(g)

GASKET

(h)

BEARING

(i)

SPACER

FIGURE P15.4.

Tolerancing

objectives

After completing this chapter, you should be able to

- Describe the purpose of conventional tolerancing and its limitations

- Use standard tables to specify an appropriate fit between two mating parts

- Explain the advantages of using geometric dimensioning and tolerancing (GD&T) over conventional tolerancing

- Recognize the datum reference frame on a drawing with geometric dimensions and tolerances

- Describe the tolerance zone shape for each geometric tolerance

- Correctly read the feature control frames on a drawing with geometric dimensions and tolerances

introduction

In the previous chapter, you learned some of the basics for displaying dimensions correctly and, to some extent, how to select appropriate dimensions to describe the size and location of features on objects. This chapter will look at dimensioning objects for **interchangeable manufacturing**. Interchangeable manufacturing is the process by which parts are made at different locations and brought together for assembly. For many industries, this process enables third-party companies to produce replacement parts or custom parts.

The first topic in this chapter deals with the amount of tolerance required. In previous chapters, the tolerance of a dimension was defined as the total amount the tolerance could vary. Since it is impossible to make anything perfectly, design engineers must define a range of acceptable tolerance for manufacturing. If you specify a small value for a tolerance, such as .0001 mm, the machining cost will be high because of the required accuracy. As the tolerance value gets larger, the cost of fabrication usually gets smaller. If you are in the business of making children's toys from plastic materials, it is unlikely that you will be specifying tolerance values such as .0001 mm. If you are designing engine parts for space missions, you may need to require very small tolerances.

It is rare to find companies that manufacture products where all parts in the final assembly have been produced at the same location. It is more likely that parts for the final assembly are manufactured at different facilities around the world. By using standard practices for tolerance dimensioning, manufacturers can be confident that parts will fit together as intended. This is critical in the specification of parts that might be manfuctured by subcontractors or by other divisions of a company.

16.01.01 Relationships between Different Parts

When doing engineering design work, it is rare to design parts that do not interact with other parts. In most cases, it is necessary to specify the intended fit between parts. Examine the WHEEL ASSEMBLY in Figure 16.01. The intent of the design is to have the WHEEL spin freely as it rolls against the ground. For this to happen, there must be a clearance of material, or space, between some of the parts in the assembly. In the case of the WHEEL ASSEMBLY, the intent is for the BUSHINGS to fit tightly into the WHEEL, the SHAFT to fit tightly within the side supports, and the BUSHINGS to spin freely around the SHAFT. The largest diameter of the SHAFT and the hole through the BUSHING are both about 3/4". To ensure that the BUSHINGS spin about the SHAFT, the designer must specify a size range for each part. Tolerance is the specific amount a particular dimension can vary. The SHAFT and BUSHING drawings appear in Figure 16.02. The size range for the largest diameter of the SHAFT is .7435-.7455, and the range for the hole in the BUSHING is .7500-.7535. If each part is machined within the stated size range, the BUSHING diameter will be larger than the SHAFT diameter and the BUSHING will be free to spin about the SHAFT.

16.01.02 Problems with Inexperience in New Engineers

One of the main obstacles for new engineers is their lack of experience. Until they gain some valuable experience on the job, they are likely to have a difficult time making all of the correct design decisions. Lack of experience can be a problem in several areas.

First, not knowing the history or function of a product can put young engineers at a disadvantage. For example, the WHEEL ASSEMBLY in Figure 16.01 has several intended fits. It is important for an engineer to know why certain fits exist between

FIGURE 16.01. A WHEEL
assembly.

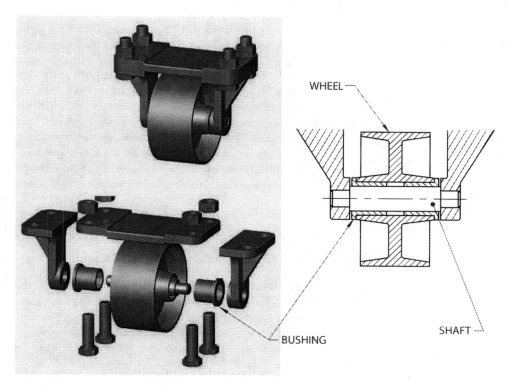

parts so the assembly will function properly. It is important for the engineer to know what materials will yield the best results within the assembly. Here are some other questions the engineer might ask:

- How will the parts be manufactured?
- Several parts in the WHEEL ASSEMBLY need to be cast. Does the company have a foundry?
- What type of machining operations can the company complete?
- What subcontractors does the company typically use?

All of these issues concerning product history and function tend to put young engineers at a disadvantage.

FIGURE 16.02. Detail drawings of the SHAFT and BUSHING.

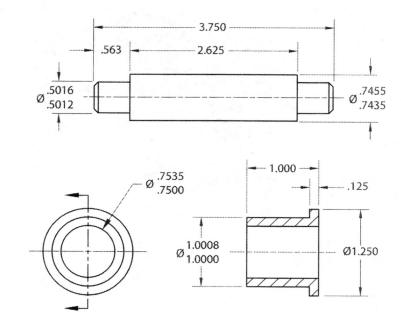

Another area that can create problems for young engineers is applying inappropriate tolerance values to dimensions. Applying too small of a tolerance value might cause problems for a machinist. For example, if an engineer applies a toleranced dimension of .750000-.750035 to the BUSHING in Figure 16.02, the machinist might not be able to machine the hole with a tolerance that small. If the machinist can machine the hole with that small of a tolerance, the cost will probably be higher than that of a larger tolerance value. However, if the engineer applies a tolerance value that is too loose (for example, .700-.750), the part may not function properly.

Inexperience also can be a problem when dealing with **geometric dimensions and tolerances**. As you will see later in the chapter, selecting an appropriate datum reference frame or coordinate system for geometric tolerancing is critical. Selecting appropriate dimensions is something that requires time and meaningful experiences on the job.

16.02 Formats for Tolerances

Tolerance dimensions can be displayed in several common formats: unilateral, bilateral, and limit dimensions. Figure 16.03 illustrates the differences between metric and inch conventions for displaying the number of decimal places. For each of these types of tolerance dimensions, a range is given from a specified basic size from which the limits were derived. For all of the metric examples in Figure 16.03, the basic size is 35. The basic size for the unilateral inch example is .500.

In a unilateral tolerance, all of the deviation is in one direction from the basic size. The tolerance is either all above or all below the basic size of the dimension. For metric dimensions, a single zero is shown without a plus or minus sign. When a designer is dimensioning in inches, the tolerance value is expressed with the same number of decimal places as the basic size and the appropriate plus or minus size is added.

Bilateral tolerances are tolerances where the deviation is divided in some way above and below the basic size of the dimension. The tolerance can be equally or unequally distributed about the basic size.

Limit dimensions are displayed with the high limit above the low limit. If the dimension is displayed on a single line, the low limit appears before the high limit.

	METRIC		INCHES	
UNILATERAL	$35\,^{+0.05}_{0}$ or $35\,^{0}_{-0.05}$		$.500\,^{+.005}_{-.000}$ not	$.500\,^{+.005}_{0}$
BILATERAL Equal	35 ± 0.05 not 35.00 ± 0.05		$.750\pm.005$ not	$.75\pm.005$
Unequal	$35\,^{+0.25}_{-0.10}$ not $35\,^{+0.25}_{-0.1}$		$1.000\,^{+.008}_{-.010}$ not	$1.000\,^{+.008}_{-.01}$
LIMIT	35.05 35.00 not	35.05 35	.250 .248 not	.25 .248

FIGURE 16.03. Formats for tolerance dimensioning in millimeters and inches.

As a designer working with tolerance dimensions, one thing you must consider is the buildup, or accumulation, of tolerances. When you are using tolerance dimensions, accumulation can occur in several ways.

16.03.01 Tolerance Buildup with Chain, Baseline, and Direct Dimensioning

Tolerance buildup, or accumulation, between features can be minimized depending on the type of dimensioning used. **Chain dimensioning** usually yields the largest accumulation of tolerance between features. The maximum variation or distance between features is equal to the sum of the intermediate distances. In Figure 16.04, the total tolerance accumulation between points X and Y is ±0.15. The distance between points X and Y is the sum of three dimensions: 20±0.05 + 25±0.05 + 25±0.05. If all three dimensions are machined to their maximum values, the result is 70.15. If they are machined to their minimum values, the result is 69.85.

   Baseline dimensioning can eliminate some of the accumulation of tolerances. In this system, the maximum variation between two features is the sum of the tolerances on the two dimensions from their origin to the two features. In Figure 16.05, the feature at X is located from the baseline with a 25 ±0.05 dimension and the feature at Y is located from the baseline with a 95 ±0.05 dimension. The tolerance buildup between the surfaces at X and Y is ±0.1. The distance between points X and Y is the difference between two dimensions: 95±0.05 - 25±0.05. If the 95±0.05 dimension is machined at its maxium value and the 25±0.05 dimension is machined at its minimum value, the result is 70.1. If the 95±0.05 dimension is machined at its minimum value and the 25±0.05 dimension is machined at its maximum value, the result is 69.9.

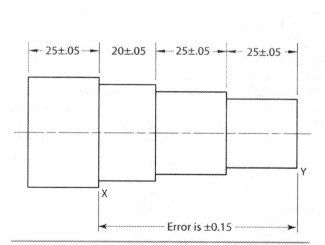

FIGURE 16.04. Tolerance accumulation with CHAIN dimensioning.

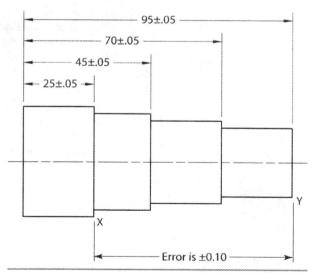

FIGURE 16.05. Tolerance accumulation with BASELINE dimensioning.

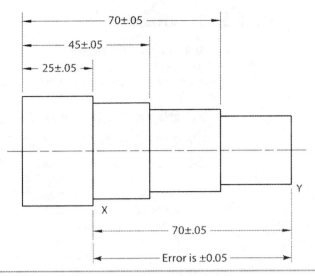

FIGURE 16.06. Tolerance accumulation with DIRECT dimensioning.

Direct dimensioning offers the best way to eliminate tolerance accumulation. This method involves placing a single dimension between two key points to minimize the tolerance accumulation. As shown in Figure 16.06, the total tolerance between features X and Y is only the tolerance on the one dimension between the two features. In this case, that tolerance is ±0.05.

16.03.02 Statistical Tolerance Control

Statistical tolerancing is a way to assign tolerances based on sound statistical practices rather than conventional tolerancing practices. It can be applied only when appropriate statistical process control methods are used for manufacturing. When conventional tolerancing methods are used, often the total assembly tolerance is divided by the number of individual parts in the assembly. A portion of this assembly tolerance is then assigned to each component. The problem with this method is that it usually results in tolerance values being more restrictive than necessary. When manufacturing processes are monitored by statistical process controls, technicians and engineers are better informed about processes for which tolerance values can be increased to reduce manufacturing costs. Figure 16.07 illustrates an example where a statistical tolerance is given with an arithmetic tolerance. In this case, the 12 ±0.05 dimension is appropriate when statistical process controls are in place. When those controls are not in place, the 12 ±0.02 dimension is applied.

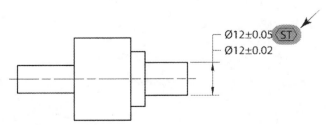

FEATURES IDENTIFIED AS STATISTICALLY TOLERACED SHALL BE PRODUCED WITH STATISTICAL PROCESS CONTROLS OR TO THE MORE RESTRICTIVE ARITHMETIC LIMITS.

FIGURE 16.07. Tolerancing with statistical process control.

16.04 Use of Tables for Fits

As mentioned at the beginning of the chapter, the intent of a design requires that you accurately specify fits between mating parts. For just about every application, you will be defining the looseness or tightness of the fit. As you design parts, you will be specifying fits using standard tables and recognized types of fits.

16.04.01 Types of Fits

Fits can be classified as one of the following:

- *Clearance fit*—Specifying the limits of size in such a way that a clearance or space always exists between mating parts. Figure 16.08 shows a machined hole with a limit dimension of 1.5000-1.5016 and a machined shaft with a limit dimension of 1.4990-1.4980. If both parts are machined within the stated limits of size, space will always exist between the two parts.

- *Interference fit*—Specifying the limits of size in such a way that an interference of material always exists between mating parts. Figure 16.09 shows a machined hole with a limit dimension of 1.5000-1.5006 and a machined shaft with a limit dimension of 1.5009-1.5013. If both parts are machined within the stated limits of size, material interference will always exist between the two parts.

- *Transition fit*—Specifying the limits of size in such a way that either a clearance or interference fit will exist when mating parts are assembled. Figure 16.10 shows a machined hole with a limit dimension of 1.5000-1.5012 and a machined shaft with a limit dimension of 1.5008-1.5015. If the hole is machined at its upper limit (1.5012) and the shaft is machined at its lower limit (1.5008), the result will be a clearance fit. On the other hand, if the hole is machined at its lower limit (1.5000) and the shaft is machined at its upper limit (1.5015), the result will be an interference fit.

You may be wondering why anyone would specify such a fit. It is almost as if the person cannot make up his or her mind about the type of fit that is necessary. Transition fits are typically associated with selective assembly. Selective assembly involves measuring parts after they are machined and matching them up with appropriate mating parts. Manufacturing parts to tight or small tolerances is expensive. With transition fits, tolerances can be "opened up," or made larger, so that manufacturing the individual parts is less expensive.

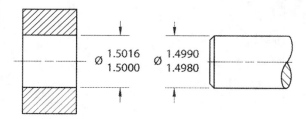

FIGURE 16.08. Specifying a CLEARANCE FIT with limit dimensioning.

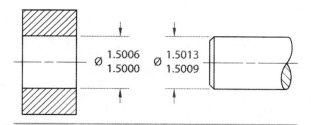

FIGURE 16.09. Specifying an INTERFERENCE FIT with limit dimensioning.

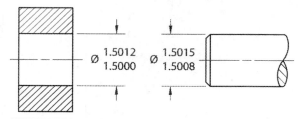

FIGURE 16.10. Specifying a TRANSITION FIT with limit dimensioning.

16.04.02 Fit Terminology

You need to be familiar with some terms as you read standard fit tables or specify fits between parts. Figure 16.11 and Figure 16.12 illustrate some of these terms.

- *Allowance*—Allowance is the difference between the maximum material limits of mating parts. It is the minimum clearance or maximum interference between parts. To calculate allowance, subtract the upper limit of the shaft dimension (largest cylinder) from the lower limit of the hole dimension (smallest hole). In Figure 16.8, the allowance is 1.5000-1.4990=.0010.

- *Tolerance*—Tolerance is the total permissible variation of a size. It is the difference between the upper limit and the lower limit.

- *Basic size*—The basic size is the size from which the limit dimensions were derived. The basic size of the parts in Figures 16.8 through 16.10 is 1.500.

- *Clearance*—Clearance refers to a fit where there is space between the two mating parts. The intent is that when assembled, the shaft will spin within the hole (see Figure 16.11).

- *Interference*—Interference is a fit where the two mating parts have intersecting nominal volumes, requiring the deformation of the parts. For example, the diameter of the shaft is larger than the diameter of the hole. When assembled, the intent is that the shaft will not spin in the hole (see Figure 16.12).

- *Hole basis or basic hole system*—In this system, the basic size is applied to the lower limit of the hole. This system is used quite often since standard tools such as reamers and broaches are designed to machine holes no less than a particular size. The shaft can then be machined to create the desired type of fit (see Figure 16.13).

- *Shaft basis or basic shaft system*—In this system, the basic size is applied to the upper limit of the shaft. The hole is then machined to create the desired type of fit. This is used when several parts with different fits are required to fit on a particular shaft (see Figure 16.14).

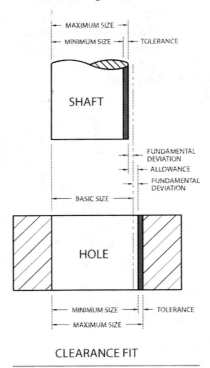

CLEARANCE FIT

FIGURE 16.11. Clearance fit terminology.

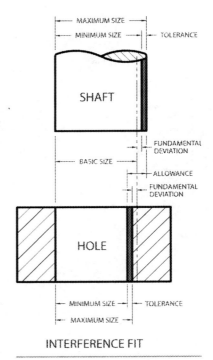

INTERFERENCE FIT

FIGURE 16.12. Interference fit terminology.

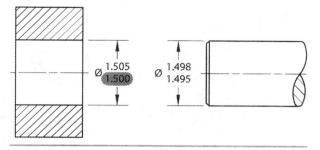

FIGURE 16.13. A basic hole system.

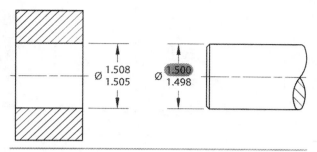

FIGURE 16.14. A basic shaft system.

16.04.03 English Fits

There are five types of fits within the English, or inch, system. These fits, for which the clearance or interference are depicted graphically in Figures 16.15 through 16.18, are established as a starting point for determining appropriate fits between mating parts [ANSI B4.1 – 1967 (R1994)]:

- ☒ RC—*Running or sliding clearance fit*—These fits provide a similar running performance, with suitable lubrication allowance, throughout the range of sizes. The clearances for the first two classes (RC1 and RC2), used chiefly as slide fits, increase more slowly with the diameter than the other two classes do; thus, accurate location is maintained even at the expense of free relative motion.

- ☒ LC—*Locational clearance fit*—These fits are intended for parts that are normally stationary but can be freely assembled or disassembled. They range from snug fits for parts requiring accuracy of location to medium clearance fits for parts shuch as spigots to looser fastener fits where freedom of assembly is of prime importance.

- ☒ LT—*Locational transition fit*—These fits are intended where accuracy of location is important but a small amount of clearance or interference is permissible. They are a compromise between clearance and interference fits.

- ☒ LN—*Locational interference fit*—These fits are intended where accuracy of location is of prime importance and where parts require rigidity and alignment with no special requirement for bore pressure. Such fits are not intended for parts designed to transmit frictional loads from one part to another by virtue of the tightness of fit, as these conditions are covered by force fits.

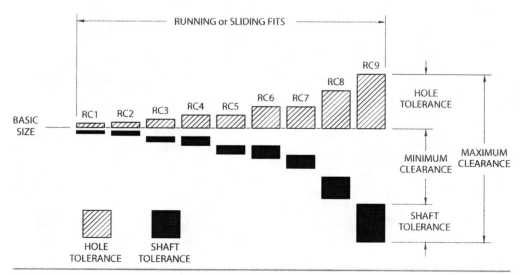

FIGURE 16.15. Running and sliding fits.

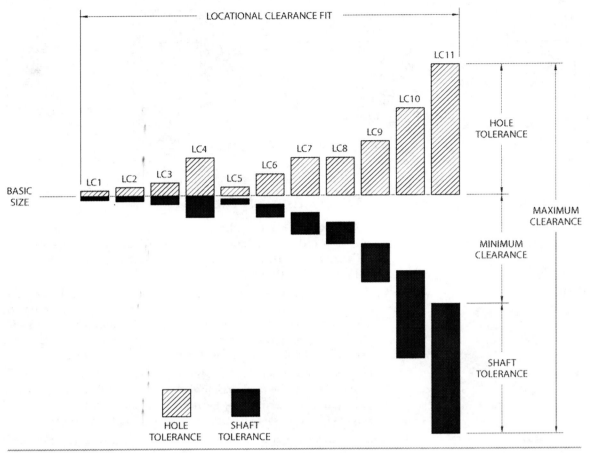

FIGURE 16.16. Locational clearance fits.

FN—*Force or shrink fit*—These types of interference fits are usually characterized by maintenance of constant bore pressures throughout the range of sizes. Therefore, the interference varies almost directly with diameter and the difference between its minimum and maximum value is small to maintain the resulting pressures within reasonable limits.

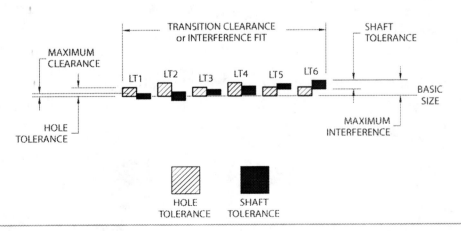

FIGURE 16.17. Locational transition fits.

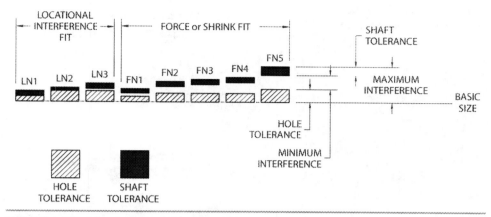

FIGURE 16.18. Locational interference and force fits.

16.04.04 Metric Fits

There are nine types of fits within the metric system. These fits are established as a starting point for determining appropriate fits between mating parts. Figure 16.19 shows the symbol designations for hole basis and shaft basis fits. The clearance and interference for these fits are depicted graphically in Figures 16.15 through 16.18.

- *Loose running fit*—These fits are for wide commercial tolerances or allowances on external members.
- *Free running fit*—These fits are not for use where accuracy is essential, but are good for large temperature variations, high running speeds, and heavy journal pressures.
- *Close running fit*—These fits are for running on accurate machines and for ensuring accurate location at moderate speeds and journal pressures.
- *Sliding fit*—These fits are not intended to run freely, but are intended to move and turn freely and locate accurately.
- *Locational clearance fit*—These fits provide snug fit for locating stationary parts; they can be freely assembled and disassembled.

	ISO SYMBOL			
	Hole Basis	Shaft Basis	DESCRIPTION	
Clearance Fits	H11/c11	C11/h11	Loose Running	More Clearance
	H9/d9	D9/h9	Free Running	
	H8/f7	F8/h7	Close Running	
	H7/g6	G7/h6	Sliding	
	H7/h6	H7/h6	Locational Clearance	
Transition Fits	H7/k6	K7/h6	Locational Transition	
	H7/n6	N7/h6	Locational Transition	More Interference
Interference Fits	H7/p6	P7/h6	Locational Interference	
	H7/s6	S7/h6	Medium Drive	
	H7/u6	U7/h6	Force	

FIGURE 16.19. Metric fit table.

FIGURE 16.20. Metric hole basis fits.

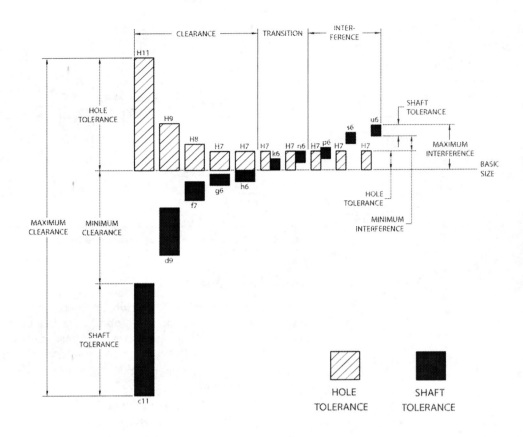

PREFERRED HOLE BASIS FITS

FIGURE 16.21. Metric shaft basis fits.

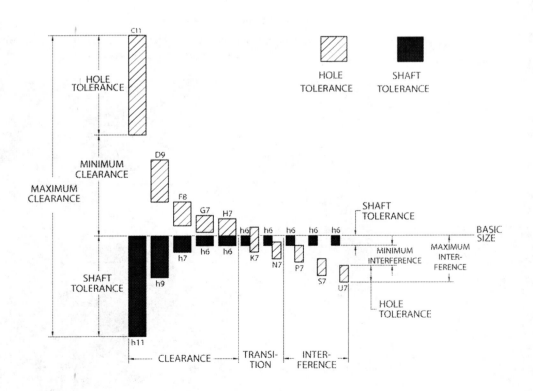

PREFERRED SHAFT BASIS FITS

- *Locational transition fit*—These fits provide for accurate location and a compromise between clearance and interference.
- *Locational interference fit*—These fits are for parts requiring rigidity and alignment with prime accuracy of location but without special bore pressure requirements.
- *Medium drive fit*—These fits are for ordinary steel parts or shrink fits on light sections—the tightest fit usable with cast iron.
- *Force fit*—These fits are suitable for parts that can be highly stressed or for shrink fits where the heavy pressure forces required are impractical.

16.04.05 Fits Tables

Figure 16.22 shows a standard table for fits in the English system of units. When specifying an inch, or English, fit between a hole and a shaft from a standard table, use the following guidelines:

- Determine the type of fit appropriate for the design and locate the corresponding table.
- Determine the basic size of the parts.
- Find the size range on the table.
- Determine the tolerances for the hole and the shaft.
- Remember that values on the English tables are in *thousandths* of an inch.

Refer to the following example to practice looking up a fit in the inch system. For this application, a *close sliding fit* is appropriate (RC1 fit) and the basic size for the parts is 1.500. On the table (see Figure 16.22), the nominal size of 1.500 falls between 1.19–1.97. The limits on the hole are -0 to +0.4. The limits on the shaft are -0.4 and -0.7. One of the most common mistakes when working with inch tables is forgetting that these limits are in *thousandths* of an inch. The upper tolerance on the hole is really

Nominal Size Range, Inches Over To	Class RC 1 Limits of Clearance	Standard Limits Hole H5	Standard Limits Shaft g4	Class RC 2 Limits of Clearance	Standard Limits Hole H6	Standard Limits Shaft g5	Class RC 3 Limits of Clearance	Standard Limits Hole H7	Standard Limits Shaft f6	Class RC 4 Limits of Clearance	Standard Limits Hole H8	Standard Limits Shaft f7
0-0.12	0.1 0.45	+0.2 -0	-0.1 -0.25	0.1 0.55	+0.25 -0	-0.1 -0.3	0.3 0.95	+0.4 -0	-0.3 -0.55	0.3 1.3	+0.6 -0	-0.3 -0.07
0.12-0.24	0.15 0.5	+0.2 -0	-0.15 -0.3	0.15 0.65	+0.3 -0	-0.15 -0.35	0.4 1.12	+0.5 -0	-0.4 -0.7	0.4 1.6	+0.7 -0	-0.4 -0.9
0.24-0.40	0.2 0.6	+0.25 -0	-0.2 -0.35	0.2 0.85	+0.4 -0	-0.2 -0.45	0.5 1.5	+0.6 -0	-0.5 -0.9	0.5 2.0	+0.9 -0	-0.5 -1.1
0.40-0.71	0.25 0.75	+0.3 -0	-0.25 -0.45	0.25 0.95	+0.4 -0	-0.25 -0.55	0.6 1.7	+0.7 -0	-0.6 -1.0	0.6 2.3	+1.0 -0	-0.6 -1.3
0.71-1.19	0.3 0.95	+0.4 -0	-0.3 -0.55	0.3 1.2	+0.5 -0	-0.3 -0.7	0.8 2.1	+0.8 -0	-0.8 -1.3	0.8 2.8	+1.2 -0	-0.8 -1.6
1.19-1.97	0.4 1.1	+0.4 -0	-0.4 -0.7	0.4 1.4	+0.6 -0	-0.4 -0.8	1.0 2.6	+1.0 -0	-1.0 -1.6	1.0 3.6	+1.6 -0	-1.0 -2.0
1.97-3.15	0.4 1.2	+0.5 -0	-0.4 -0.7	0.4 1.6	+0.7 -0	-0.4 -0.9	1.2 3.1	+1.2 -0	-1.2 -1.9	1.2 4.2	+1.8 -0	-1.2 -2.4
3.15-4.73	0.5 1.5	+0.6 -0	-0.5 -0.9	0.5 2.0	+0.9 -0	-0.5 -1.1	1.4 3.7	+1.4 -0	-1.4 -2.3	1.4 5.0	+2.2 -0	-0.4 -2.8
4.73-7.09	0.6 1.8	+0.7 -0	-0.6 -1.1	0.6 2.3	+1.0 -0	-0.6 -1.3	1.6 4.2	+1.6 -0	-1.6 -2.6	1.6 5.7	+2.5 -0	-1.6 -3.2
7.09-9.85	0.6 2.0	+0.8 -0	-0.6 -1.2	0.6 2.6	+1.2 -0	-0.6 -1.4	2.0 5.0	+1.8 -0	-2.0 -3.2	2.0 6.6	+2.8 -0	-2.0 -3.8
9.85-12.41	0.8 2.3	+0.9 -0	-0.8 -1.4	0.8 2.9	+1.2 -0	-0.8 -1.7	2.5 5.7	+2.0 -0	-2.5 -3.7	2.5 7.5	+3.0 -0	-2.5 -4.5
12.41-15.75	1.0 2.7	+1.0 -0	-1.0 -1.7	1.0 3.4	+1.4 -0	-1.0 -2.0	3.0 6.6	+2.2 -0	-3.0 -4.4	3.0 8.7	+3.5 -0	-3.0 -5.2

* From ANSI B4.1 – 1967 (R1994). For larger diameters, see the standard.

FIGURE 16.22. American National Standard running and sliding fits. *Reprinted from ASME B4.1-1967 (R1994) and ASME B4.2-1978 (R1994), by permission of The American Society of Mechanical Engineers. All rights reserved.*

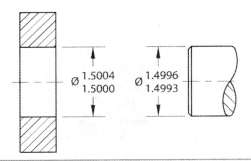

FIGURE 16.23. A close sliding fit.

+0.0004. The values for the shaft are really -0.0004 and -0.0007. When these values from the table are added or subtracted from the basic size, the results are the dimensions shown in Figure 16.23.

Figure 16.24 shows a standard table for fits in the metric system of units. Specifying fits from ISO, or metric, tables is a little easier. The tables provide the direct values, so there is no need to add or subtract. Follow these guidelines to determine metric fits:

- Determine the type of fit appropriate for the design and locate the corresponding table.
- Determine the basic size of the parts.
- Find the size range on the table.
- Determine the tolerances for the hole and the shaft.

To practice looking up a metric fit, you will use a *loose running fit* with a basic size of 25. In Figure 16.24, find 25 on the left side of the table. Look to the right under the Hole and Shaft columns. The result is the dimensions shown in Figure 16.25.

Preferred Metric Hole Basis Clearance Fits – American National Standard

Dimensions are in millimeters.

Basic Size		Loose Running			Free Running			Close Running		
		Hole H11	Shaft c11	Fit	Hole H9	Shaft d9	Fit	Hole H8	Shaft f7	Fit
1	Max	1.060	0.940	0.180	1.025	0.980	0.070	1.014	0.994	0.030
	Min	1.060	0.880	0.060	1.000	0.955	0.020	1.000	0.984	0.006
20	Max	20.130	19.890	0.370	20.052	19.935	0.169	20.033	19.980	0.074
	Min	20.000	19.760	0.110	20.000	19.883	0.065	20.000	19.959	0.020
25	Max	25.130	24.890	0.370	25.052	24.935	0.169	25.033	24.980	0.074
	Min	25.000	24.760	0.110	25.000	24.833	0.065	25.000	24.959	0.020

From ANSI B4.2 – 1978 (R1984). For larger diameters, see the standard.

FIGURE 16.24. Metric hole basis clearance fits table. *Reprinted from ASME B4.1-1967 (R1994) and ASME B4.2-1978 (R1994), by permission of The American Society of Mechanical Engineers. All rights reserved.*

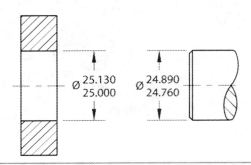

FIGURE 16.25. A loose running fit.

16.05 Conventional Tolerancing versus Geometric Tolerancing

Before you move on to geometric dimensioning and tolerancing (GD&T), it is important to understand some of the limitations of conventional tolerancing—the limit or plus/minus system of tolerancing. To begin, you will look at some terminology that is used throughout the rest of the chapter.

16.05.01 Features With and Without Size

Professionals who deal with engineering parts use a specific language, especially concerning dimensioning and tolerancing. When talking about drawings and 3-D models, they must be able to identify features with size and features without size (see Figure 16.26). A feature is a general term that applies to an actual portion of a part, such as a surface, pin, tab, hole, or slot. A **feature with size** is a cylindrical or spherical surface or a set of two opposed elements or opposed parallel surfaces associated with a size dimension. The 40 mm wide slot in Figure 16.27 is a feature of size. The feature contains two equal and opposing parallel surfaces. Notice how the normal vectors from each surface point in opposite directions. The feature defined by the 30 mm dimension is not a feature of size. Even though the normal vectors are opposing, the surfaces are not of equal size.

A **feature without size** is typically a planar surface or a feature where the normal vectors point in the same direction. The feature defined by the 30 mm dimension in Figure 16.28 is not a feature of size since the normal vectors of the two surfaces point in the same direction.

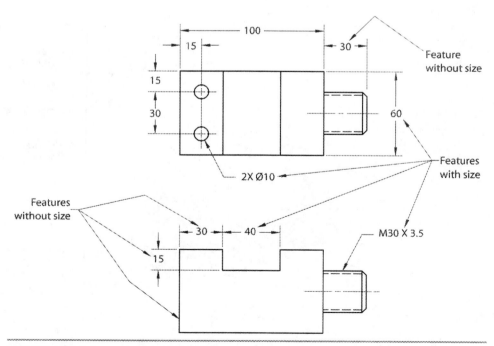

FIGURE 16.26. Features with and without size.

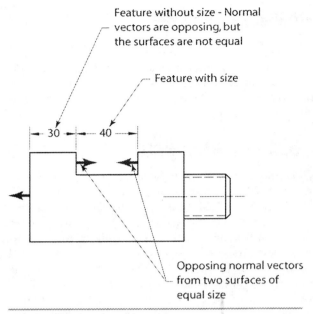

Feature without size - Normal
vectors are opposing, but
the surfaces are not equal

Feature with size

30   40

Opposing normal vectors
from two surfaces of
equal size

FIGURE 16.27. Features with and without size.

Feature without size
Normal vectors are pointing in
the same direction

30

FIGURE 16.28. A feature without size.

16.05.02 Conventional Tolerancing and Form

Sometimes it is difficult to think about imperfect parts when all of the models and drawings that you generate have sharp corners and flat surfaces like those in Figure 16.29. When parts are finally produced, imperfections exist, even if you cannot see them with the naked eye. Surfaces may be wavy or bumpy, may have dips in them, or may be angled slightly (see Figure 16.30). If you use conventional tolerancing to control form, you

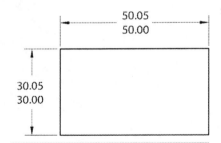

50.05
50.00

30.05
30.00

FIGURE 16.29. Conventional tolerance dimensioning of a block.

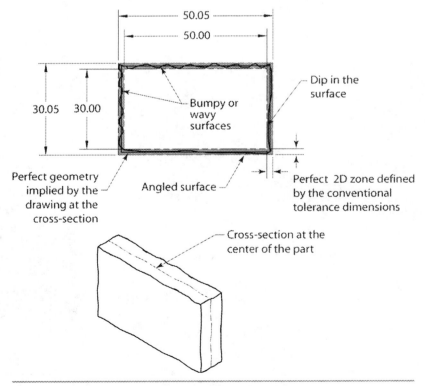

50.05

50.00

30.05   30.00

Bumpy or
wavy
surfaces

Dip in the
surface

Perfect geometry
implied by the
drawing at the
cross-section

Angled surface

Perfect 2D zone defined
by the conventional
tolerance dimensions

Cross-section at the
center of the part

FIGURE 16.30. How conventional tolerancing controls surfaces.

FIGURE 16.31. A WEDGE BLOCK assembly.

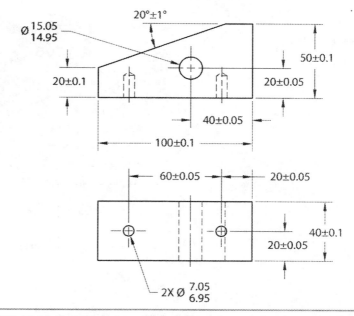

FIGURE 16.32. A WEDGE BLOCK drawing with conventional tolerancing.

must understand the extent to which this works. Where only a conventional tolerance of size is specified, the limits of size of an individual feature prescribe the extent to which variations in its geometric form, as well as size, are allowed (Rule 1). Figure 16.29 shows a rectangular block with two size dimensions. When you are using conventional tolerancing, Rule 1 states that the actual size of the object must be within the boundaries defined by the limit dimensions at *each cross section*. What this means is that conventional tolerancing is a 2-D system. When the rectangular block in Figure 16.30 is inspected, it must be checked at the front, at the back, and at all cross sections. Since the drawing does not specify where dimensions originate, two inspectors may measure the part differently. This could lead to accepting parts that do not function or rejecting parts that actually work.

Examine the WEDGE BLOCK assembly in Figure 16.31. The purpose of the blocks is to keep the cylinder centered. The blocks mate against three surfaces and have three holes machined in them (see Figure 16.32). When the dimensions that describe the outside shape of the part are inspected, measurements can be taken at each cross-sectional area moving from the front of the part to the back. A measurement taken from the front of the part may yield a different result than one taken at the back of the part (see the imperfect part in Figure 16.33). Like the rectangular block in Figure 16.29, an inspector might accept parts that do not actually work in the assembly or reject parts that would work.

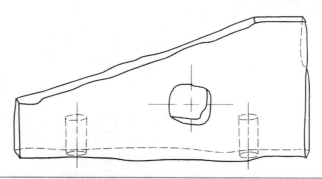

FIGURE 16.33. Imperfect geometry of the WEDGE BLOCK.

FIGURE 16.34. Conventional tolerancing when locating holes.

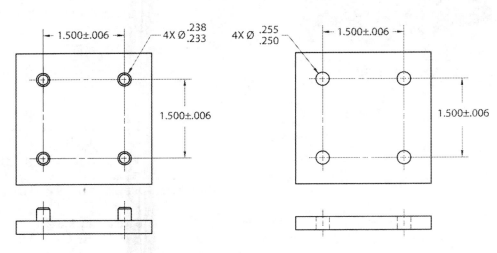

16.05.03 Location of Holes and Pins with Conventional Tolerancing

Another potential problem occurs when holes are located using conventional tolerance dimensions. Examine the two parts in Figure 16.34. The parts are designed so that there will be a clearance fit between the pins and the holes. The location dimensions for the holes (1.500 ±.006) will yield square tolerance zones for each part (see Figure 16.35). Now you will take a closer look at some examples where the holes and pins fall at the extreme edges of their tolerance zones.

When a pin is machined to the far right of the square zone and the hole is machined to the far left of the square zone, the result is surface contact between the two parts (see Figure 16.36). This is acceptable for the assembly since the parts will still

FIGURE 16.35. Square tolerance zones from conventional tolerancing.

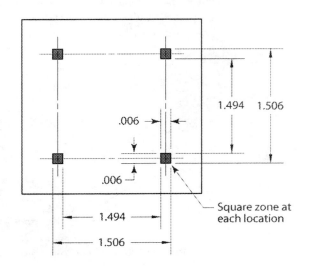

FIGURE 16.36. A pin and a hole at the extreme horizontal positions of the square tolerance zone.

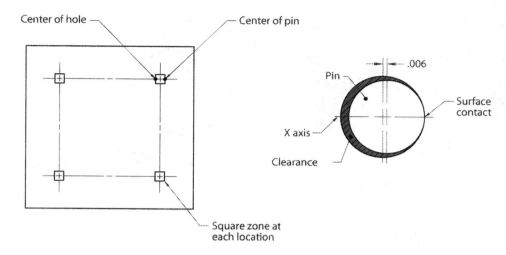

function under these conditions. Surface contact is also the result when the two features are located at the extreme ends of the y-axis (see Figure 16.37). Again, this is acceptable. The parts will still work.

A problem occurs when the center of the hole and the center of the pin are located at the extreme diagonals within the tolerance zone (see Figure 16.38). In this situation, material interference will result, which will not work for the assembly. The parts will not fit or function properly. You may be thinking that all that needs to be done to make things work is to specify a larger hole size or a smaller pin size. Usually, this is not a good idea since tolerances between holes and pins are taken from standard tables. The only other way to correct this problem when using limit dimensions to locate the center of holes is to reduce the size of the square tolerance zone. Any time you need to reduce a tolerance value, it usually costs more to produce the parts. If you stay with the same values for the diameters of the holes and pins and continue to use conventional tolerancing to locate the centers, you must reduce the tolerances on the location dimensions from ±.006 to ±.004. The result is that you always pass parts that will function. Unfortunately, you also reject parts that will function properly. When a hole is drilled at position 1 in Figure 16.39 within the ±.004 square zone, the part passes inspection and works properly. A hole drilled at position 2 falls outside the ±.004 square zone, so it fails inspection. You know from Figure 16.36 and Figure 16.37 that the parts will function in this situation. You will come back to these parts after some discussion about GD&T.

FIGURE 16.37. A pin and a hole at the extreme vertical positions of the square tolerance zone.

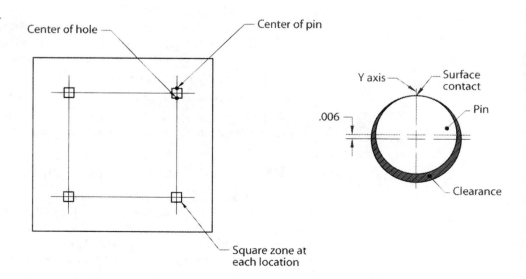

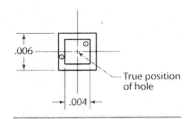

FIGURE 16.39. The results of changing the size of the square tolerance zone.

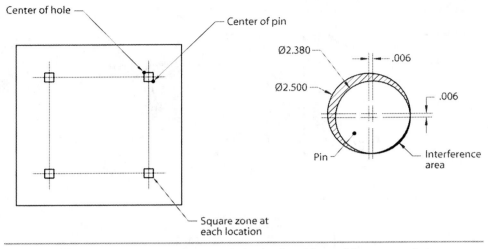

FIGURE 16.38. A pin and a hole at the extreme diagonal positions of the square tolerance zone.

16.06 Geometric Dimensioning and Tolerancing (GD&T)

Many students have trouble understanding geometric dimensioning and tolerancing (GD&T). GD&T has even been referred to as Gloom, Doom, and Terror. If you try to keep things simple in the beginning, you should be able to apply appropriate tolerances to objects without confusing your boss, a machinist, or a quality control person.

Geometric dimensioning and tolerancing (GD&T) is a 3-D mathematical system that allows a designer to describe the form, orientation, and location of features on a part within precise tolerance zones. Because it uses symbols instead of words, GD&T is an international language that is understood by technicians and engineers around the world. For these reasons, there are several advantages of using GD&T instead of conventional tolerancing:

- *The system allows the designer to clearly specify design intent.* The location of datums allows manufacturing engineers, machinists, and quality control personnel to easily recognize part functionality.
- *There is better communication throughout the design process.* Manufacturing engineers and machinists are able to make better decisions about how things are made. Quality control personnel are able to make better choices for inspection.
- *The system is set up so that almost nothing can be interpreted in more than one way.* This is extremely valuable when hiring a subcontractor to manufacture parts. You want to make sure everything works when the parts are assembled.

Just two items are required within this system:

- A datum reference frame to immobilize and orient the part.
- Specific form, orientation, and location tolerances that describe 2-D and 3-D tolerance zones within which all part geometry must fall.

16.06.01 The Datum Reference Frame

Usually, errors related to GD&T have something to do with how the **datum reference frame** was established (or not established). The datum reference frame is a theoretical system made up of three mutually perpendicular planes, or **datums**, established by real features on the object. This concept of a 3-D system should not be new to you. From the time you began plotting points on graph paper in mathematics, science, or graphics

FIGURE 16.40. Components of
the theoretical datum system.

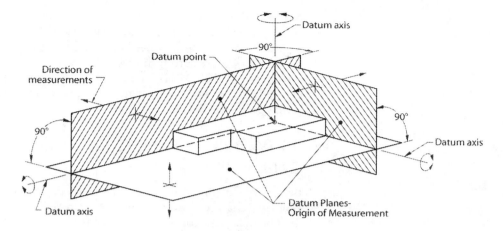

class, you were using a 3-D coordinate system. When working with GD&T, you need to
keep two things in mind:

- *The things you cannot see*: The imaginary or theoretical coordinate system and perfect
  part geometry that exists within the CAD software, CNC manufacturing software,
  or inspection software

- *The things you can see*: The real features on the finished object

Figure 16.40 shows the items that make up the theoretical datum reference frame.
As stated earlier, the key part of the system is the three mutually perpendicular planes.
The origin or datum point is defined by the intersection of the three planes. Datum
axes are defined by the intersection of two of the planes. As you begin applying geometric
tolerances, the goal is to add just enough datums to immobilize the part or elimate
all degrees-of-freedom, or DOFs (translational and rotational).

Figure 16.41 illustrates some terminology related to datums. The previous paragraph
talked about the datum plane, which is a theoretical perfect plane that exists in
one's mind and in the CAD, CNC, and inspection software. To establish these theoretical
datums, datum simulators must be used. Datum simulators can be a number of

FIGURE 16.41. Datum
terminology.

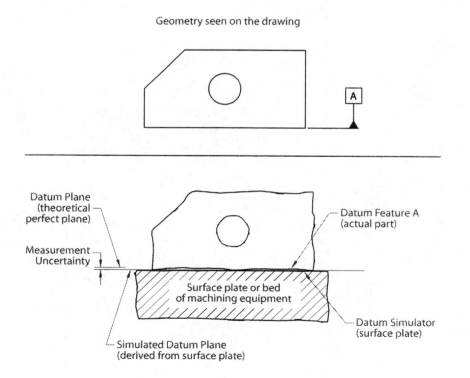

different things. When parts are being manufactured, machine beds, lathe chucks or collets, gage pins, and vises are used to establish datums. When parts are being inspected, datums are established using granite tabletops, surface plates, and angle plates. All of these datum simulators must be at least *ten times better in quality* than the tolerances specified on the drawings to be considered datum simulators. Simulated datums are derived from the datum simulators coming in contact with features on the actual part or on the datum features.

16.06.02 Geometry Characteristic Symbols and Feature Control Frames

Before considering the specific tolerances, take a look at Figure 16.42. Notice how the geometry characteristic symbols are organized. The form tolerances are for individual features. They are not related to any datums. The profile tolerances may or may not be related to datums. The orientation, location, and runout tolerances must be related to datums. As you explore the individual symbols, you will see why certain tolerances should be related to datums and why others should not.

GD&T is a technical language. Like any language, some people use it in a conversational way. Others can read it but not write it, and some designers are experts who can read and write the language fluently.

The main focus of the language is the **feature control frame**. The feature control frame contains the geometric characteristic symbol, the geometric tolerance, and the relative datums (see Figure 16.43). To understand the language, you must be able to put the symbols in the feature control frame into a form that you can read. Figure 16.43 shows the different parts of the feature control frame. One of the fourteen geometric characteristic symbols will appear in the first section of the frame. In the second section of the feature, control frame is where the tolerance information is displayed. This section will include information about the shape of the zone (such as a diameter symbol for cylindrical zones), the size of the zone, and any material condition modifiers (such as the maximum material condition, MMC, or the least material condition, LMC).

Now you will practice reading a couple of feature control frames before looking at each of the fourteen geometric characteristic symbols. Figure 16.44 shows a feature control frame with a perpendicularity tolerance of 0.05 that is related to one datum.

	TYPE OF TOLERANCE	CHARACTERISTIC	SYM
FOR INDIVIDUAL FEATURES	FORM	STRAIGHTNESS	—
		FLATNESS	▱
		CIRCULARITY	○
		CYLINDRICITY	⌭
FOR INDIVIDUAL OR RELATED FEATURES	PROFILE	PROFILE OF A LINE	⌒
		PROFILE OF A SURFACE	⌓
FOR RELATED FEATURES	ORIENTATION	ANGULARITY	∠
		PERPENDICULARITY	⊥
		PARALLELISM	//
	LOCATION	POSITION	⊕
		CONCENTRICITY	◎
		SYMMETRY	�
	RUNOUT	CIRCULAR RUNOUT	↗
		TOTAL RUNOUT	↗↗

FIGURE 16.42. Geometric characteristic symbols.

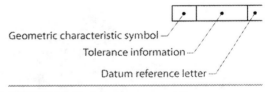

Geometric characteristic symbol ⌐
Tolerance information ⌐
Datum reference letter ⌐

FIGURE 16.43. A feature control frame.

⊥	0.05	A

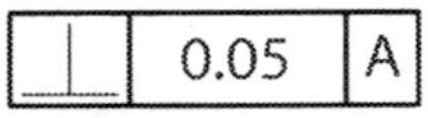

FIGURE 16.44. A feature control frame with the perpendicularity tolerance.

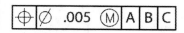

FIGURE 16.45. A feature control frame with the position tolerance.

As you read the feature control frame, try to take each segment separately. You might read the first example as follows: The feature must be *perpendicular* within a *five-hundredths of a millimeter* tolerance zone relative to *datum feature A*.

The example in Figure 16.45 can be read as follows: The features must be *positioned* within a *five-thousandths of an inch cylindrical* tolerance zone at *maximum material condition* relative to primary *datum feature A*, secondary *datum feature B*, and tertiary *datum feature C*.

16.06.03 Order of Precedence for Datums

As you apply datums to a part, you must specify the order of precedence. Examine the WEDGE BLOCK in Figure 16.46. Since there is a large hole passing through the part for the socket head screw, it is critical that the hole be perpendicular to the back surface of the part and that the hole be located properly. Now examine the drawing for the WEDGE BLOCK. Directly under the size tolerance for the hole (14.95-15.05) is a feature control frame indicating that a position tolerance is used to control the orientation and location of the axis of the hole. The precedence of the datums for this geometric tolerance is datum feature A, datum feature B, and datum feature C. Datum feature A is the

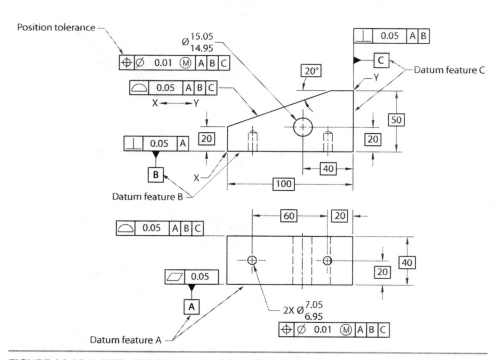

FIGURE 16.46. A WEDGE BLOCK assembly and detail drawing.

back surface (see the bottom view of the part), datum feature feature B is the bottom surface of the part, and datum feature C is the right side surface of the part.

To establish the datum reference frame for manufacturing or inspection, a part has to be placed in the machine or loaded in a specific order. Assume for this example that a quality control person is inspecting the position of the large hole through the part. The datums are listed in the order A, B, and C. The primary datum plane is established by a minimum three-point contact with the back surface of the object (datum feature A in Figure 16.47a). Once the primary datum plane is set, the secondary datum plane must be perpendicular to it. Therefore, to establish the secondary datum plane, only a two-point contact with the bottom surface (datum feature B in Figure 16.47b) is necessary. Finally, the tertiary datum plane, which is mutually perpendicular to the first two datum planes, can be established by a one-point contact with the right-hand surface (datum feature C in Figure 16.47c).

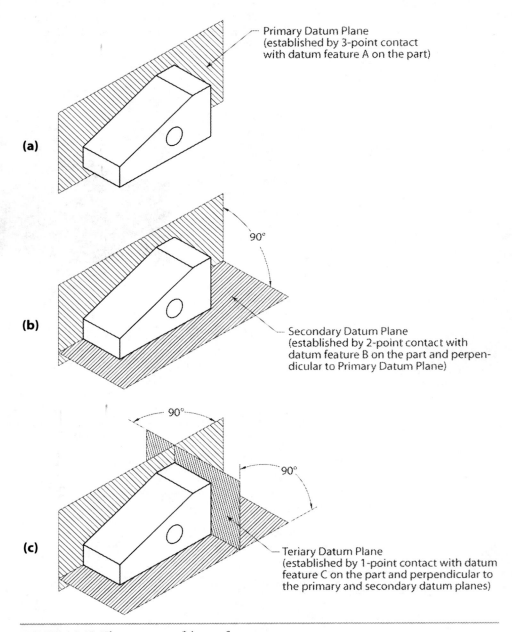

FIGURE 16.47. The sequence of datum features.

FIGURE 16.48. The cylindrical tolerance zone of the position tolerance.

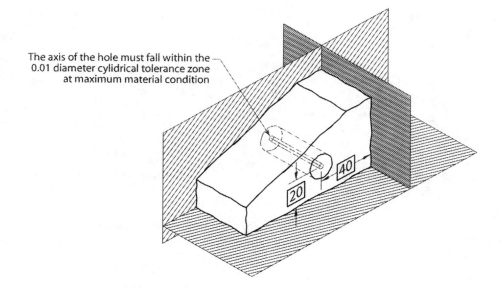

The axis of the hole must fall within the 0.01 diameter cylidrical tolerance zone at maximum material condition

Once the datum reference frame is established, the inspector can check the position of the hole. If the hole is machined at maximum material condition (14.95-the smallest hole will generate the most material), the size of the cylindrical tolerance zone is 0.01. The axis of the hole must fall within this cylinder, which is located from the datums by the 20 and 40 basic dimensions. The imperfections in the geometry of the part must fall within the theoretically perfect tolerance zones located from the established datums.

16.06.04 Position Tolerances versus Conventional Tolerances

Section 16.05.03 looked at using conventional tolerancing to locate the centers of holes and pins. That section discussed some problems that might result from the square tolerance zones established with this type of tolerance method. An alternative to using conventional tolerancing is using the geometric tolerance of position.

Figure 16.49 shows the same part as Figure 16.34 with the four holes except that it is dimensioned using geometric dimensions. Look at how the holes are dimensioned on this part. Notice that the size of the holes are dimensioned the same as before (.250-.255). Conventional tolerancing is still an excellent way to specify the sizes of holes. The main difference here is that the locations of the holes are not

FIGURE 16.49. Geometric dimensioning and tolerancing of the PLATE.

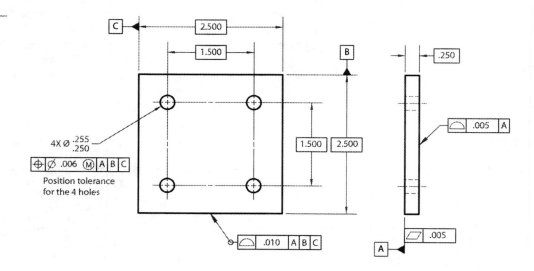

4X Ø .255 / .250

Position tolerance for the 4 holes

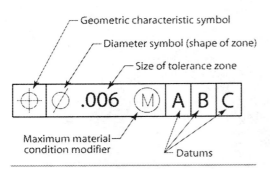

Geometric characteristic symbol

Diameter symbol (shape of zone)

Size of tolerance zone

⊕ | ⌀ | .006 | Ⓜ | A | B | C

Maximum material condition modifier

Datums

FIGURE 16.50. The feature control frame for the PLATE position tolerance.

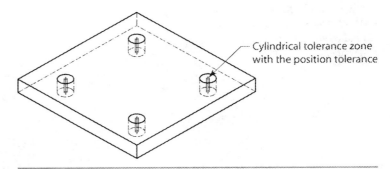

Cylindrical tolerance zone with the position tolerance

FIGURE 16.51. Cylindrical tolerance zones for the position tolerance.

ACTUAL SIZE OF HOLE	SIZE OF CYLINDRICAL TOLERANCE ZONE
.250	.006
.251	.007
.252	.008
.253	.009
.254	.010
.255	.011

FIGURE 16.52. Effects of the maximum material condition modifier on the position tolerance.

dimensioned with limit dimensions, but with **basic dimensions**, which are sometimes called true position dimensions. Basic dimensions (those with a box around them) are theoretically exact. They locate the perfect position of features from clearly identified datums. For the part in Figure 16.49, three datums are used (A, B, and C). The tolerance for the location of the holes is given in a feature control frame (see Figure 16.50). This particular feature control frame indicates that *the four holes must be positioned within a .006 cylindrical tolerance zone at maximum material condition relative to primary datum feature A, secondary datum feature B, and tertiary datum feature C.* Instead of a square tolerance zone, you now have a circular or cylindrical zone (see Figure 16.51).

The **maximum material condition** (MMC) modifier allows the size of the zone to change if the size of the hole changes. MMC is the condition in which a feature of size contains the maximum amount of material within the stated limits of size. The counterpart of MMC is the *least material condition* (LMC), which is the condition in which a feature of size contains the minimum amount of material within the stated limits of size. As mentioned earlier, the size of the four holes is .250-.255. The feature control frame states that at MMC, the size of the cylindrical zone is .006. MMC for a hole is the smallest hole; in this case, .250. As the hole departs from MMC, you can add *bonus tolerance* to .006. Figure 16.52 illustrates the potential tolerance zone sizes based on the actual hole size after it is machined.

Now compare the differences between conventional tolerancing square zones and the cylindrical zones of geometric dimensioning for some potential hole locations. Figure 16.53 shows the tolerance zones discussed previously (see Figure 16.39) combined in one figure. It includes the original square zone of .006 and the modified square zone of .004. It also includes the two cylindrical zones from the geometric tolerancing: n.006 (MMC) and n.011 (LMC). Also in the figure are four potential hole locations. If a hole is machined at location 1, it would pass inspection under all methods of tolerancing discussed since it falls within the .004 square zone. A hole machined with its center at position 2 would pass inspection under the original drawing, which specified a square zone of .006, or under the drawing that uses geometric tolerances. Notice, however, that if the zone size is reduced to .004, under the conventional tolerancing method, the part would not pass inspection. This is a problem since the part would work under the initial design conditions. The last two potential hole positions, 3 and 4, represent locations

FIGURE 16.53. Cylindrical tolerance zones for the position tolerance.

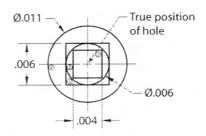

⌀.011

True position of hole

.006

⌀.006

.004

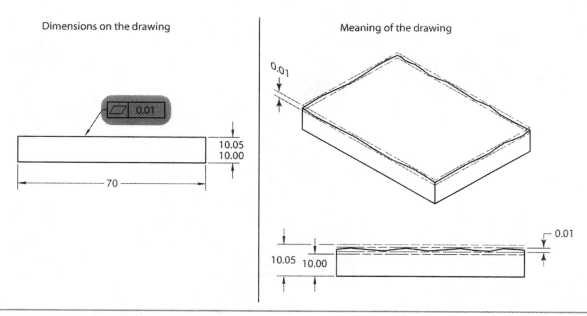

FIGURE 16.54. The flatness tolerance.

that would fail inspection if the material condition was not considered. With the MMC modifier specified in the feature control frame, these two possible hole centers would pass inspection if the size of the hole departed enough from the MMC.

16.06.05 Form Tolerances

Form tolerances are for individual features and are not related to any datums. This group of geometric tolerances includes straightness, flatness, circularity (roundness), and cylindricity. They control individual features such as surface or line elements within the surface. The shape of the tolerance zones might be two-dimensional (space between two parallel lines or two concentric circles) or three-dimensional (space between two parallel planes, between two concentric cylinders, or within a cylindrical zone).

Flatness-Flatness specifies a 3-D tolerance zone defined by two parallel planes. All points on the specified surface must fall between the two imaginary planes. The tolerance specified in the feature control frame must be less than the tolerance on the size dimension for the part. For the geometric tolerance in Figure 16.54, the feature control frame might be read as follows: The feature must be *flat* within *one-hundredth of a millimeter.*

Figure 16.55 illustrates one method for inspecting flatness. Moving a dial indicator over the surface is time-consuming, but this type of inspection method is fairly good. The full indicator movement (FIM) reading must not exceed the total flatness tolerance.

FIGURE 16.55. Inspecting the flatness of a feature.

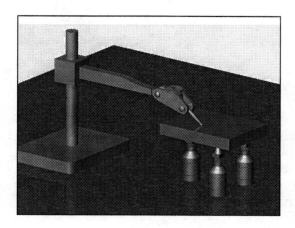

FIGURE 16.56. Straightness of a surface.

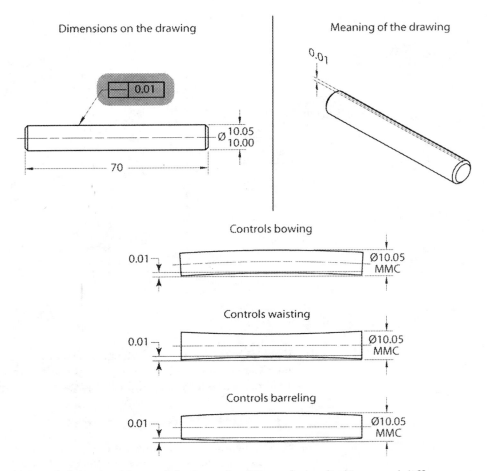

Dimensions on the drawing

Meaning of the drawing

Controls bowing

Controls waisting

Controls barreling

Straightness—The straightness tolerance can be applied in several different ways. If applied as shown in Figure 16.56, the zone is defined by two parallel lines to create a 2-D zone. The tolerance is view-specific, meaning the two parallel lines must move from left to right, not from front to back. The feature control frame reads as follows: Each line element on the surface must be *straight* within *five-hundredths of a millimeter*.

Inspecting straightness is done similarly to the way flatness is checked. The main difference is that the dial indicator is passed over a surface in a straight line. After the FIM is checked, the dial is reset and the indicator is passed over the surface again using a different line element. This is repeated until the whole surface has been checked.

Another way to apply straightness is when you are concerned about the size of a cylindrical feature, such as a machined shaft, but you want to allow the shaft to bend or bow beyond the perfect form limits. Figure 16.57 shows straightness applied to an axis.

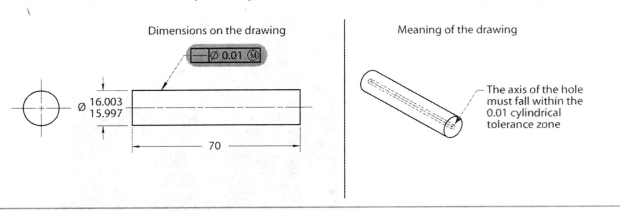

Dimensions on the drawing

Meaning of the drawing

The axis of the hole must fall within the 0.01 cylindrical tolerance zone

FIGURE 16.57. Straightness of an axis.

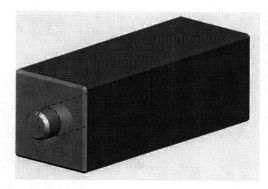

Because the diameter symbol is specified in the feature control, you know that the tolerance applies to the axis of the shaft instead of to the cylindrical surface. For this tolerance, all derived points on the axis of the shaft must fall within the cylindrical zone. Since the straightness is applied to a feature of size, material condition modifiers such as MMC and LMC can be applied. The feature control frame can be read as follows: The feature (axis of the shaft) must be *straight* within a *one-hundredth of a millimeter cylindrical* tolerance zone at *maximum material condition*. Because a MMC modifier is used, the size of the tolerance zone can increase proportionally as the size of the shaft departs from the MMC.

Because this tolerance is concerned with the axis of a feature (something that cannot be physically touched), this type of straightness is difficult to inspect. If you are inspecting the straightness of an axis for a shaft, a **functional gage** like the one in Figure 16.58 is used. The size of the hole in the gage block is the virtual size of the shaft (MMC plus the tolerance of 0.01). If the shaft can pass through the hole, the part is acceptable.

Circularity (Roundness)—Circularity or roundness is a 2-D control. For shafts, all points within any plane perpendicular to the axis of the shaft must be equidistant from that axis. Circularity specifies a tolerance zone bounded by two concentric circles. The circularity tolerance must be less than the size tolerance. A good analogy of this control is a stack of pennies. The circularity tolerance would control how round each penny is but not the straightness of the whole stack. This tolerance keeps the cylinder from barrelling, tapering, or wasting (see Figure 16.56).

Figure 16.59 illustrates the correct method for applying circularity to a cylinder. The feature control frame reads as follows: The feature (each circular element) must be *round* within *one-tenth of a millimeter* tolerance zone.

Dimensions on the drawing

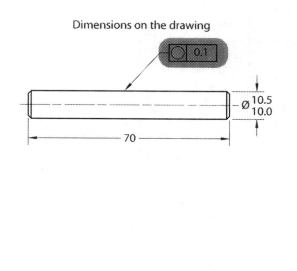

Meaning of the drawing

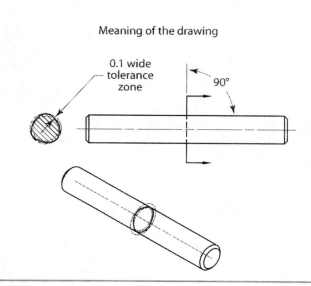

FIGURE 16.59. The circularity or roundness of a feature.

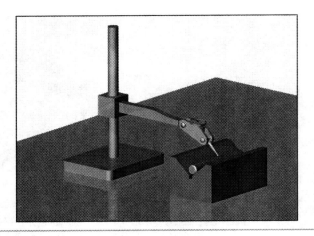

FIGURE 16.60. Inspecting circularity.

Inspecting circularity for cylinders is typically done with a v-block and dial indicator (see Figure 16.60) or with a v-anvil micrometer.

Cylindricity-The cylindricity tolerance controls a cylindrical surface so that all points are equidistant from a common axis. It is the most complex form of tolerance. Inspecting the tolerance also is very difficult. The tolerance zone is a 3-D zone defined by two concentric cylinders. All points on the surface of the shaft must fall between the two concentric cylinders. The feature control frame in Figure 16.61 reads as follows: The cylindricity of the feature must be within a twenty-five hundredths of a millimeter tolerance zone.

There are a couple of different accepted techniques for inspecting cylindricity. Figure 16.62 shows a way to inspect cylindricity using a total runout technique. The shaft is spun about two center points. After one complete rotation, the point of the indicator is moved in a straight line parallel to the axis of the shaft. After the point of the indicator moves over the complete surface of interest, FIM is recorded.

16.06.06 Profile Tolerances

Profile of a line—Profile of a line specifies a *2-D tolerance zone* defined by two contours. The tolerance may specify a datum reference. When a datum reference is not specified, the

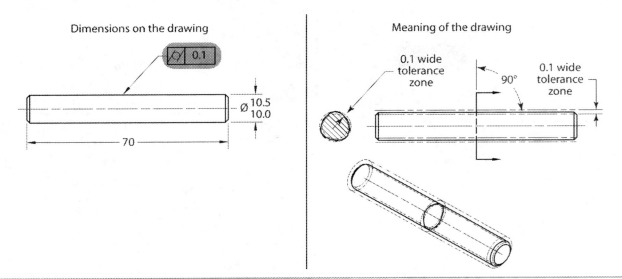

FIGURE 16.61. The cylindricity tolerance.

FIGURE 16.62. Inspection technique for cylindricity.

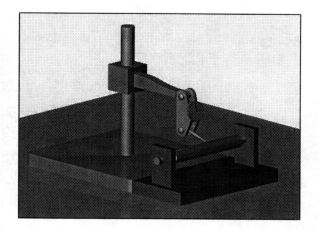

tolerance controls only the shape of the contour. When datums are specified, the tolerance controls the shape of the contour as well as the size and/or location of the contour.

Figure 16.63 illustrates profile of a line. The feature control frame reads as follows: Each feature line profile must be within a five-hundredth of a millimeter tolerance zone relative to primary datum feature A, secondary datum feature B, and tertiary datum feature C. Unless otherwise specified, the tolerance specified in the feature control frame is equally disposed on either side of the perfect geometry (0.025 above and 0.025 below).

FIGURE 16.63. Profile of a line.

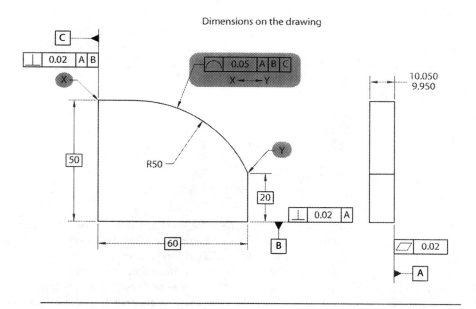

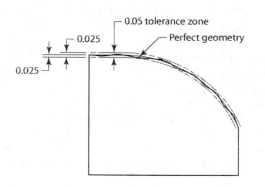

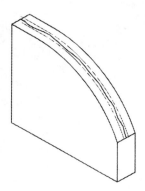

FIGURE 16.64. Profile of a surface.

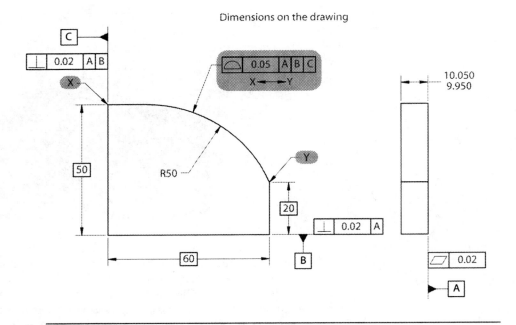

Dimensions on the drawing

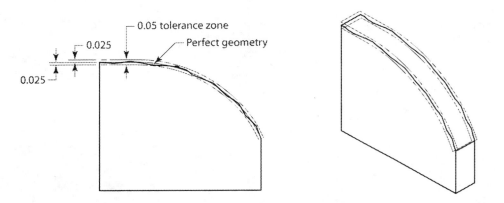

Meaning of the drawing

— 0.05 tolerance zone
— Perfect geometry
0.025
0.025

Profile of a surface—Profile of a surface specifies a *3-D tolerance zone* defined by two contoured surfaces. Like profile of a line, the tolerance may specify a datum reference. When a datum reference is not specified, the tolerance controls only the shape of the contour. When datums are specified, the tolerance controls the shape of the contour as well as the size and/or location of the contour. Figure 16.64 illustrates profile of a surface. The feature control frame reads as follows: The surface profile must be within a five-hundredth of a millimeter tolerance zone relative to primary datum feature A, secondary datum feature B, and teriary datum feature C. Like profile of a line, the tolerance specified in the feature control frame is equally disposed on either side of the perfect geometry (0.025 above and 0.025 below) unless specified otherwise.

Both profile of a line and profile of a surface can control surfaces in other ways. As indicated earlier, profile tolerances are equally distributed about the perfect geometry of the feature. This is referred to as a *bilateral-equal* distribution. Figure 16.65 illustrates three additional ways to describe the tolerance zones for the profile of a line or the profile of a surface. In Figure 16.65a, the 0.05 tolerance zone is on the outside of the perfect geometry. This is called *unilateral-outside*. Figure 16.65b shows an example of *unilateral-inside* since all of the tolerance zone is specified inside the perfect geometry. The last example in Figure 16.65c can be used when an unequal distribution is desired. The profile tolerance here specifies a *bilateral-unequal* distribution where 0.02 is indicated outside

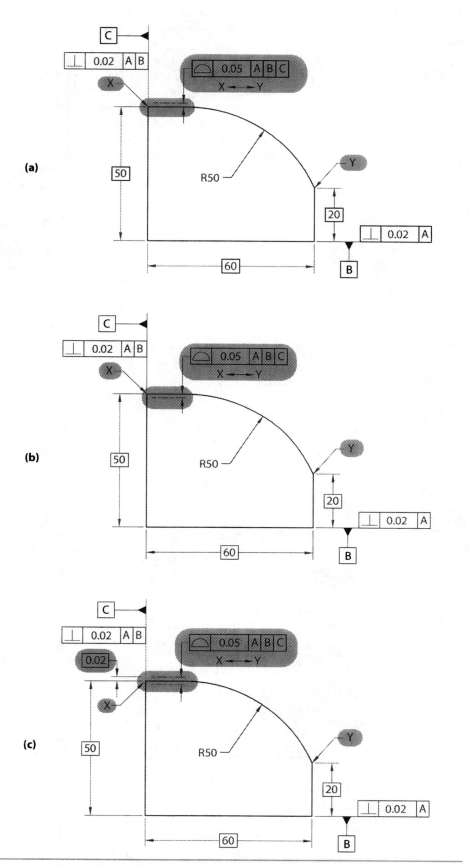

FIGURE 16.65. Tolerance distributions for the profile tolerance.

the perfect geometry using a basic dimension and the remaining 0.03 is inside the perfect geometry.

Profile of a surface also can be used to make sure two or more surfaces are coplanar. This can be specified for an object such as the one in Figure 16.66 when datums are applied (see Figure 16.67) or when datums are not applied (see Figure 16.68).

Inspection of profile tolerances—Profile tolerances can be inspected in a couple of different ways. Optical comparitors along with overlay charts are frequently used to inspect profile tolerances. These tools work best for parts such as gaskets and plates and for other thin parts. When a datum reference frame is applied to a tolerance, mechanical gaging can be used to inspect parts. For this method, a master part or gage is created to guide a dial indicator as it traces over the surface of the part being inspected.

FIGURE 16.66. Profile of a surface also can be used to make sure two or more surfaces are coplanar.

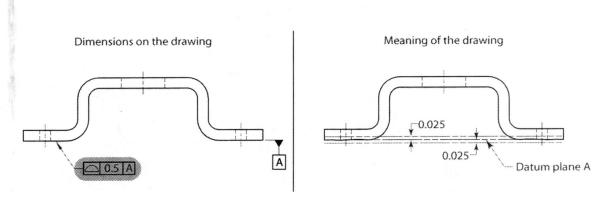

FIGURE 16.67. Using profile with a datum to make two surfaces coplanar.

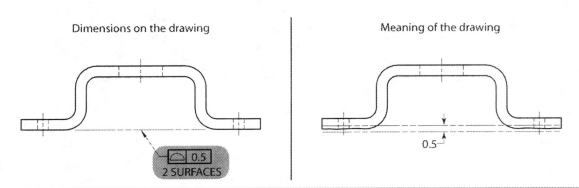

FIGURE 16.68. Using profile without a datum to make two surfaces coplanar.

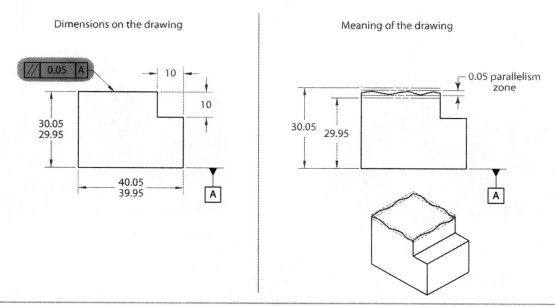

FIGURE 16.69. Parallelism tolerance used to control a surface.

16.06.07 Orientation Tolerances

Parallelism—Parallelism specifies a 3-D tolerance zone that can control the orientation of a surface or axis of a hole or cylinder relative to a datum. When applied to a surface, the 3-D zone is defined by the area between two parallel planes. When applied to an axis, the 3-D zone is defined by the area within a cylinder. In either case, the tolerance must include a datum reference. Figure 16.69 illustrates parallelism applied to a surface. The feature control frame reads as follows: The feature must be parallel within five-hundredths of a millimeter tolerance zone relative to datum feature A.

When parallelism is applied to an axis (see Figure 16.70), the tolerance zone is a cylinder. Since the tolerance is applied to a feature of size (a hole), a material condition modifier may be used. In this case, the axis of the hole must fall within the 0.05 cylidrical tolerance zone. The axis of the cylindrical tolerance zone is parallel to datum axis A.

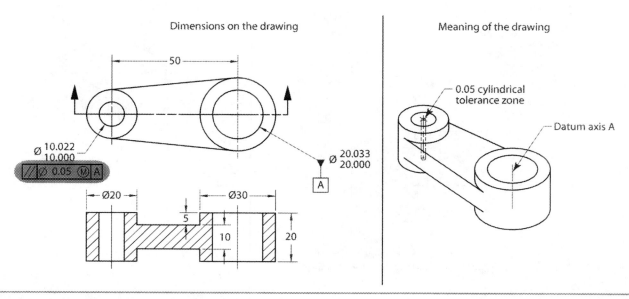

FIGURE 16.70. Parallelism tolerance used to control an axis.

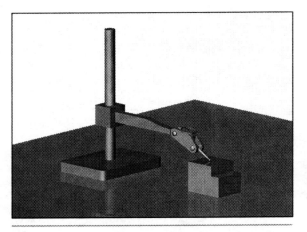

FIGURE 16.71. Inspecting the parallelism of a surface.

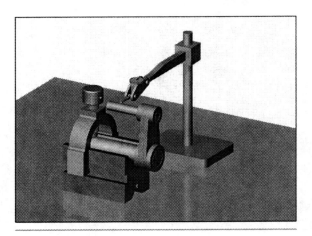

FIGURE 16.72. Inspecting the parallelism of an axis.

When parallelism for a flat surface is inspected, a surface plate is typically used with a dial indicator (see Figure 16.71). The FIM of the dial must not exceed the tolerance specified on the drawing. When axis-to-axis parallelism is inspected, gage pins must be inserted into the datum hole and the controlled hole. The datum hole is locked into a V-BLOCK, and a dial indicator is used to check the parallelism (see Figure 16.72).

Perpendicularity—Perpendicularity specifies a 3-D tolerance zone that can control the orientation of a surface or axis of a hole or cylinder relative to a datum. When applied to a surface, the 3-D zone is defined by the area between two parallel planes. When applied to an axis, the 3-D zone is defined by the area within a cylinder. In either case, the tolerance must include a datum reference. Figure 16.73 illustrates perpendicularity applied to a surface. The feature control frame reads as follows: The feature must be perpendicular within five-hundredths of a millimeter tolerance zone relative to datum feature A.

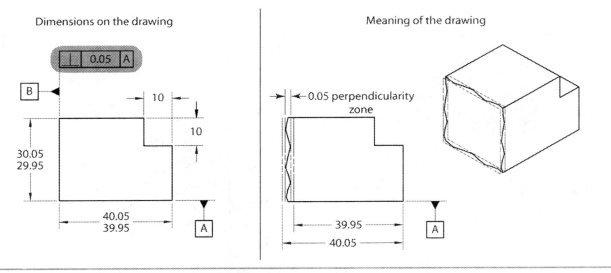

FIGURE 16.73. Perpendicularity tolerance used to control a surface.

Dimensions on the drawing

Meaning of the drawing

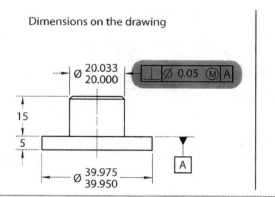

Ø 20.033
20.000

⊥ Ø 0.05 Ⓜ A

15

5

Ø 39.975
39.950

A

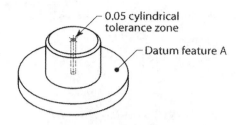

0.05 cylindrical
tolerance zone

Datum feature A

FIGURE 16.74. Perpendicularity tolerance used to control an axis.

When perpendicularity is applied to an axis (see Figure 16.74), the tolerance zone is a cylinder. Since the tolerance is applied to a feature of size (a cylinder), a material condition modifier may be used. In this case, the axis of the cylinder must fall within the 0.05 cylidrical tolerance zone. The axis of the cylindrical tolerance zone is perpendicular to datum axis A.

Inspecting perpendicularity can be accomplished in many ways. A common method for inspecting perpendicularity between two surfaces is to use a right-angle plate method (see Figure 16.75). Inspecting the perpendicularity of an axis is similar to inspecting the parallelism of an axis. Gage pins can be inserted into holes, and a dial caliper can be used.

Angularity—One of the disadvantages of using plus-minus dimensioning to control angular surfaces has to do with the shape of the resultant zone. Figure 16.76 illustrates the zone that is defined by the note ALL ANGULAR DIMENSIONS +/- 1° UNLESS OTHERWISE SPECIFIED. Notice that a wedge-shaped zone is created. This is a problem since more tolerance is accepted to the top left of the surface than to the bottom right.

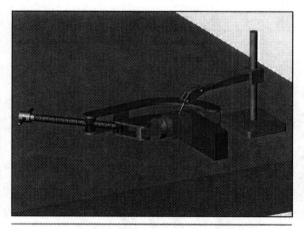

FIGURE 16.75. Inspecting the perpendicularity between two surfaces.

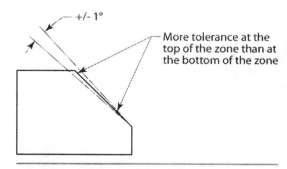

+/- 1°

More tolerance at the top of the zone than at the bottom of the zone

FIGURE 16.76. The tolerance zone when conventional tolerancing is used to control angles.

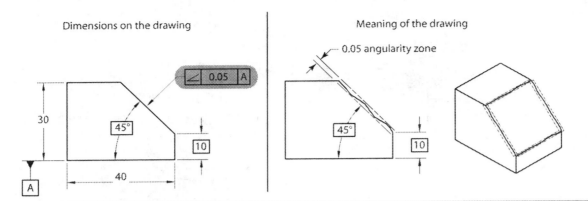

FIGURE 16.77. Angularity tolerance used to control a surface.

Angularity specifies a 3-D tolerance zone that can control the orientation of a surface or axis of a hole or cylinder relative to a datum. When applied to a surface, the 3-D zone is defined by the area between two parallel planes. When applied to an axis, the 3-D zone is defined by the area within a cylinder. In either case, the tolerance must include a datum reference and a basic dimension specifying the angle from one or more datums. The feature control frame in Figure 16.77 reads as follows: The feature must be at an angle of 45° within five-hundredths of a millimeter tolerance zone relative to datum feature A.

Angularity also can be inspected many different ways. Figure 16.78 illustrates one popular way. A sine bar is used in combination with precision cylinders and blocks to orient the angled surface parallel to the tabletop. A dial indictor is then used to investigate the FIM.

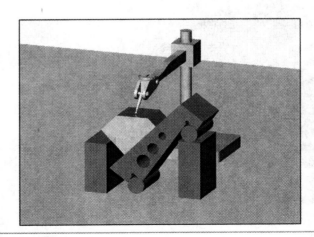

FIGURE 16.78. Inspecting the angularity between two surfaces.

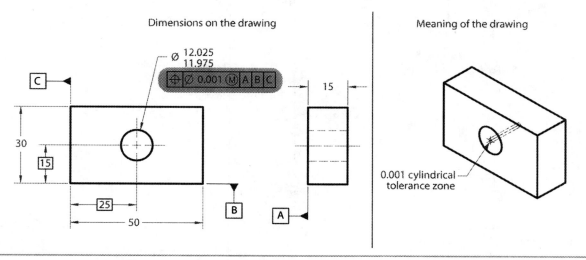

FIGURE 16.79. Using the position tolerance to locate the axis of a hole.

16.06.08 Location Tolerances

Position—The position tolerance is one of the most fequently used geometric tolerances. It can be used to control the orientation and location of a center, an axis, or a center plane of a feature of size. When the location of a hole or cylindrical feature of size needs to be controlled, position establishes a 3-D cylindrical tolerance zone within which the axis of the feature must fall. When the location of a center plane needs to be controlled, the position tolerance establishes a 3-D zone defined by two parallel planes. In any case, the zones are located using basic dimensions from specified datum features. There are other uses of the position tolerance, but the most common ones are described above. The feature control frame in Figure 16.79 reads as follows: The feature must be positioned within a one-thousandth of a millimeter cylindrical tolerance zone at maximum material condition relative to primary datum feature A, secondary datum feature B, and tertiary datum feature C.

Figure 16.80 illustrates one method for inspecting the position tolerance when it is applied to a hole feature. In this case, an open setup technique is used with surface plates, a gage pin, a clamp, and a dial indicator. Similar techniques are used when the location of more than one feature is inspected.

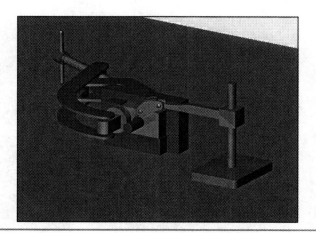

FIGURE 16.80. Inspecting the position of a hole using a gage pin.

Dimensions on the drawing

Meaning of the drawing

◎ ∅ 0.001 A

∅ 25.0 / 24.9

∅ 14.0 / 13.9

A

|—15—|—20—|

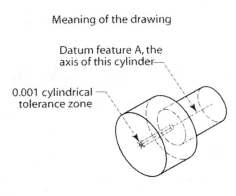

Datum feature A, the axis of this cylinder—

0.001 cylindrical tolerance zone

FIGURE 16.81. Concentricity applied to a cylinder.

Concentricity—Concentricity is a geometric tolerance used to control the *axis-to-axis* relationship between two features. The feature control frame in Figure 16.81 reads as follows: The feature must be concentric within a four-tenths of a millimeter cylindrical tolerance zone relative to datum feature A.

In theory, this may be easier to understand than it is to inspect. Since concentricity requires an inspector to determine all median points along a feature, it requires some complicated inspection techniques. Diametrically opposed indicators are required to accurately determine concentricity (see Figure 16.82). For objects such as the one in Figure 16.81, runout tolerances provide better inspection methods (see the section on inspecting runout later in the chapter). For an object like the one in Figure 16.83, runout would be a bad choice since a dial indicator would need to be used to make contact with the hexagonal surfaces.

Symmetry—In some ways, symmetry and concentricity are very similar. The main difference is that symmetry is typically concerned with the position of a *center plane* relative to an axis or a center plane of a datum feature. Figure 16.84 illustrates a part with the symmetry tolerance. The feature control frame in the figure reads as follows: The center plane of the feature must be symmetric within a five-hundredths of a millimeter tolerance zone relative to datum feature A.

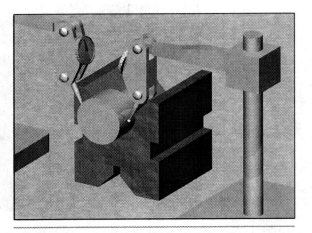

FIGURE 16.82. Inspecting concentricity with diametrically opposed indicators.

FIGURE 16.83. Concentricity applied to a hexagonal feature.

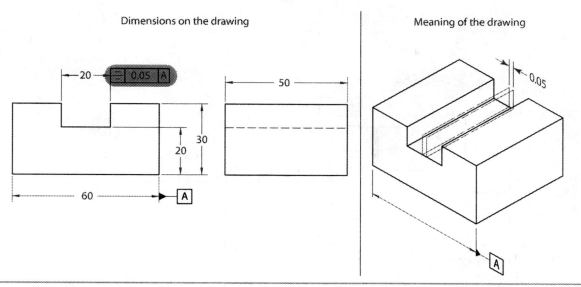

FIGURE 16.84. Symmetry of two surfaces about a median plane.

Since it is necessary to determine the median points on the feature, symmetry is difficult to inspect. For this reason, position and profile tolerances are frequently used instead of symmetry.

16.06.09 Runout Tolerances

Circular runout—Circular runout is a 2-D control similar to circularity or roundness. The main difference is that circular runout controls a surface relative to a datum axis. The feature control frame in Figure 16.85 reads as follows: The circular runout of the feature must be within a two-hundredths of a millimeter tolerance zone relative to datum feature A.

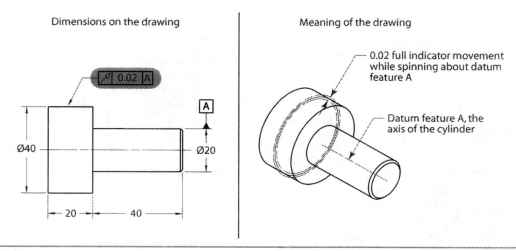

FIGURE 16.85. Circular runout.

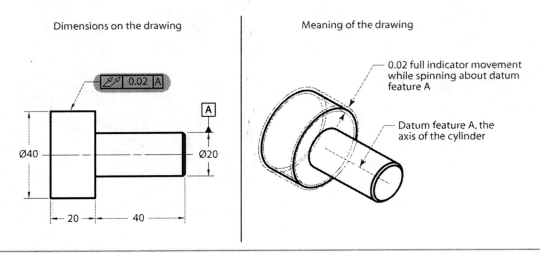

Dimensions on the drawing

Meaning of the drawing

0.02 full indicator movement while spinning about datum feature A

Datum feature A, the axis of the cylinder

Ø40

Ø20

A

20   40

FIGURE 16.86. Total runout applied to a cylindrical surface.

Total runout—Total runout is a 3-D control for rotating parts relative to a datum axis. When applied to a cylindrical surface, it controls circularity, concentricity, straightness, taper, and surface profile (see Figure 16.86). It also can be applied to a flat surface to control wobble, perpendicularity, and flatness (see Figure 16.87). The feature control frame in Figure 16.86 reads as follows: The total runout of the cylindrical feature must be within a two-hundredths of a millimeter tolerance zone relative to datum feature A.

When using a V-Block and a dial indicator to inspect runout, the FIM must be within the specified tolerance as the part is spinning about the datum feature (see Figure 16.88). For circular runout, the dial is reset after each revolution of the part. For total runout, the indicator is passed over the entire surface before the FIM is examined.

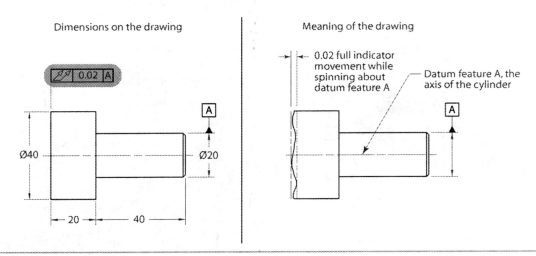

Dimensions on the drawing

Meaning of the drawing

0.02 full indicator movement while spinning about datum feature A

Datum feature A, the axis of the cylinder

A

Ø40

Ø20

A

20   40

FIGURE 16.87. Total runout applied to a flat surface.

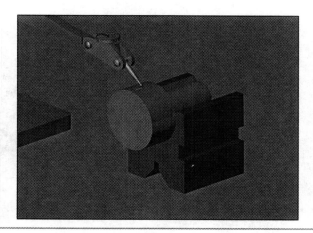

FIGURE 16.88. Inspecting runout using a V-Block.

   Multiple datums—Since one of the main goals of geometric tolerancing is to apply tolerances based on how parts function, careful specification of datums is necessary. Figure 16.89 illustrates how a multiple datum can be specified when the runout tolerance is used. Since the SHAFT spins about both SUPPORTS, the datum axis is determined by both ends of the SHAFT. Figure 16.90 illustrates an inspection technique for a multiple datum.

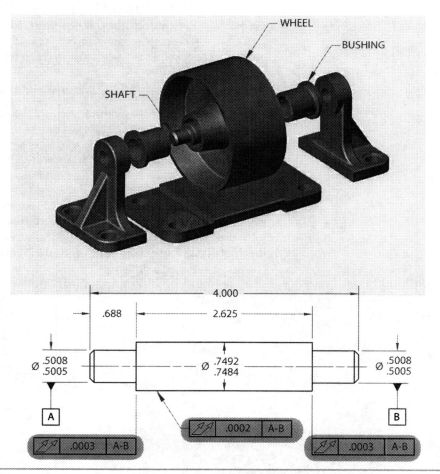

FIGURE 16.89. Using a multiple datum with the runout tolerance.

FIGURE 16.90. Inspecting a part with a multiple datum.

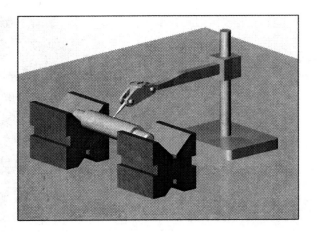

CAUTION

As stated earlier in the chapter, one of the challenges for new engineers is their lack of experience. You may make some mistakes before you fully understand how the concepts of dimensioning and tolerancing relate to your engineering work. What follows are some of the common errors that are made due to inexperience.

Tolerances Too Tight or Too Loose

Earlier, Section 16.01.02 discussed how applying inappropriate tolerances can create problems for manufacturing. When you apply tolerances that are too small or too tight, manufacturing becomes more difficult and expensive. Applying tolerances that are too large or too loose may cause parts to function improperly.

Misreading Standard Tolerance Tables

One of the most common errors made by those without much experience in assigning tolerances is misreading the tables. Look at an example where a *close sliding fit* (RC1) is being applied to a hole and shaft that have a nominal size of *.500*. Looking at the table in Figure 16.91, notice that the limits on the hole are shown as +0.3 and -0. The limits on the shaft are -0.25 and -0.45. It would not make much sense to have the dimension on the hole read .500-.800 and the dimension on the shaft be .050-.250. These tolerances are much too large. The key point to remember about the tables associated with the English system is that the values are shown in thousandths of an inch. So values of +0.3 and -0 on the table mean +0.0003 and -0, respectively. Values of -0.25 and -0.45 mean -0.00025 and -0.00045, respectively. Figure 16.92 shows the correct way to display the dimensions on a drawing.

Nominal Size Range, Inches Over To	Limits of Clearance	Class RC 1	
		Standard Limits	
		Hole H5	Shaft g4
0–0.12	0.1	+0.2	–0.1
	0.45	–0	–0.25
0.12–0.24	0.15	+0.2	–0.15
	0.5	–0	–0.3
0.24–0.40	0.2	+0.25	–0.2
	0.6	–0	–0.35
0.40–0.71	0.25	+0.3	–0.25
	0.75	–0	–0.45

FIGURE 16.91. English fit table.

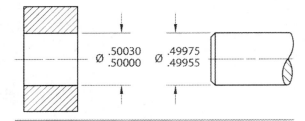

Ø .50030 / .50000   Ø .49975 / .49955

FIGURE 16.92. Clearance fit.

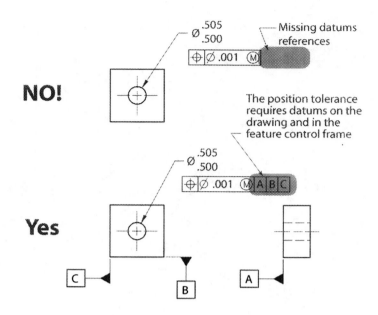

FIGURE 16.93. Omitting datums when they are necessary.

Missing datums references

NO!

Ø .505 / .500

⊕ Ø .001 Ⓜ

The position tolerance requires datums on the drawing and in the feature control frame

Yes

Ø .505 / .500

⊕ Ø .001 Ⓜ A B C

C

B

A

No Datums for Geometric Tolerances That Require Datums

Figure 16.93 illustrates a case where the position tolerance is specified for the location of a hole but no datums are given in the feature control frame and none are shown on the drawing. As you start to use geometric dimensions and tolerances, it is recommended that you keep a table or chart handy that shows which geometric tolerances need a datum reference. Figure 16.94 is a good example of this type of table.

Adding Unrequired Datums

Adding datums when they are not required is usually the result of not taking the time to fully understand each tolerance. This is closely related to the information discussed in the last section. Most often datums are incorrectly applied to tolerances that do not require datums, such as the form tolerances of straightness, flatness, circularity, and cylindricity (see Figure 16.94). Form tolerances control the form of an individual feature, not the relationship of that feature to something else.

FIGURE 16.94. Datum requirement table for geometric tolerances.

DATUM REQUIREMENT	TYPE OF TOLERANCE	CHARACTERISTIC	SYM
DATUMS ARE NOT ALLOWED	FORM	STRAIGHTNESS	—
		FLATNESS	▱
		CIRCULARITY	○
		CYLINDRICITY	⌭
DATUMS REQUIRED MOST OF THE TIME	PROFILE	PROFILE OF A LINE	⌒
		PROFILE OF A SURFACE	⌓
DATUMS ARE ALWAYS REQUIRED	ORIENTATION	ANGULARITY	∠
		PERPENDICULARITY	⊥
		PARALLELISM	∥
	LOCATION	POSITION	⊕
		CONCENTRICITY	◎
		SYMMETRY	⋚
	RUNOUT	CIRCULAR RUNOUT	↗
		TOTAL RUNOUT	↗↗

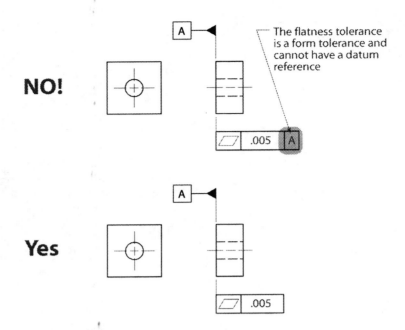

FIGURE 16.95. Adding datums when they are not necessary.

Examine the drawing in Figure 16.95. Notice how the feature control frame for the incorrect version of the tolerance includes a reference to datum feature A. This is wrong for a couple of reasons. First, since flatness is a form tolerance, no datums can be listed in the feature control frame. Second, the geometric tolerance is applied to what is identified as datum feature A, which is itself.

Tolerances That Cannot Be Inspected

Because you tend to learn GD&T in a classroom environment, almost everything you know is based on theory and not on actual hands-on practice. This can lead to problems even when you correctly apply tolerances on a drawing. In addition to knowing the correct ways to add geometric tolerances to a drawing, you must know the inspection capabilities of your company. For example, if you correctly specify a cylindricity tolerance on a drawing (as in Figure 16.61) but your company does not have total runout inspection equipment (see Figure 16.62) or precision spindles for checking cylindricity, the drawing tolerances are useless. As you get settled into your first engineering job, it is a good idea to get to know the quality control people as well as the capabilities they have for inspecting geometric tolerances.

Material Condition Modifier for a Feature Not of Size

Another potential error is the result of not being able to properly recognize features with size. Examine the drawing in Figure 16.96. Notice how a maximum material condition modifier is added to the parallelism feature control frame. In this case, the parallelism tolerance is applied to a planar surface, which is not a feature with size. Therefore, a material condition modifier cannot be applied. The correct way of specifying the tolerance is shown without the maximum material condition modifier.

Incorrect Application of Datum Feature Symbols

The last error that is frequently made has to do with applying datum feature symbols. This mistake also is related to not being able to distinguish between features with size and features without size. Figure 16.97 and Figure 16.98 show the same object dimensioned two different ways. In Figure 16.97, the datum feature symbols are used to specify the top left corner of the left view as the origin of the datum reference frame. Datums feature B and datam feature C are used to specify the outside surfaces as

FIGURE 16.96. Applying
material condition modifiers to
features with size.

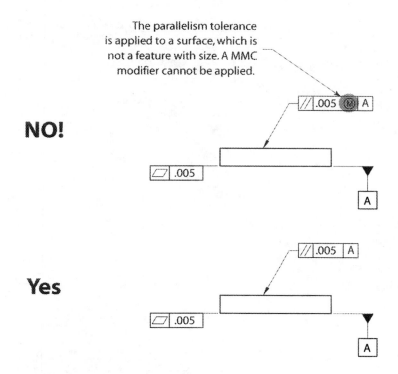

The parallelism tolerance
is applied to a surface, which is
not a feature with size. A MMC
modifier cannot be applied.

NO!

Yes

datum features. Since these datum features are surfaces (features without size), no
material condition modifiers can be applied. When you examine the feature control
frames for the two position tolerances, notice that there are no material condition
modifiers after the B and C.

For the object in Figure 16.98, the datum feature symbols for datums B and C are
specified differently. Notice how each is aligned with the corresponding dimension.
Datum feature B is the median plane running vertically through the center of the
part. Datum feature C is the median plane running horizontally through the center of

FIGURE 16.97. Datum feature
symbols used to specify a surface as a datum.

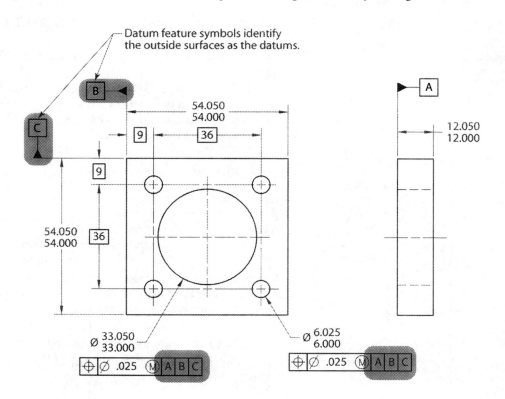

Datum feature symbols identify
the outside surfaces as the datums.

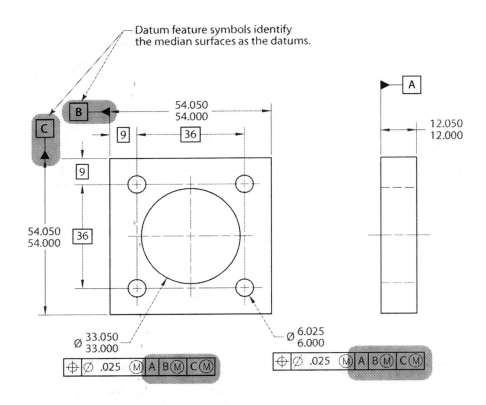

the part. In this case, the origin of the datum reference frame is the center of the rectangle. These datum features are now based on sizes—the two 54 dimensions. They are features with size, so material condition modifiers can be applied. Notice the maximum material condition modifiers after the B and C in the feature control frames.

16.07 Examples of Specifying Fits and Geometric Tolerances

The following examples should give you a head start on applying conventional tolerancing and GD&T to your designs. The first example will walk you through specifying a clearance fit between two parts in an assembly using the standard inch table for a sliding fit. The second is a step-by-step example of applying geometric tolerances to a simple rectangular block with a hole in it.

16.07.01 Specifying the Fit between Two Parts

Earlier, Section 16.01.02 discussed how applying inappropriate tolerances can create problems for manufacturing. Look at an assembly to see how to apply appropriate tolerances based on how the part functions. Examine the coupling assembly in Figure 16.99.

For this exercise, assume there is a clearance fit between the STUD and the BUSHING. Use the guidelines from Section 16.04.05 for determining fits in inches:

- *Determine the type of fit appropriate for the design and locate the corresponding table.* For this exercise, you will use a *sliding fit* (RC2), which is intended for accurate location. It will allow the parts to move and turn easily.

- *Determine the basic or nominal size.* The nominal size of the hole in the BUSHING and the largest diameter of the STUD is **9/16" (.5625)**.

- *Find the size range on the table* (see Figure 16.100). This size falls within the **0.40-0.71** category.

FIGURE 16.99. Coupling assembly.

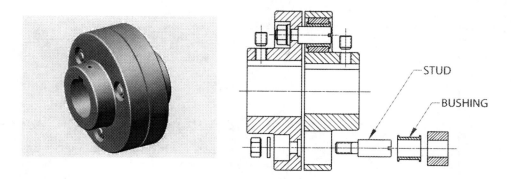

STUD

BUSHING

- *Determine the tolerances for the hole and the shaft.* The limits on the hole for the BUSHING are **-0** and **+0.4**. The limits on the diameter of the SHAFT are **-0.55** and **-0.25**.

- *Remember that values are in thousandths of an inch on the English tables.* Begin by calculating the size of the hole in the BUSHING. The nominal size is .5625, so you will add the upper and lower limits to this value.

.5625 + .0004 = .56290

.5625 + 0 = .56250

Limit dimension for hole in BUSHING: .56250-.56290

Do the same for the larger diameter of the STUD.

.5625 - .00025 = .56225

.5625 - .00055 = .56195

Limit dimension for hole in STUD: .56195-.56225

Figure 16.101 shows the resulting dimension values for the STUD and the BUSHING.

Nominal Size Range, Inches		Class RC 1			Class RC 2			Class RC 3			Class RC 4		
			Standard Limits			Standard Limits			Standard Limits			Standard Limits	
Over To	Limits of Clearance	Hole H5	Shaft g4	Limits of Clearance	Hole H6	Shaft g5	Limits of Clearance	Hole H7	Shaft f6	Limits of Clearance	Hole H8	Shaft f7
0-0.12	0.1 0.45	+0.2 -0	-0.1 -0.25	0.1 0.55	+0.25 -0	-0.1 -0.3	0.3 0.95	+0.4 -0	-0.3 -0.55	0.3 1.3	+0.6 -0	-0.3 -0.07
0.12-0.24	0.15 0.5	+0.2 -0	-0.15 -0.3	0.15 0.65	+0.3 -0	-0.15 -0.35	0.4 1.12	+0.5 -0	-0.4 -0.7	0.4 1.6	+0.7 -0	-0.4 -0.9
0.24-0.40	0.2 0.6	+0.25 -0	-0.2 -0.35	0.2 0.85	+0.4 -0	-0.2 -0.45	0.5 1.5	+0.6 -0	-0.5 -0.9	0.5 2.0	+0.9 -0	-0.5 -1.1
0.40-0.71	0.25 0.75	+0.3 -0	-0.25 -0.45	0.25 0.95	+0.4 -0	-0.25 -0.55	0.6 1.7	+0.7 -0	-0.6 -1.0	0.6 2.3	+1.0 -0	-0.6 -1.3
0.71-1.19	0.3 0.95	+0.4 -0	-0.3 -0.55	0.3 1.2	+0.5 -0	-0.3 -0.7	0.8 2.1	+0.8 -0	-0.8 -1.3	0.8 2.8	+1.2 -0	-0.8 -1.6
1.19-1.97	0.4 1.1	+0.4 -0	-0.4 -0.7	0.4 1.4	+0.6 -0	-0.4 -0.8	1.0 2.6	+1.0 -0	-1.0 -1.6	1.0 3.6	+1.6 -0	-1.0 -2.0
1.97-3.15	0.4 1.2	+0.5 -0	-0.4 -0.7	0.4 1.6	+0.7 -0	-0.4 -0.9	1.2 3.1	+1.2 -0	-1.2 -1.9	1.2 4.2	+1.8 -0	-1.2 -2.4
3.15-4.73	0.5 1.5	+0.6 -0	-0.5 -0.9	0.5 2.0	+0.9 -0	-0.5 -1.1	1.4 3.7	+1.4 -0	-1.4 -2.3	1.4 5.0	+2.2 -0	-0.4 -2.8
4.73-7.09	0.6 1.8	+0.7 -0	-0.6 -1.1	0.6 2.3	+1.0 -0	-0.6 -1.3	1.6 4.2	+1.6 -0	-1.6 -2.6	1.6 5.7	+2.5 -0	-1.6 -3.2
7.09-9.85	0.6 2.0	+0.8 -0	-0.6 -1.2	0.6 2.6	+1.2 -0	-0.6 -1.4	2.0 5.0	+1.8 -0	-2.0 -3.2	2.0 6.6	+2.8 -0	-2.0 -3.8
9.85-12.41	0.8 2.3	+0.9 -0	-0.8 -1.4	0.8 2.9	+1.2 -0	-0.8 -1.7	2.5 5.7	+2.0 -0	-2.5 -3.7	2.5 7.5	+3.0 -0	-2.5 -4.5
12.41-15.75	1.0 2.7	+1.0 -0	-1.0 -1.7	1.0 3.4	+1.4 -0	-1.0 -2.0	3.0 6.6	+2.2 -0	-3.0 -4.4	3.0 8.7	+3.5 -0	-3.0 -5.2

* From ANSI B4.1 – 1967 (R1994). For larger diameters, see the standard.

FIGURE 16.100. American National Standard running and sliding fits. *Reprinted from ASME B4.1-1967 (R1994) and ASME B4.2-1978 (R1994), by permission of The American Society of Mechanical Engineers. All rights reserved.*

FIGURE 16.101. Limit
dimensions for the STUD and
BUSHING.

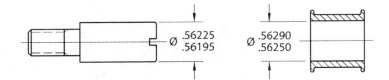

Ø .56225
  .56195

Ø .56290
  .56250

16.07.02 Adding Geometric Dimensions

Becoming an expert in GD&T will take quite a bit of experience. There are some basic guidelines you can keep in mind as you add geometric dimensions to a drawing to make sure you are as thorough as possible. In this section, you will use the PLATE ASSEMBLY as an example (see Figure 16.102). Notice how the PLATE fits against three surfaces on the BASE and how the SCREW passes through both parts. It is critical that logical datums be selected if the assembly is to function correctly. For this example, you will look at how you might apply geometric dimensions to the PLATE.

Start by establishing the datum reference frame for the PLATE (see Figure 16.103). As you identify datum features, you can use any letters. The most common ones are A, B, and C in a three-datum feature system; however, you also can use D, E, and F or M, N, and O. Since the large flat surface on the bottom of the PLATE has most contact with the BASE, identify it as primary datum feature A. The back surface of the PLATE is the next largest, so you identify it as secondary datum feature B. Finally, identify the left-hand surface of the part as datum feature C. These datum features establish a datum reference frame with the origin of the 3-D coordinate system at the back left bottom corner. All geometric tolerances that you use will be based on this coordinate system.

Now that you have established the datum features, you must control them with geometric tolerances. Since they are all surfaces, this will be fairly easy. Planar surfaces used as primary datums are typically controlled with a flatness tolerance. This is what

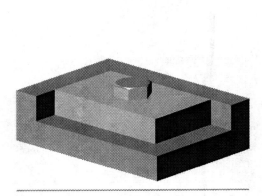

FIGURE 16.102. PLATE ASSEMBLY.

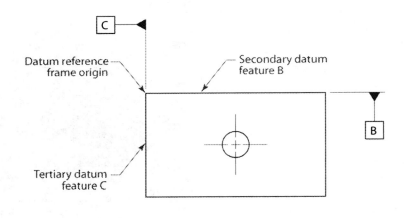

Datum reference frame origin

Secondary datum feature B

Tertiary datum feature C

B

C

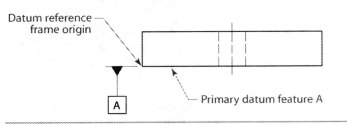

Datum reference frame origin

Primary datum feature A

A

FIGURE 16.103. Establishing the datums on the PLATE.

FIGURE 16.104. Controlling
the datums on the PLATE.

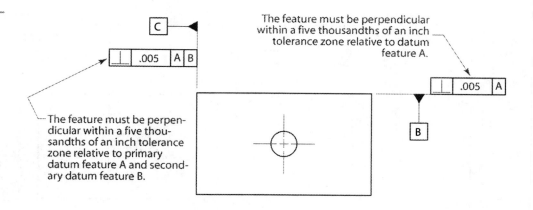

The feature must be perpendicular within a five thousandths of an inch tolerance zone relative to datum feature A.

The feature must be perpendicular within a five thousandths of an inch tolerance zone relative to primary datum feature A and secondary datum feature B.

The feature must be flat within a five thousandths of an inch tolerance zone.

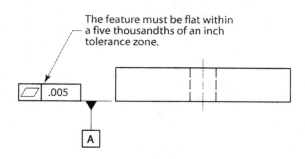

was done with datum feature A. All points on the bottom surface must fall between two imaginary planes that are five-thousandths of an inch apart. The other two surfaces are controlled with the perpendicularity tolerance. Datum feature B is controlled relative to datum feature A first. Like the flatness tolerance, all points on the back surface must fall between two imaginary planes that are five-thousandths of an inch apart. In this case, the imaginary planes are perpendicular to datum feature A. The left side of the object is controlled in the same manner. For this tolerance, the imaginary planes used to establish the tolerance zone are perpendicular to datum feature A and datum feature B (see Figure 16.104).

To control the location and orientation of the machined hole, a position tolerance is used (see Figure 16.105). Basic dimensions are used to locate the theoretically exact position of the center of the hole. Remember that these dimensions do not have any tolerance. The tolerance for the axis of the hole will be taken care of in the feature control frame for the position tolerance. This example uses a tolerance of .010. Since a diameter symbol is in front of this tolerance, the shape of the zone is a cylinder. (See Section 16.06.03 for another example of the position tolerance.) The hole is positioned relative to all of the datums.

The last thing you will do is control the other surfaces of the part (see Figure 16.106). One way to control the top surface of the part is with the parallelism tolerance. If you do this, you must use a conventional tolerance dimension to locate the top surface from the bottom of the part. The top surface must fall between two parallel imaginary planes that are five-thousandths of an inch apart. The orientation of the two imaginary planes is controlled by the upper and lower tolerances of the limit dimension (.495-.505).

To control the front and right surfaces, a profile of a surface is used. The tolerance zone for this tolerance is established by the two basic dimensions locating the surfaces (1.500 and 2.500). Imaginary planes .010 apart are equally disposed about the perfect geometry of the part. All points must fall between these imaginary planes. See Section 16.06.06 for a more detailed explanation of the profile tolerance.

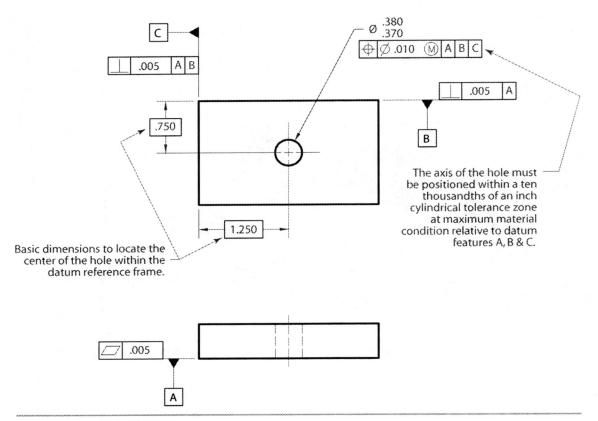

FIGURE 16.105. Positioning the hole on the PLATE.

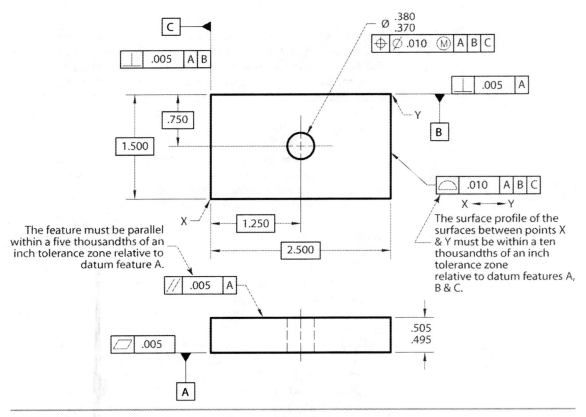

FIGURE 16.106. Controlling the other surfaces on the PLATE.

16.08 Chapter Summary

This chapter covered basic information related to conventional tolerancing and GD&T. It began with a discussion of interchangeable manufacturing and explained why it is important to the way modern industry functions. The chapter looked at several topics within conventional tolerancing, such as what tolerance stack-up is, how to specify English and metric fits, and how tolerance dimensions control form and location. With these topics as a foundation, the chapter covered the basics of geometric dimensioning and tolerancing. Included was a discussion of the advantages of geometric tolerancing over conventional tolerancing, the importance of the datum reference frame to establish a coordinate system for design manufacturing and inspection, an explanation of how to read feature control frames, and a description of each geometric tolerance with an example of how to inspect each one.

16.09 glossary of key terms

allowance: The difference between the maximum material limits of mating parts. It is the minimum clearance or maximum interference between parts.

baseline dimensioning: A method for specifiying the location of features on a part whereby all the locations are relative to a common feature or edge.

basic dimension: A dimension that is theoretically exact. It is identified by a box around the dimension. It locates the perfect position of features from clearly identified datums.

chain dimensioning: A method for specifiying the location of features on a part whereby the location of each feature is successively specified relative to the location of the previous feature.

clearance: A type of fit where space exists between two mating parts.

datum: A theoretical plane or axis established by real features on an object for the purpose of defining the datum reference frame.

datum reference frame: A system of three mutually perpendicular planes used as the coordinate system for geometric dimensioning.

direct dimensioning: Dimensioning between two key points to minimize tolerance accumulation.

feature control frame: The main alphabet of the language of geometric dimensioning and tolerancing. These boxes contain the geometric characteristic symbol, the geometric tolerances, and the relative datums.

feature with size: A cylindrical or spherical surface or a set of two opposed elements or opposed parallel surfaces associated with a size dimension. Typical features with size are holes, cylinders, spheres, and opposite sides of a rectangular block.

feature without size: A planar surface or a feature where the normal vectors point in the same direction.

functional gage: An inspection tool built uniquely for the purpose of quickly checking a specific dimension or geometric condition on a part to determine whether or not it fall within tolerance limits.

geometric dimensioning and tolerancing (GD&T): A 3-D mathematical system that allows a designer to describe the form, orientation, and location of features on a part within precise tolerance zones.

interchangeable manufacturing: A process by which parts are made at different locations and brought together for assembly. For many industries, this process opens the door for third-party companies to produce replacement parts or custom parts.

interference: A fit where two mating parts have intersecting nominal volumes, requiring the deformation of the parts . For example, the diameter of the shaft is larger than the diameter of the hole. When assembled, the intent is that the shaft will not spin in the hole.

maximum material condition: The condition in which a feature of size contains the maximum amount of material within the stated limits of size.

statistical tolerancing: A way to assign tolerances based on sound statistical practices rather than conventional tolerancing practices.

16.10 questions for review

1. Describe interchangeable manufacturing. List two products that you use daily that rely on interchangeable manufacturing.

2. Describe the difference between baseline and chain dimensioning. Make two sketches of the object in Figure 16.106 and dimension it using the two methods of dimensioning.

3. How can you tell if a dimension on a drawing is appropriate for statistical process control applications?

4. What are the differences between clearance, interference, and transition fits? Give an example of a design that requires a clearance fit. Give an example of a design that requires an interference fit.

5. What is allowance as it relates to tolerance dimensioning? If the diameter of a hole is dimensioned as .500-.505 and the diameter of the mating shaft is .495-.498, what is the allowance?

6. Define tolerance as it relates to limit dimensioning. What is the tolerance for the hole in question 5? for the shaft?

7. Define the following terms: feature, feature with size, and feature without size.

8. List three advantages of GD&T over conventional tolerancing.

9. What is the theoretical coordinate system used in geometric dimensioning and tolerancing that consists of three mutually perpendicular planes?

10. Define the following: datum plane, datum simulator, and simulated datum. Give three examples of datum simulators.

11. What are the parts of a feature control frame?

12. Describe how the maximum material condition modifier is used to allow bonus tolerance for a feature.

13. Describe the difference between a flatness tolerance and a parallelism tolerance for a surface. Do these tolerances control form? orientation? location?

14. Describe the difference between the tolerance zone shape for straightness of a surface element and straightness of an axis.

15. What are the three ways in which profile of a line and profile of a surface can be specified relative to the perfect geometry implied on the drawing?

16. Describe the difference between circularity and circular runout.

17. Identify the geometric tolerances that require datum references.

16.11 problems

1. Using the tables in the back of the book, add the limit dimensions for the machined hole and shaft shown in Figure P16.1 per the following specifications. If instructed, determine the allowance for each system.

   a. RC1 fit with a basic size of .7500 inches
   b. RC9 fit with a basic size of 1.0000 inches
   c. FN3 fit with a basic size of .5000 inches
   d. FN5 fit with a basic size of 2.0000 inches
   e. LT1 fit with a basic size of .8750 inches
   f. LT6 fit with a basic size of 3.0000 inches
   g. LN1 fit with a basic size of .3750 inches
   h. LN3 fit with a basic size of 4.0000 inches
   i. LC1 fit with a basic size of .6250 inches
   j. LC11 fit with a basic size of .5000 inches
   k. Loose running fit (H11/c11) with a basic size of 5.000 millimeters
   l. Close running fit (H8/f7) with a basic size of 25.000 millimeters
   m. Locational transition fit (H7/n6) with a basic size of 10.000 millimeters
   n. Medium drive fit (H7/s6) with a basic size of 15.000 millimeters
   o. Sliding fit (G7/h6) with a basic size of 20.000 millimeters

16.11 problems (continued)

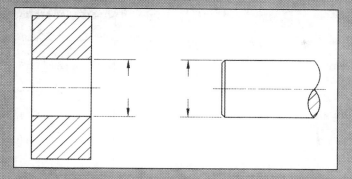

FIGURE P16.1.

2. Given the dimensions in the drawing shown in Figure P16.2, circle the value that represents the maximum material condition value for each dimension.

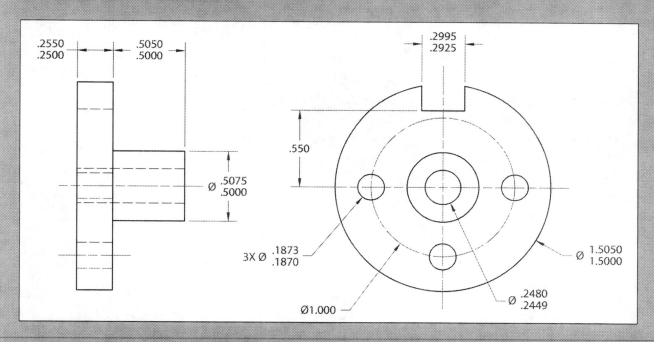

FIGURE P16.2.

16.11 problems (continued)

3. On the machined block shown in Figure P16.3, circle the dimensions that represent features with size.

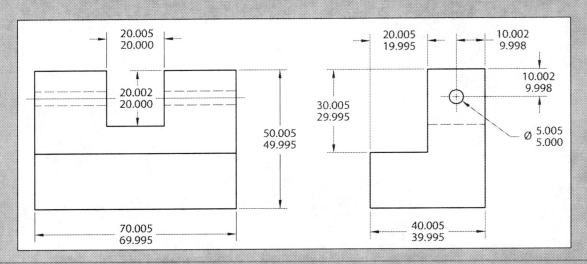

FIGURE P16.3.

4. On the drawing shown in Figure P16.4, apply datum feature symbols per the following specifications:
   a. Identify the left-hand face in the left-side view as datum feature A.
   b. Identify the bottom surface in the front view as datum feature B.
   c. Identify the median plane of the slot in the front view as datum feature C.
   d. Identify the axis of the large hole as datum feature D.

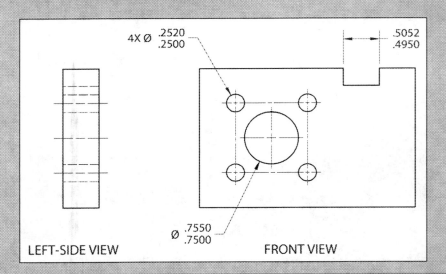

FIGURE P16.4.

5. Given the following sentence descriptions of the geometric tolerance information, correctly sketch the feature control frames for each.

   a. The feature must be flat within a tenth of a millimeter tolerance zone.

   b. The feature must be straight within a thousandth of an inch tolerance zone.

   c. The feature must be round within five-tenths of a millimeter tolerance zone.

   d. The feature (planar surface) must be perpendicular within a five-thousandths of an inch tolerance zone relative to datum feature A.

   e. The feature (axis of a cylinder) must be perpendicular within a one-hundredth of a millimeter cylindrical tolerance zone at maximum material condition relative to datum feature D.

   f. The feature (planar surface) must be parallel within a thousandth of an inch tolerance zone relative to datum feature A.

   g. The feature (axis of a cylinder) must be parallel within a three-hundredths of a millimeter cylindrical tolerance zone at maximum material condition relative to datum feature M.

   h. The total runout of the surface must be within a five-hundredths of a millimeter tolerance zone relative to datum feature A.

   i. The total surface profile of the surface must be within a two-thousandths of an inch tolerance zone relative to datum feature A.

   j. The features (axis of a hole) must be positioned within a five-thousandths of a millimeter cylindrical tolerance zone at maximum material condition relative to primary datum feature D, secondary datum feature E, and tertiary datum feature F.

6. Given the following feature control frames, write the sentence descriptions for each.

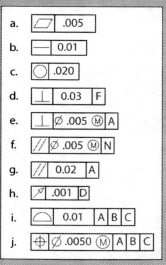

FIGURE P16.6.

16.11 problems (continued)

7. Place the item number of the following terms in the bold circles on the drawing in Figure P16.7 to identify each symbol.

   a. Basic dimension

   b. Feature control frame

   c. Maximum material condition modifier

   d. Datum feature symbol

   e. Statistical tolerance symbol

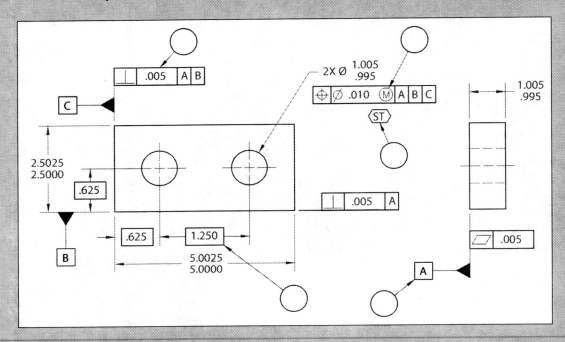

FIGURE P16.7.

16.11 problems (continued)

8. Given the drawing in Figure P16.8 and the sentence descriptions of the geometric tolerance information below, correctly dimension the drawing.

   a. Identify the left-hand surface in the SIDE VIEW as datum feature A. Control it with a flatness tolerance of .005.

   b. Identify the bottom surface in the FRONT VIEW as datum feature B. Control it with a perpendicularity tolerance of .005 relative to datum feature A.

   c. Identify the left-hand surface in the FRONT VIEW as datum feature C. Control it with a perpendicularity tolerance of .005 relative to primary datum feature A and secondary datum feature B.

   d. Make all dimensions basic except for the two limit dimensions.

   e. Add a position tolerance for the machined hole. The hole must be positioned within a ten-thousandths of an inch cylindrical tolerance zone at maximum material condition relative to primary datum feature A, secondary datum feature B, and tertiary datum feature C.

   f. In the FRONT VIEW, identify the top left corner as point X and the lower right corner as point Y. On either the top surface or the right-hand surface, add a profile of a surface tolerance of .010 relative to primary datum feature A, secondary datum feature B, and tertiary datum feature C. Under the feature control frame, identify that the tolerance applies between points X and Y.

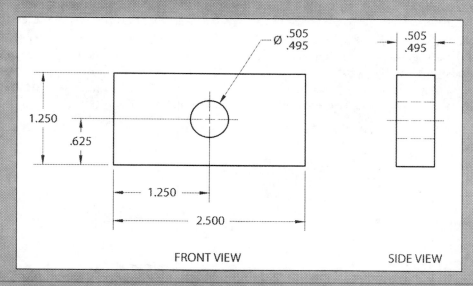

FIGURE P16.8.

16.11 problems (continued)

9. Given the drawing in Figure P16.9 and the sentence descriptions of the geometric tolerance information below, correctly dimension the drawing.

a. Identify the right-hand surface of the large cylinder in the SIDE VIEW as datum feature A. Control it with a flatness tolerance of .0050.

b. Apply a perpendicularity tolerance to the axis of the .5000-.5075 cylinder in the SIDE VIEW. The feature must be perpendicular with a .0030 cylindrical tolerance zone at maximum material condition relative to datum feature A. Identify the axis of this cylinder as datum feature B.

c. Identify the median plane of the .2925-.2995 slot in the FRONT VIEW as datum feature C. Control this with a position tolerance of .0035 at maximum material condition relative to primary datum feature A and secondary datum feature B at maximum material condition.

d. Make the .5500, 1.0000, and 1.5000 dimensions basic.

e. Add a position tolerance for the .2449-.2480 hole. The hole must be positioned within a .0025 of an inch cylindrical tolerance zone at maximum material condition relative to primary datum feature A and secondary datum feature B at maximum material condition.

f. Add a position tolerance for the .1870-.1873 holes. The holes must be positioned within a .0001 of an inch cylindrical tolerance zone at maximum material condition relative to primary datum feature A, secondary datum feature B at maximum material condition, and tertiary datum feature C at maximum material condition.

g. In the FRONT VIEW on the horizontal surface of the slot, add a profile of a surface tolerance of .0020 relative to primary datum feature A, secondary datum feature B at maximum material condition, and tertiary datum feature C at maximum material condition.

h. In the FRONT VIEW on the largest diameter, add a profile of a surface tolerance of .0020 relative to primary datum feature A and secondary datum feature B at maximum material condition.

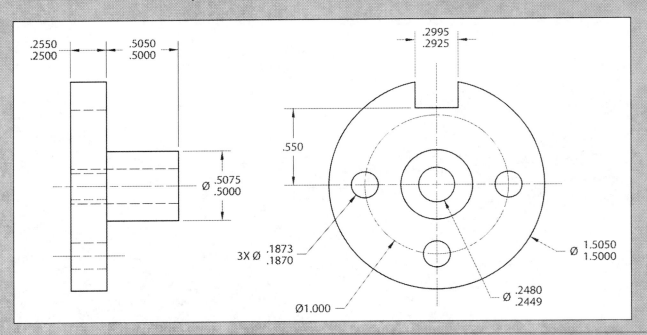

FIGURE P16.9.

Working Drawings

objectives

After completing this chapter, you should be able to

- Specify the contents, formatting, and organization of engineering drawings
- Correctly prepare and interpret formal, professional engineering drawings
- Discuss the primary differences between drawings used in manufacturing projects and those used in construction projects
- Effectively use scales to measure the length of lines on a drawing

18.01

introduction

In this chapter, you will learn about conventions and practices used in real-world engineering drawings. You will learn about two primary types of drawings—manufacturing and construction. **Manufacturing drawings** are used by engineers other than just mechanical engineers, and **construction drawings** are used by engineers other than just civil engineers; however, for the sake of simplicity in terminology, this chapter will sometimes refer to working drawings as "mechanical engineering drawings" or as "civil engineering drawings" since those two disciplines are concerned primarily with manufacturing and construction drawings, respectively. As a further simplification, the term *object* or *part* will refer to the mechanical parts that have been designed as well as a civil infrastructure project. Manufacturing drawings are used for products such as bicycles and toasters. Construction drawings are used for roads and bridges. Mechanical drawings depict products that are mass-produced; civil drawings represent unique projects that are known as **one-offs**. (A one-off is a system for which only one such system is constructed.) Although there are similarities between manufacturing and construction drawings, there are also significant differences. In the following sections, you will learn about manufacturing working drawings and construction working drawings. In particular, in the discussion of construction drawings, you will learn about the characteristics that set them apart from typical manufacturing drawings.

When parts and assemblies are ready for fabrication or when structures are ready for construction, the drawings must be presented in a format that is considered formal and professional. There are several reasons for this formality. First and foremost, the drawings must be able to stand on their own without any vagueness or ambiguity. They must be interpreted the same way when viewed by different people. In fact, for complex projects (in particular, for construction projects), many people will view the drawings. Also, the engineer responsible for the design may not be available to answer questions that arise during manufacturing or construction. Formal drawings need to be formatted in such a way that relevant information concerning the specifications, records, and identification of the part is easy to locate and is included with the drawing.

Next, an engineering drawing is considered a legal document and, as such, must contain a certain amount of information concerning the history of and responsibilities for the design. In the case of a set of construction drawings, the seal and signature of a registered **professional engineer (PE)** is typically a requirement. Finally, since engineering drawings are usually presented to third parties for cost estimation or fabrication, the presentation of the drawing is a reflection of the quality of the originator. Drawings that are presented well reflect favorably on the person or company that made the drawings.

When fabricated parts and assemblies are later used in the field or when infrastructure projects are constructed in the field, additional people may need to see the design drawings. These people sometimes include technicians and assemblers who install the parts in the final working environment; salespeople who ensure that the parts are compatible with other products produced by different companies; subcontractors who construct specific systems in the project, such as the wiring or plumbing; maintenance people who repair or replace the parts in the field; government inspectors who monitor the progress of a civil works project; and for certain types of systems, engineers or technicians who are responsible for the removal, recycling, or disposal of the parts at their end of life.

If you have decided that you would like someone else to make your parts or device for you, you must produce a set of formal documents known as **working drawings** to send to the fabricator. In civil engineering projects, contractors bid on projects based on the working drawings and specifications. Working drawings show each part or structure in all of the views necessary to fully define their features, their sizes and tolerances, and the way they are to be assembled into the completed product. Consequently, much of what you have learned in the previous chapters concerning orthogonal projection, pictorial views, dimensioning, and tolerancing is used extensively in working drawings. In the ideal case, once you have produced a set of working drawings and they are delivered to the fabricator or contractor, your systems should be able to be fabricated correctly without any further intervention from you. No one should need to call you with questions concerning any feature of the part or the way the part is to be made. In large construction projects, this is rarely the case and the engineer who designed the structure is often extensively involved in overseeing final construction of the project.

Once a drawing leaves your hands as the responsible engineer, it is likely to be reproduced many times and viewed many times by different people. You must have confidence that the information contained on the drawing will be interpreted correctly by every person who views it. In a complex manufacturing project, for example, the first person who will likely see the drawing is a buyer who must evaluate the operations required to fabricate the system and the degree of difficulty of fabrication. Thus, a fabricator with the capability to produce the part will be selected. For construction projects, the first people to see the drawings are usually the contractors who bid on the project. Contractors estimate project costs based on the drawings and specifications; the person with the lowest estimate, or bid, is typically awarded the project. The selected fabricator or contractor must then produce the part or **assembly** as specified on the drawings. Inspectors measure and test the part or materials to ensure that they meet the criteria defined in the drawings and specifications. The engineers and technicians who are responsible for installing the part in the final product must know the sizes of the part's features and their allowable variation so that any special tooling required for the installation can be built. The subcontractors who install various systems on a construction project must know how their portion fits in with the overall structure. This process of design and specification, fabrication, inspection, and installation is shown in Figure 18.01 for the prototype production of a computer disk drive spindle, a typical manufacturing project. Not shown is the special tooling required to ensure the proper alignment of the parts when they are assembled.

When you finish making a working drawing, you have created part of a legal document. Engineering drawings are, in fact, legally binding documents. Once an agreement between you and the fabricator or contractor has been reached for the manufacture or construction of a part or system, the engineering drawing becomes the focal point of the agreement. A working drawing is part of a contract in which a fabricator or contractor agrees to make the specified part in accordance with all of the requirements indicated on the drawing in exchange for an agreed amount of money, products, or services. For manufactured products, an additional agreement usually outlines what information, if any, can be shared with others besides the fabricator. If any information required to make the part is missing on the working drawing, the contract may not be able to be completed. In the worst-case scenario, if any information on the working drawing can be easily misinterpreted, an error in the part may result. In either case, as the originator of the drawing, the fault would lie with you and you may be required to compensate the fabricator or contractor for whatever time and effort was expended in the attempt to make the part.

Manufactured parts that meet all of the requirements specified on the drawing must be purchased for the agreed-upon volume, delivery schedule, and price.

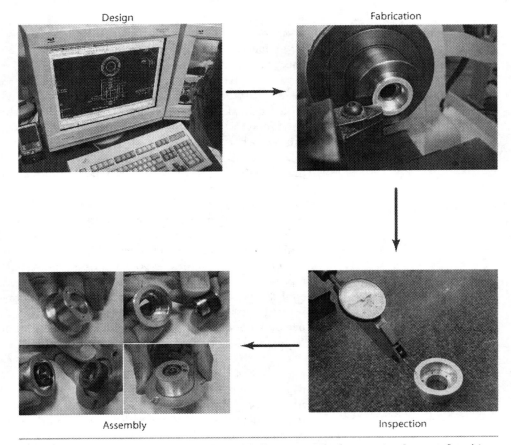

FIGURE 18.01. Some steps in the product development cycle that require the use of working drawings.

Contractors must be paid the agreed-upon amount when the structure is completed. On the other hand, for manufactured products, you can reject delivered parts that fail to meet any specification of the drawing. For construction projects, contractors must typically redo the portion of the structure that is not in keeping with the drawings and specifications—eating into their profit margin for the project. If there is an error on the drawing, the buyer must still purchase the manufactured parts if they have been made according to the drawing given to the fabricator. For construction engineering projects, the design firm may have to pay for cost overruns due to incorrect design information on the drawings. Information that is missing on a drawing (and then misinterpreted by the fabricator) is most often considered the fault of the designer. For example, if the numerical dimensions for a part to be manufactured are meant to be in centimeters, this information is missing on the drawing, and the numerical dimensions are interpreted as inches, the error is considered the buyer's fault. Still, these parts must be purchased. Since construction projects are one-off designs, missing dimensions or missing information is a relatively frequent occurrence. Contractors and engineers typically remain in close contact during the construction phase so that these issues can be easily resolved in the field.

Working drawings can usually be distinguished from less formal drawings by their formatting. Just as courts require all submitted legal documents to adhere to a required format and colleges and universities require graduate theses to have a uniform appearance, engineering working drawings also have a prescribed presentation form. Informal drawings, such as those shown in Figure 18.02, have no required formatting and can appear on any size paper; multiview presentations are not required, and dimensions

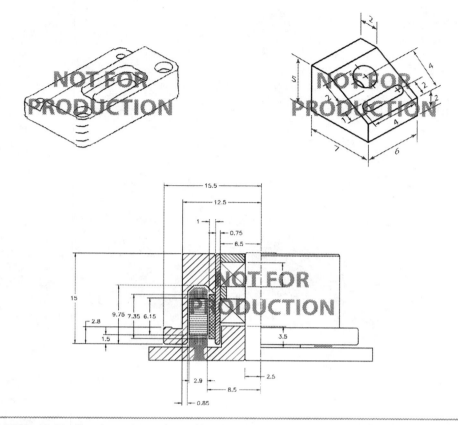

FIGURE 18.02. Sketches, pictorials, and layouts are helpful for visualization and initial sizing but are usually not considered complete, formal drawings.

frequently appear on pictorials. Informal drawings can be sketches, can be made with mechanical instruments or CAD, and can include many parts on a single page. Working drawings, on the other hand, are to be of specific sizes and include borders and headers containing specific information. Specific views and presentation techniques are expected. Most of all, working drawings must be complete in providing the information required to make the parts they describe. This is not to say, however, that only working drawings can be legal documents. In civil engineering practice, written specifications usually accompany the drawings and are considered part of the project's legal documentation.

Under certain conditions, informal drawings (even sketches) can be considered legal documents. If, for example, you or your buyer gives an informal drawing to a fabricator with instructions to make the part, even the informal drawing becomes part of the legal contract. The drawing just will not look very nice—or professional. Another example involves patent disputes. The courts may consider the notes and sketches you make in your engineering notebook to be legal documents for establishing the date of conception of an idea. For this purpose, you should have a witness sign and date any notes, sketches, or drawings that you produce that may lead to a patent.

In the engineering and business worlds, appearances are important. The progression from informal drawings to formal drawings, as shown in Figure 18.03, is in many ways a transition in appearance and presentation. Many people consider a formal engineering drawing to be not only a means of information transfer but also a work of art. The presentation of this document can reflect well or poorly on its originator. For that reason, the formal drawings you submit should be well organized, neat, and polished—a part of engineering professionalism.

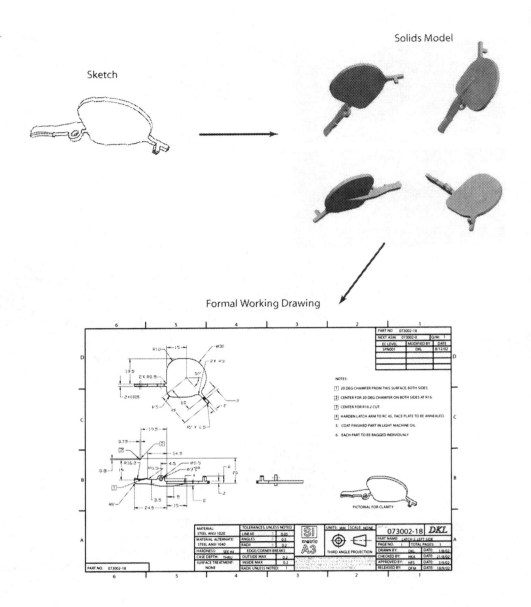

FIGURE 18.03. The typical progression of the design of a part from a conceptual hand sketch to a computer 3-D model to a formal working drawing extracted from the model.

18.03 Sheet Sizes

The first step in making a formal working drawing is to choose an appropriate sheet size. This statement might sound strange today, when computers can generate a drawing of almost any size with the part views shown in any scale. However, most working drawings need to be printed for easy viewing, perhaps by a machinist trying to make the parts in a shop, a contractor examining the drawing in the preparation of a bid, or a group of engineers sitting around a conference table reviewing the design. When a working drawing is printed to its intended size, it must be readable.

Most of the world, with the exception of the United States, uses **international sheet sizes**. The most common international sizes are A4, A3, A2, A1, and A0. Size A4 is 297 mm × 210 mm. (For anyone not well-versed in metric sizes, this is approximately the size of the paper used in a computer printer.) If the horizontal dimension size is larger than the vertical size, the paper orientation is known as **landscape**; otherwise, the orientation is called **portrait**. Landscape paper orientation is used almost exclusively in engineering working drawings. The next largest paper size, A3, is generated by

FIGURE 18.04. Some relative standard sheet sizes, international and US, used for formal drawings.

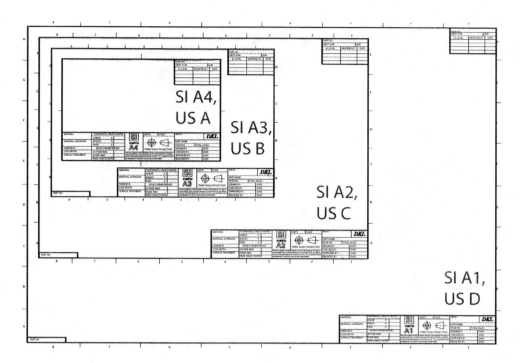

SI A4, US A

SI A3, US B

SI A2, US C

SI A1, US D

attaching two A4 "sheets" along their lengths, producing a sheet that is twice the area of an A4 sheet, or 420 mm × 297 mm. The A2 sheet (594 mm × 420 mm) is similarly produced by putting together two A3 sheets. The A1 (840 mm × 594 mm) and A0 (1188 mm × 840 mm) sizes are generated similarly. The A0 size is generally accepted as the largest size that will fit, without rolling or folding, inside available cabinets made for drawing storage.

US sheet sizes, which are designated A, B, C, D, and E, are close to the international sheet sizes. Size A paper is 11" × 8.5" and is commonly called letter size. As with the international paper sizes, each increasing US sheet size is generated by attaching its two smaller sizes along their lengths. Thus, a B size sheet is 17" × 11", a C size sheet is 22" × 17", etc. An E size sheet, which is 44" × 34", is the largest drawing size that will fit easily inside a common filing cabinet for drawings. Civil engineering drawings are usually drawn on E size paper unless a bound book of B size drawings is created for a project. The common International and US sheet sizes are shown in Figure 18.04.

Some caution is necessary when you are printing a drawing less than its full size, which provides convenience in printing, copying, and handling. In large construction projects, printing a drawing to less than full size is a necessity. The font size used for the dimensions and notes on a working drawing is usually 3 mm to 6 mm in height and is independent of the size of the drawing; that is, the font size on an A4 drawing is the same as that on an A0 drawing. If you want to see the notes and dimensions printed to their full size, the drawing needs to be printed to its full size. If, for example, an A1 or A0 size drawing is reduced to an A4 size, the notes and dimensions may be reduced to the point where they are no longer legible. This effect is demonstrated in Figure 18.05 as larger drawings are reduced to a smaller sheet size. Fortunately, a larger printer, such as the one shown in Figure 18.06, is fairly easy to find, and drawings can be easily printed to a size that is legible and convenient for handling.

The previous discussion covered working drawings in a generic way. The similarities and some differences between manufacturing and construction drawings were discussed. In the following sections, the discussion of manufacturing and construction drawings will diverge. You will first learn about manufacturing drawings and then about construction drawings.

FIGURE 18.05. Geometry and letter font size reduction when larger drawings are printed to smaller sheets.

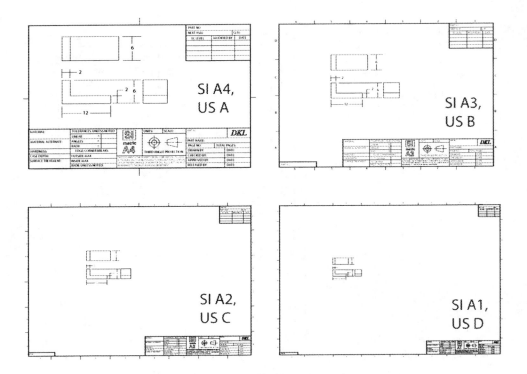

FIGURE 18.06. An ink-jet printer capable of creating a full size International A0 or US size E drawing.

18.04 The Formal Drawing Header in Manufacturing Drawings

In addition to the information about the geometries of the parts or assemblies, working drawings need to contain other information. There must be information, for example, on how each part can be uniquely identified; otherwise, it may be difficult to locate specific parts and drawings among the vast numbers of parts being manufactured or assembled at any given time. Also, there must be some information about the history of a part or an assembly; otherwise, it may be difficult to distinguish modified new parts from original old parts as the design progresses. If the design for a part does change with time, there must be a way of recording those changes so that everyone working with the part knows what it looks like, how it fits into other parts, and how it performs in the completed device. Is it a new style part or an old style part? If it is an old style part, how old is it? How many changes has it undergone? Can the old style be used instead of the new style?

There also must be a sense of accountability for the design of a part. Who made the drawing? Which engineer was responsible for the part's proper function? Who approved the release of the drawing outside the company? When were those things done? Is the information contained on a drawing considered confidential to the originator? Most of those questions can be answered by examining the drawing header, which is described next.

A **header** is a printed frame or outline on which a drawing is created. Drawing headers are usually unique to the company that produces the drawing, but they follow a similar format and contain the same type of information. A typical header for a manufacturing drawing is shown in Figure 18.07. A heavy line **border** defines the limit of the formal drawing area. Any added markings that are to be a part of the drawing must be inside this border. On some headers, evenly spaced **location grid** marks appear in the horizontal and vertical directions outside the border. The location grid on a drawing, similar to the location grid on a street map, helps readers of the drawing locate areas on the sheet where specific features can be found. For large drawings with many features, the location grid is particularly useful. If, for example, you were told to look for a specific feature at location C5 on the drawing, you would immediately begin looking at the double highlighted area shown in Figure 18.07. A major part of the header is the **main title block**. The main title block contains most of the information required to identify the part on the drawing as well as to track its progress in the design cycle. The main title block provides space for specifying the material and the material processing required to fabricate the part. Some companies provide a **secondary title block** for additional information a company would like to see included on its manufacturing drawings.

The main title block contains information on how to interpret what is seen on the drawing, as highlighted in the magnified portion shown in Figure 18.08. The definition of the units for the dimensions is specified there. Usually the units are specified as MM (millimeters), CM (centimeters), M (meters), IN (inches), or FT (feet). In addition, words and/or graphics specify whether the orthogonal views on the drawing are produced using first-angle projection, which is popular internationally, or using third-angle projection, which is used in the United States. The scale of the drawing is defined as "the ratio of the size of the actual part to the size of the image of the part shown on the drawing when the drawing is printed to its full sheet size."

FIGURE 18.07. A typical header for a formal engineering drawing.

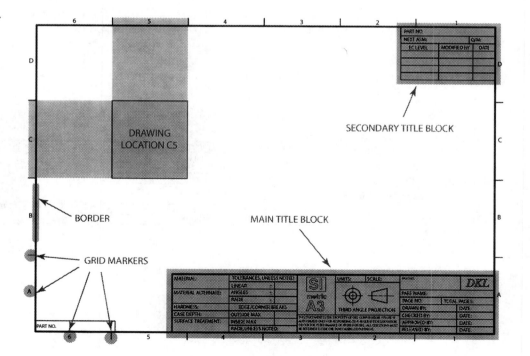

MATERIAL:	TOLERANCES, UNLESS NOTED		SI	UNITS:	SCALE:	PART NO.		DKL
	LINEAR	±	metric					
MATERIAL ALTERNATE:	ANGLES	±	A3			PART NAME:		
	RADII	±				PAGE NO.	TOTAL PAGES:	
HARDNESS:	EDGE/CORNER BREAKS			THIRD ANGLE PROJECTION		DRAWN BY:		DATE:
CASE DEPTH:	OUTSIDE MAX		THIS DOCUMENT IS THE PROPERTY OF DKL CORPORATION. ITS USE IS AUTHORIZED ONLY FOR RESPONDING TO A REQUEST FOR QUOTATION OR FOR THE PERFORMANCE OF WORK FOR DKL. ALL QUESTIONS MUST BE REFERRED TO THE DKL PURCHASING DEPARTMENT.			CHECKED BY:		DATE:
SURFACE TREATMENT:	INSIDE MAX					APPROVED BY:		DATE:
	RADII, UNLESS NOTED:					RELEASED BY:		DATE:

The main title block also contains information about who owns the drawing and the information it contains, as indicated in Figure 18.09. A manufacturing drawing and any of its copies are usually considered the property of the company for which the part is made. Usually the name, initial, or logo of the company (in this case, DKL Corporation) is displayed and some sort of message expresses how the information contained in the drawing can be used and distributed. If this information is considered confidential, or proprietary, it is clearly marked as such. The purpose of these statements is to ensure that the information contained in the drawings is not freely distributed, especially to the company's competitors.

The main means of identification of a part is through its **part number**, as highlighted in Figure 18.10. Every individual part that is fabricated according to the same drawing (or a copy of it) carries the same part number. Ideally, all parts with the same part number should be interchangeable. When it is important to identify each part fabricated from the same drawing, those parts can be assigned unique serial numbers. Since assemblies and subassemblies are often handled and transported as complete units, they also are assigned part numbers. Every company has its own method of assigning part numbers. Some are alphanumeric strings, some include information on the date the number was assigned, and some include coded information on the project type or the location of the engineering facility. Whether an individual part, a subassembly, or a full assembly is defined, part numbers must be unique within a company. A firm usually has an internal accounting system for assigning and tracking part numbers to ensure that no two unique parts are given the same number. In addition to the part number, a part, subassembly, or full assembly is usually given a **part name**. A part name is given for convenience and is usually based on a part's function or appearance, such as L-bracket, or Base Plate, or Pillow Block A. Part names do not have to be unique since they are meant to provide temporary convenience for identifying parts while they are in fabrication or use. A company could have several L-brackets defined for use in various assemblies; however, each unique L-bracket is defined by a unique number.

If a part is modified during its life, the drawing is given an **EC Level** number. EC is an acronym for Engineering Change; it also may be called Revision Level or something similar depending on the terminology a company uses. The existence of an EC Level

MATERIAL:	TOLERANCES, UNLESS NOTED		SI	UNITS:	SCALE:	PART NO.		DKL
	LINEAR	±	metric					
MATERIAL ALTERNATE:	ANGLES	±	A3			PART NAME:		
	RADII	±				PAGE NO.	TOTAL PAGES:	
HARDNESS:	EDGE/CORNER BREAKS			THIRD ANGLE PROJECTION		DRAWN BY:		DATE:
CASE DEPTH:	OUTSIDE MAX		THIS DOCUMENT IS THE PROPERTY OF DKL CORPORATION. ITS USE IS AUTHORIZED ONLY FOR RESPONDING TO A REQUEST FOR QUOTATION OR FOR THE PERFORMANCE OF WORK FOR DKL. ALL QUESTIONS MUST BE REFERRED TO THE DKL PURCHASING DEPARTMENT.			CHECKED BY:		DATE:
SURFACE TREATMENT:	INSIDE MAX					APPROVED BY:		DATE:
	RADII, UNLESS NOTED:					RELEASED BY:		DATE:

FIGURE 18.10. The part name,
part number, and revision (or
EC) number uniquely distinguishes this part from different
parts or earlier versions of the
same part.

FIGURE 18.10. The part name,
part number, and revision (or
EC) number uniquely distinguishes this part from different
parts or earlier versions of the
same part.

PART NO.		
NEXT ASM:		Q/M:
EC LEVEL	MODIFIED BY	DATE

MATERIAL:	TOLERANCES, UNLESS NOTED			SI metric A3	UNITS:	SCALE:	PART NO.		DKL
	LINEAR	±							
MATERIAL ALTERNATE:	ANGLES	±					PART NAME:		
	RADII	±			THIRD ANGLE PROJECTION		PAGE NO.	TOTAL PAGES:	
HARDNESS:	EDGE/CORNER BREAKS						DRAWN BY:		DATE:
CASE DEPTH:	OUTSIDE MAX			THIS DOCUMENT IS THE PROPERTY OF DKL CORPORATION. ITS USE IS			CHECKED BY:		DATE:
SURFACE TREATMENT:	INSIDE MAX			AUTHORIZED ONLY FOR RESPONDING TO A REQUEST FOR QUOTATION OR FOR THE PERFORMANCE OF WORK FOR DKL. ALL QUESTIONS MUST			APPROVED BY:		DATE:
	RADII, UNLESS NOTED:			BE REFERRED TO THE DKL PURCHASING DEPARTMENT.			RELEASED BY:		DATE:

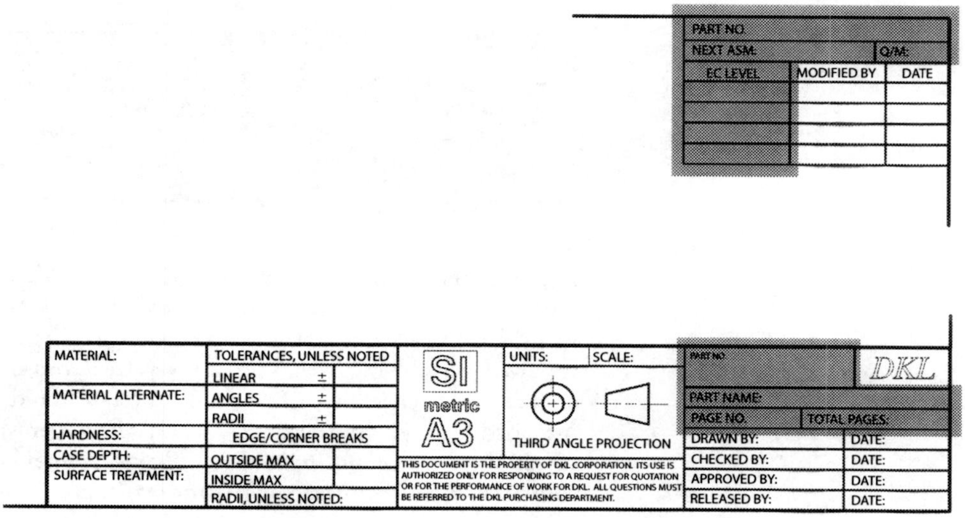

number is an indication that the original design has been updated in some way (e.g.,
changes in the material or in one or more dimensions or tolerances). In Figure 18.10,
the EC Level appears on the secondary title block. Different parts and assemblies can
have the same EC Level number if they are from the same product and were updated at
the same time. As with part numbers, EC Level numbers can be an alphanumeric string
and cannot be reused on the same part or assembly after they have been assigned. If the
design of a part has changed significantly to the point where it is no longer interchangeable with the older versions of the part, that part should be assigned a new part
number rather than a new EC Level number.

Drawings with large numbers of detail views and notes may require more than one
sheet. In this case, each sheet must have a page number and specify the total pages in
the entire drawing. Some companies require that each part specifies its next assembly,
which is the part number of the assembly or subassembly into which the part is to be
immediately installed. If the next assembly requires more than one of a particular part,
that quantity is specified as the **quantity per machine (Q/M)**.

A chain of responsibility is required for all manufacturing drawings. The people
responsible for the creation of a drawing must be identifiable should any questions arise
about the drawing's contents. Every formal drawing has areas for **approval signatures**
in the main title block, as shown in Figure 18.11, where the appropriate people can initial

FIGURE 18.11. Signatures and
dates help establish the history
of development and leave a trail
of accountability.

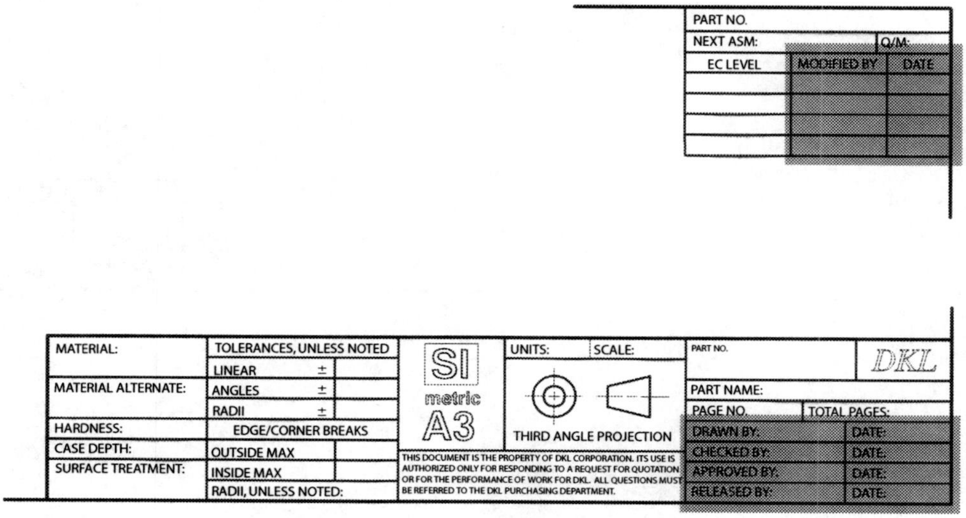

PART NO.		
NEXT ASM:		Q/M:
EC LEVEL	MODIFIED BY	DATE

MATERIAL:	TOLERANCES, UNLESS NOTED			SI metric A3	UNITS:	SCALE:	PART NO.		DKL
	LINEAR	±							
MATERIAL ALTERNATE:	ANGLES	±					PART NAME:		
	RADII	±			THIRD ANGLE PROJECTION		PAGE NO.	TOTAL PAGES:	
HARDNESS:	EDGE/CORNER BREAKS						DRAWN BY:		DATE:
CASE DEPTH:	OUTSIDE MAX			THIS DOCUMENT IS THE PROPERTY OF DKL CORPORATION. ITS USE IS			CHECKED BY:		DATE:
SURFACE TREATMENT:	INSIDE MAX			AUTHORIZED ONLY FOR RESPONDING TO A REQUEST FOR QUOTATION OR FOR THE PERFORMANCE OF WORK FOR DKL. ALL QUESTIONS MUST			APPROVED BY:		DATE:
	RADII, UNLESS NOTED:			BE REFERRED TO THE DKL PURCHASING DEPARTMENT.			RELEASED BY:		DATE:

MATERIAL:	TOLERANCES, UNLESS NOTED						UNITS:	SCALE:	PART NO.		*DKL*
	LINEAR	±									
MATERIAL ALTERNATE:	ANGLES	±							PART NAME:		
	RADII	±							PAGE NO.	TOTAL PAGES:	
HARDNESS:	EDGE/CORNER BREAKS					THIRD ANGLE PROJECTION			DRAWN BY:	DATE:	
CASE DEPTH:	OUTSIDE MAX								CHECKED BY:	DATE:	
SURFACE TREATMENT:	INSIDE MAX								APPROVED BY:	DATE:	
	RADII, UNLESS NOTED:								RELEASED BY:	DATE:	

and date the drawing. (However, with most CAD drawings, the initials are no longer handwritten; rather, they are inserted as a drawing note.) The required signatures usually include those of the drafter who made the drawing (drawn by . . .), the person who reviewed the drawing to make sure it was free from errors (checked by . . .), the designer or engineer who checked to make sure the fabricated part would fit and function in its intended manner (approved by . . .), and a manager who checked that the formal drawing would meet all accounting and security requirements when delivered to a fabricator outside the company (released by . . .). In smaller companies, it is common to see two or more of these functions performed by the same person.

The main title block usually includes spaces where additional information required for the fabrication of the part is contained, as shown in Figure 18.12. The reason for these spaces is to prompt the entry of additional information; usually the information required for the fabrication of the parts is included on the drawing. Typical additional information might include the material from which the part is made and any special heat treatment or surface treatments that are required. Other important information includes the **default tolerances**, which are the dimensional tolerances that may be assumed when no tolerance appears with the dimension. Using default tolerance in this manner saves effort in assigning a tolerance to every dimension when the tolerances are the same and generally gives the drawing a neater appearance. Default tolerances can be specified to be different according to the number of decimal places shown on the dimension. Dimensions that have one, two, or three decimal places can be assigned different default tolerances, usually with stricter tolerances used as the number of decimal places increases.

If the drawing extends to multiple pages, the header blocks on the subsequent pages can be simplified, as shown in Figure 18.13. These simplified blocks are called **continuation blocks** and usually contain information that identifies the sheets as being part of a larger drawing. This information includes the part number, EC number, and sheet number of the drawing. The size of the sheet is also included in case the sheets of the drawing are of different sizes.

If the company has no preferred standard title blocks for its drawings, ANSI has recommended the use of some generic title blocks, which are shown in Figure 18.14.

SI metric A3		UNITS:	SCALE:	PART NO.		*DKL*
				PART NAME:		
	THIRD ANGLE PROJECTION			PAGE NO.	TOTAL PAGES:	
				EC NUMBER:		

FIGURE 18.14. An ANSI standard title block and continuation sheet block for US sheet sizes A, B, and C (above) and for sizes D and larger (below). Dimensions shown are in inches.

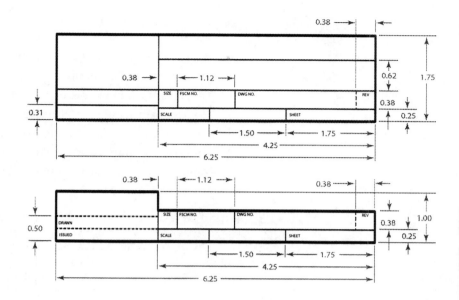

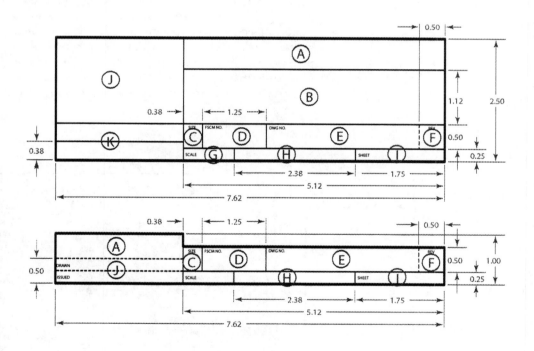

The information contained in the generic ANSI title blocks is representative of that expected to be contained in most formal drawing title blocks. This information is entered in the proper areas of the ANSI title block as indicated in Figure 18.14 and as listed here:

A. A statement of origin or ownership of the drawing

B. The title of the part or drawing

C. The size of the sheet when the drawing is printed to its full size

D. The Federal Supply Code for Manufacturers (FSCM) number if the work is being done for the federal government

E. The drawing number or part number

F. The revision, or EC, number

G. The ratio of the item size shown on the drawing versus that of the actual item

H. The approximate weight of the item if it is heavy

I. The page number (for drawings with multiple pages)

J. Names of the drafter and checker, with dates

K. Names of any additional people needed to approve the drawing, with dates

18.05 The Drawing Area for Manufactured Parts

The drawing area is defined as the area inside the border of the drawing. It is informally subdivided in an area reserved for showing geometry and an area for the **notes**, as shown in Figure 18.15. Notes are usually listed in one corner of the drawing, and the rest of the drawing area is dedicated to showing the views of the part.

18.05.01 Geometry Presentation

The size of the sheet and the scale of the object should be selected so that the area reserved for showing the object's geometry is uncluttered, even after the dimensions are added. These choices are rather subjective, and looking at how other (good) formal drawings have been prepared gives you some clues about how to make these choices. Simple objects with few geometric features and dimensions generally require smaller sheets. Complicated objects with many features and dimensions require larger sheets or perhaps multiple sheets. Some consideration, however, should be given toward handling convenience. Smaller sheets are easier to store and carry, whereas larger sheets are more difficult to store but are better for showing to a group of people.

FIGURE 18.15. For clarity, text notes are kept in a separate area on a formal drawing so a reader can look in a single location to find all of them.

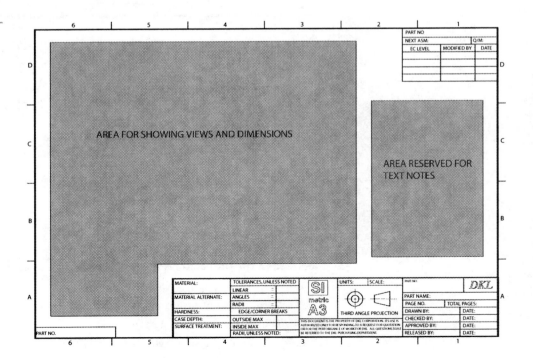

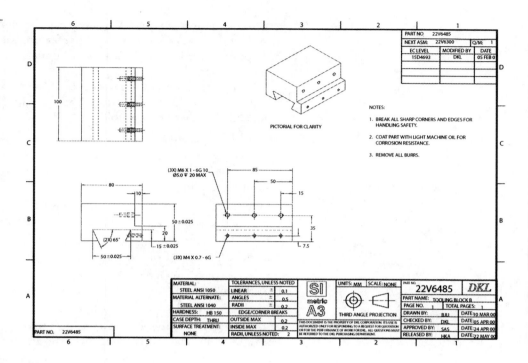

FIGURE 18.16. A formal drawing of a tooling block presented in the preferred multiview configuration showing all hidden lines. All of its features can be shown using the top, front, and right-side views.

18.05.02 Object Views

Whether the object is a part or an assembly, its geometry must be presented using the rule of orthogonal projection and multiview representation. Further, unless there is a good reason not to do so, the views to be shown are those of the preferred configuration (i.e., the front, top, and right-side views, as shown in Figure 18.16). Cases where more or fewer than three orthographic views should be used are shown in the chapter on orthogonal projection and multiview drawings. A more complex part requiring more views is shown in Figure 18.17. For this part, a left-side view has been added to

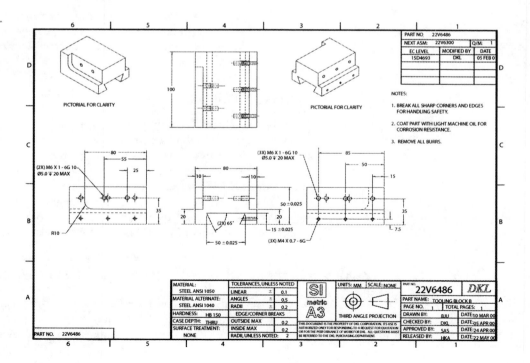

FIGURE 18.17. This modified tooling block requires an additional left-side view in order to show the features on that side.

show a cutout and threaded holes on that side of the object. Using the preferred configuration and hidden lines alone to show those features would have required that dimensions be applied to the hidden lines, which produces views that are more complex and difficult to interpret.

The orientation of the object must be such that these three views show as many visible edges in their true length as possible. The guidelines for adding additional drawing details and additional views are as follows:

1. Start by showing the object in the preferred configuration (i.e., the top, front, and right-side views). Orient the object such that as many edges as possible are shown in their true length in these views. If a view adds no additional information to the presentation, it may be removed.

2. Add more of the standard orthogonal views (e.g., left-side, bottom, and/or back view) as necessary so that dimensioning can be applied to visible edges or features only.

3. Add all hidden lines from the exterior edges and interior detail that are not visible.

4. If there are too many hidden lines and the views are confusing, remove the hidden lines that are not necessary for fully defining the geometry or features of the object.

5. If there are still too many hidden lines and the views are still confusing, add more of the standard orthogonal views as necessary to reduce the number of hidden lines and to maintain full definition of the object's geometry.

6. Use shorthand notation to define screw threads and the size and depth of counterbored and countersunk holes and slots. Otherwise, add section views to clarify the interior details.

7. If the hidden lines from different interior details cross or overlap, add section views to clarify the interior details.

8. If any edges cannot be seen in their true lengths in the standard orthogonal views, add auxiliary views so these true lengths can be seen.

9. If features cannot be seen clearly and cannot be defined because they are small, add detail views with a magnified scale.

10. Add the appropriate dimensions and tolerance specifications for the object. If the drawing starts to look crowded, transfer everything to a larger-sized sheet.

For people with a great deal of drawing experience, most of those steps can be done mentally. Then the general rule for presenting the object becomes simply, "Start with the preferred configuration; then add or subtract whatever views are necessary to best show all of the geometry."

18.05.03 Notes

The notes on a formal drawing refer to special processing, handling, or assembly procedures that are required on a part or an assembly that cannot be specified by the dimensions and tolerances on the part or by the materials specifications in the title block. The notes are usually numbered according to each specific requirement and listed together in the same area of the drawing. Notes on a drawing might include "This surface to be free of plating" or "Part to be cleaned and degreased when completed" or "All internal edges to be free of burrs." Generally speaking, a note is added whenever you want something done to a part and you do not know how else to specify it.

18.06 Parts, Subassemblies, and Assemblies

An engineered device is composed of one or more pieces, and one of the purposes of manufacturing drawings is to document how those pieces should be made and how the pieces should be put together to make the device. A set of drawings must contain

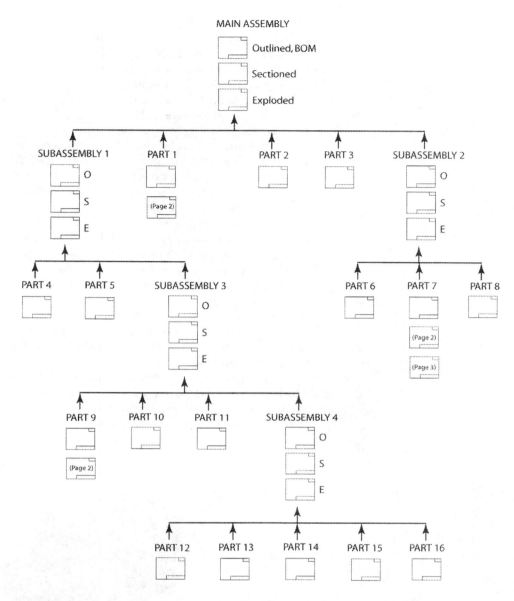

FIGURE 18.18. A set of drawings for a project is organized like the roots of a tree. Individual parts fit into subassemblies or the main assembly. Subassemblies fit into higher subassemblies or the main assembly.

enough information so that any manufacturer with the proper fabrication tools and skills can make all of the pieces and put them together properly. This fabrication must be possible from the information available on the drawings, without consultation with the engineers, designers, or drafters who made the drawings. A set of manufacturing drawings is structured like the roots of a tree, as shown in Figure 18.18.

At the very top of the root structure is the **main assembly** for the device. Assembly drawings are required to show how to put the main assembly together and how all of the pieces look and fit when this is done. The main assembly is composed of smaller individual parts that can be made especially for the device or purchased as commercially available parts. Examples of common commercial parts include screws, bolts, washers, nuts, and rivets.

Assembly drawings contain information that identifies the parts or subassemblies in the assembly. This is done with **balloons** and arrows pointing to each part. Balloons are closed geometric shapes, not necessarily circular, that contain a number. Depending on individual company practices, the number inside the balloon can be the part number or an **item number** that is referenced to the part number and listed with the drawing's notes. Some companies like to include the quantity of each part inside the balloon along with the item or part number.

The main assembly also can be composed of smaller **subassemblies**, which are collections of custom-made and/or commercially available parts that have already been put together and installed in the main assembly as a single piece. A large project may have several levels of subassemblies in the main assembly. Each subassembly needs its own layout drawing and assembly drawing for the various sub-subassemblies, or parts, that go into it. Finally, each custom-made part requires a **detail drawing** that shows the geometry, dimensions, tolerances, materials, and all other information needed to fabricate the part.

At this time, a more precise definition of a part is needed. The most common interpretation of a **part** is that it is a single object made from a single, contiguous material. Most metal, plastic, or wooden objects, for example, fall under this definition. Up until the twentieth century, this definition was correct. Since that time, products have become increasingly complex in their construction and use of different materials. Is an electric motor a single part; or is it a collection of parts, otherwise known as an assembly? What about the headlight module on a car? Imagine an electric circuit board with various electronic components installed on it. If you were the user of the board, you would probably consider it to be a single part. However, if you were its manufacturer, you would probably consider it to be an assembly. Therefore, the definition of a part depends on how you expect to receive it from the manufacturer making it for you. You can generally refer to an object as a single part, even though it may be composed of many different pieces and be made of many different materials, when you expect the fabricator to deliver it to you as a single unit with only its external dimensions and functional requirements specified.

Consider the drawings that would be necessary for the product shown in Figure 18.19, which shows a vise clamp used for holding work pieces during machining operations. All of the drawings necessary to fabricate this device will be discussed, with more detail on the type and method of presentation of information for each type of drawing.

FIGURE 18.19. A 3-D computer-generated model of a machine vise.

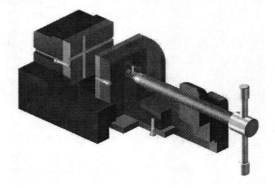

FIGURE 18.20. An exploded assembly drawing including a bill of materials for a machine vise.

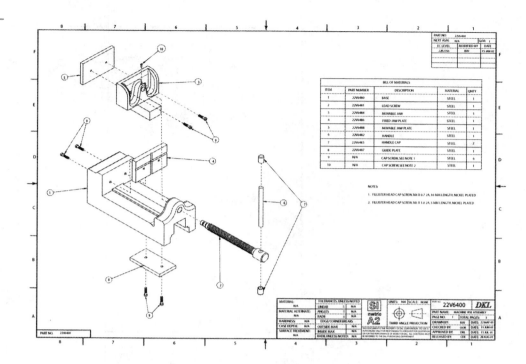

The bill of materials table within the figure:

ITEM	PART NUMBER	DESCRIPTION	MATERIAL	QNTY
1	22V6480	BASE	STEEL	1
2	22V6481	LEAD SCREW	STEEL	1
3	22V6484	MOVABLE JAW	STEEL	1
4	22V6486	FIXED JAW PLATE	STEEL	1
5	22V6488	MOVABLE JAW PLATE	STEEL	1
6	22V6482	HANDLE	STEEL	1
7	22V6483	HANDLE CAP	STEEL	2
8	22V6487	GUIDE PLATE	STEEL	1
9	N/A	CAP SCREW, SEE NOTE 1	STEEL	6
10	N/A	CAP SCREW, SEE NOTE 2	STEEL	1

NOTES:

1. FILLISTER HEAD CAP SCREW, M4 X 0.7 2A, 10 MM LENGTH, NICKEL PLATED
2. FILLISTER HEAD CAP SCREW, M6 X 1.0 2A, 5 MM LENGTH, NICKEL PLATED

18.06.01 Exploded Assembly Drawings

Exploded assembly drawings show how various parts and pieces that compose an assembly or subassembly are put together. Rather than showing everything in their final position, as with a layout drawing, an assembly drawing shows the parts of a device in a disassembled state. The assembly drawing for the vise clamp is shown in Figure 18.20. The various parts are shown in their final resting orientation, but not necessarily in their final location. Instead, the parts are located such that they are removed from their final location in the opposite direction of manufacturing insertion. The path of insertion for each part is then shown using a dashed path called a **trail**. Therefore, the trail of each part shows the fabricator how that part is to be placed in the device to create the final configuration.

Since assembly drawings are used to show a process rather than precise geometry, using a pictorial presentation is preferred to using a multiview presentation. Neither part nor assembly dimensions are shown, except for occasional reference dimensions for convenience only. As with a layout drawing, assembly drawings use numbered balloons and arrows pointing to each piece to identify their parts or subassemblies. The item number in each balloon must correspond to the same item number in the layout drawing and is then listed with its corresponding part number and part name in the assembly drawing's notes.

18.06.02 Outline Assembly Drawings

Outline assembly drawings, sometimes called **layout drawings**, are used to show the fit and function of all of the various pieces that go into a completed assembly or subassembly. The main outline assembly drawing for the vise clamp is shown in Figure 18.21. An outline assembly drawing shows the final product in its final configuration using the multiview format required for all working drawings. Sometimes isometric or other pictorial views are included for additional clarity. Section views are added to reveal parts that cannot be seen externally, and magnified detail views are used to show parts that are too small to recognize. Note that the dimensions for the individual parts are not shown in

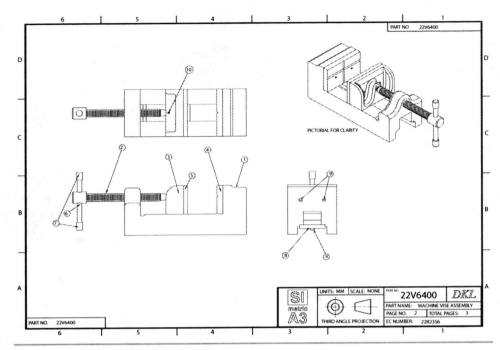

FIGURE 18.21. An outline assembly drawing of the machine vise.

any assembly drawing. That information is contained in the detail drawings. Information pertaining to tolerances and materials on the drawing header are left blank since that information is contained in the detail drawing for the individual part and does not need to be repeated for the assembled device.

If any **assembly dimensions** are required, they must be shown with their tolerances on the layout drawing. Assembly dimensions show where parts must be placed relative to other parts when the device is being put together (e.g., when a special alignment between parts is required and no features on the individual parts provide for this alignment). An example of when assembly dimensions are required is when a smaller block is to be welded or bonded to a larger plate. Unless there are features on the plate for locating the block, assembly dimensions must be supplied. If the parts are to be welded together, specification for the welds must be placed on the layout drawing.

Reference dimensions, if used at all, should be used sparingly and must be clearly identified and placed inside parentheses. These dimensions already exist on or can be extracted from other drawings. They are shown mostly for the convenience of the reader and are usually used to show gross sizes, such as the overall width, height, and length of a device. The reason reference dimensions are used sparingly is because errors sometimes occur when the dimension on a part changes and the change is forgotten on the reference dimension.

The notes on a layout drawing are used to specify any special procedures or processes needed to put the device together and any tests that are necessary to ensure that the device will work in its intended manner. The notes also list the definitions of the item numbers referenced in the multiview presentation.

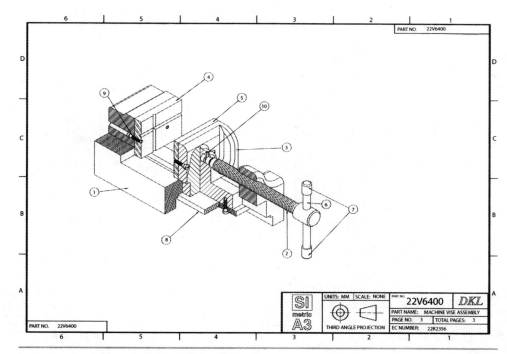

FIGURE 18.22. A sectioned assembly drawing of the machine vise.

18.06.03 Sectioned Assembly Drawings

A **sectioned assembly drawing** is a pictorial or orthogonal view(s) that shows all of the various pieces of an assembly or a subassembly in their final resting position. For purposes of revealing otherwise hidden parts, some parts have been cut away. The cut surfaces are indicated by the use of section lines. A section line pattern is usually used for each part to aid in its distinction. The various pieces within the assembly are identified using numbered balloons with the same item numbers used in the other assembly drawings. A sectioned assembly drawing for the vise clamp is shown in Figure 18.22. Although sectioned assembly drawings are difficult to create, especially without the use of 3-D modeling, such drawings offer unparalleled clarity for showing how various parts fit together to make a complete device. Whenever possible, a sectioned assembly drawing should be included in a drawing set.

18.06.04 The Bill of Materials

The **bill of materials (BOM)** for a device is not an actual drawing, but rather a text list of its parts, subassemblies, and subassembly parts. The BOM, which can appear on any one of the assembly drawings or as a separate drawing or document, is used mainly by a fabricator to check that all of the drawings and materials needed to make the device are available. Commercial parts are also included on this list. Although not a drawing, a BOM is usually printed as a table on an assembly drawing to emphasize that this list is considered a member of the set of drawings for the device. The BOM is often included as part of the layout or assembly drawing.

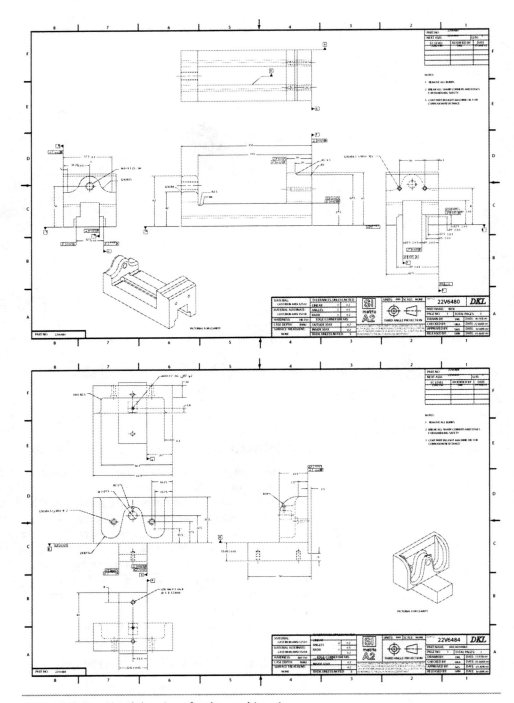

FIGURE 18.23. Detail drawings for the machine vise.

The typical information included on a BOM of an assembly includes the item number (if the bill is included as part of the layout or assembly drawing), the corresponding part number, its part name, the material from which the part is made, and the number of times the part is used in the assembly. Subassemblies have their own BOMs. When the main assembly contains subassemblies, the part numbers and names for those subassemblies are listed on the main BOM. The various parts and sub-subassemblies are listed on the BOM for each respective subassembly. If commercial parts are used, their

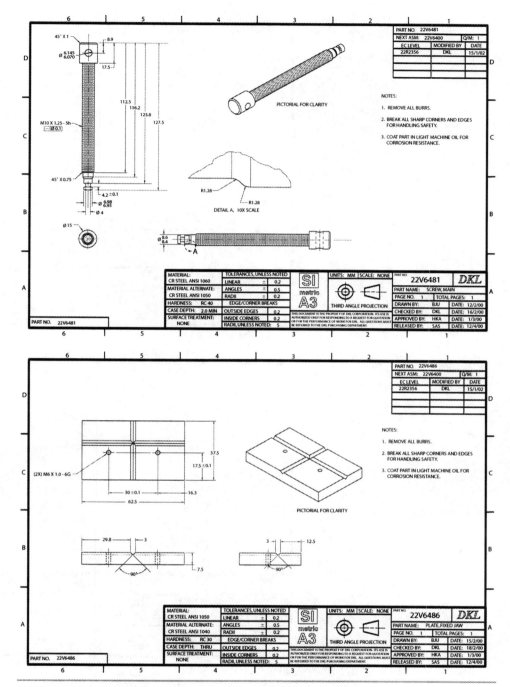

FIGURE 18.23. (CONTINUED) Detail drawings for the machine vise.

descriptions must be included on the BOM. These descriptions must contain enough information for the parts to be acquired without subsequent explanation.

18.06.05 Manufacturing Detail Drawings

A detail drawing shows all of the geometry, dimensions, tolerances, material, and processes needed to fabricate a single part. Each custom-made part must have its own detail drawing. Some companies even require that commercially available parts have

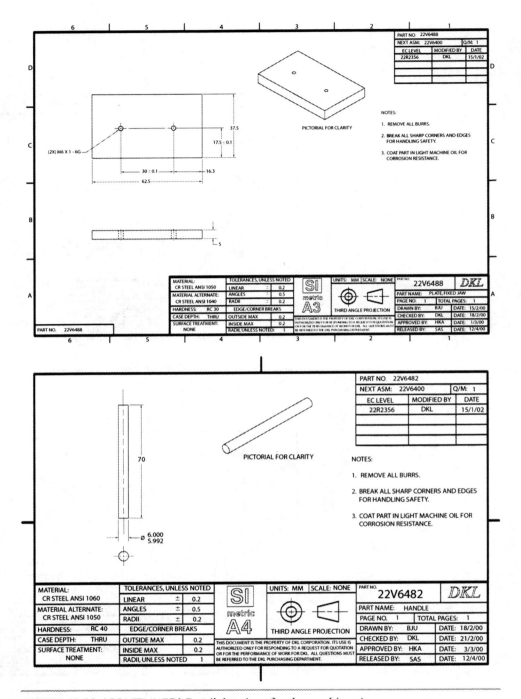

FIGURE 18.23. (CONTINUED) Detail drawings for the machine vise.

their own detail drawings placed on that company's header to ensure that these parts will fit and function properly with the custom-made parts. The detail drawings for the parts of the vise clamp are shown in Figure 18.23. The drawings shown in Figure 18.16 and Figure 18.17 are also classified as detail drawings.

The detail drawing for each part shows it using the multiview format required for all manufacturing drawings. Sometimes isometric or other pictorial views are included for additional clarity. Section views are added as necessary to reveal interior features. Magnified detail views are added as necessary to show features that would otherwise be too small to dimension. All of the dimensions for each part must be shown.

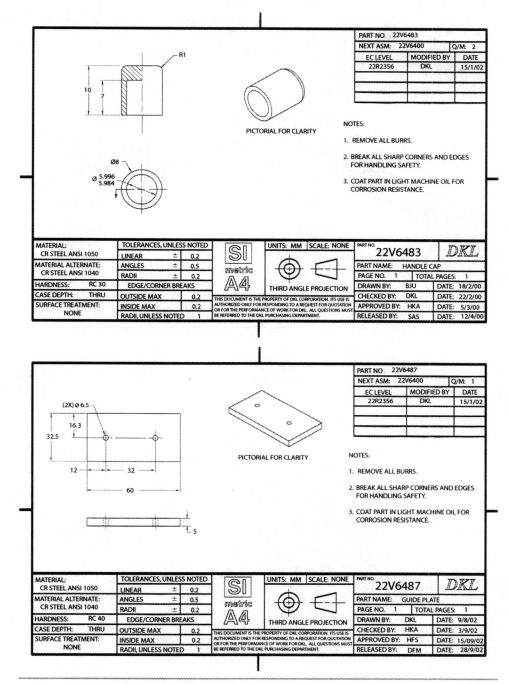

FIGURE 18.23. (CONTINUED) Detail drawings for the machine vise.

Information pertaining to tolerances and materials on the drawing header is also included.

The notes on a detail drawing are used to specify any special procedures or processes needed to fabricate or finish the part that are not evident from the dimensions and tolerances and any tests that are necessary to ensure that the part works in its intended manner. Putting a closed geometric shape, usually a box, around the note number highlights a note that refers to a particular feature on the part. A leader arrow then points to that feature and is annotated "See note X," which tells the reader of the drawing that a special instruction in the notes is associated with that feature.

FIGURE 18.24. Three-dimensional computer-generated models of a disposable one-cell flashlight.

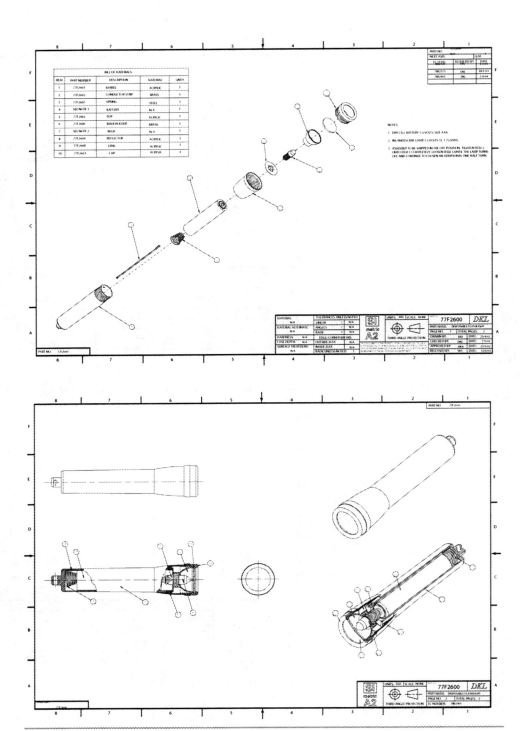

FIGURE 18.25. Working drawings for the disposable flashlight.

18.06.06 More Examples of Manufacturing Drawings

The 3-D model of a small, inexpensive flashlight is shown in a complete state and in a sectioned state in Figure 18.24. The working drawings for this product are shown in Figure 18.25. The assembly drawings show how the individual pieces fit together, and the detail drawings show the required sizes of the custom parts. The complete assembly drawing is three pages long and includes exploded, outline, and sectioned views as well

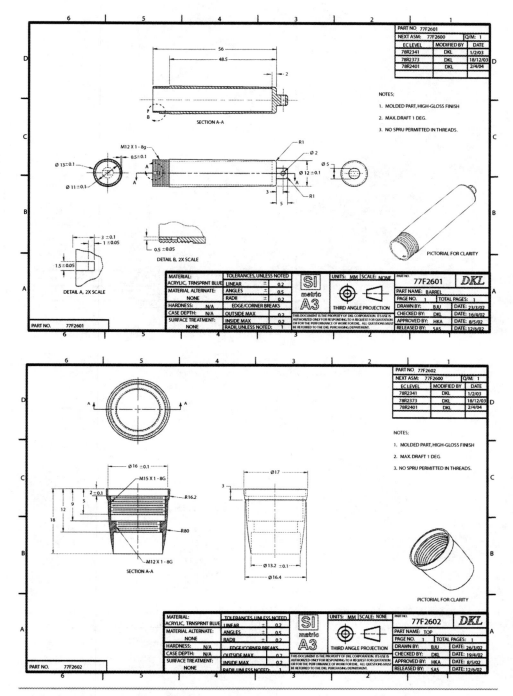

FIGURE 18.25. (CONTINUED) Working drawings for the disposable flashlight.

as a BOM. For this intended low-cost, high-volume product (more than 100,000 per month), many of the pieces will be molded from plastic. The product has been designed such that stringent tolerances on the dimensions are not required for the parts to fit together and function. Two of the parts, the battery and the light bulb, are commercially available; thus, detail drawings are not needed for them. The assembly drawings, however, show all of the parts, including the battery and bulb. The BOM, located on the first page of the assembly drawing, specifies enough information about these two parts so that they may be purchased.

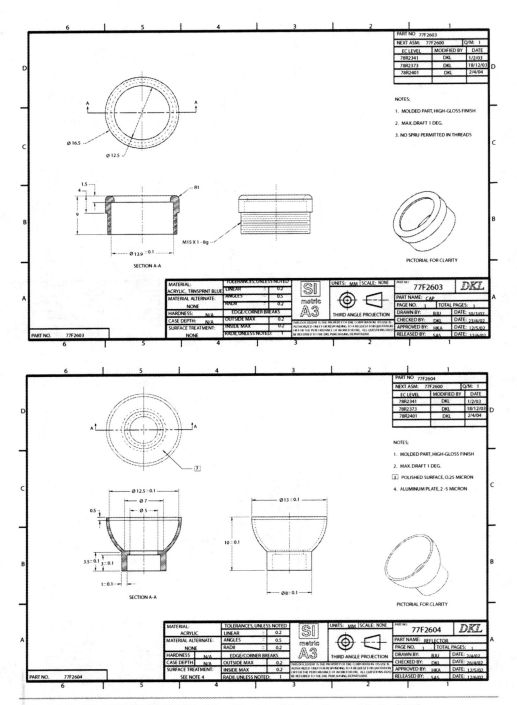

FIGURE 18.25. (CONTINUED) Working drawings for the disposable flashlight.

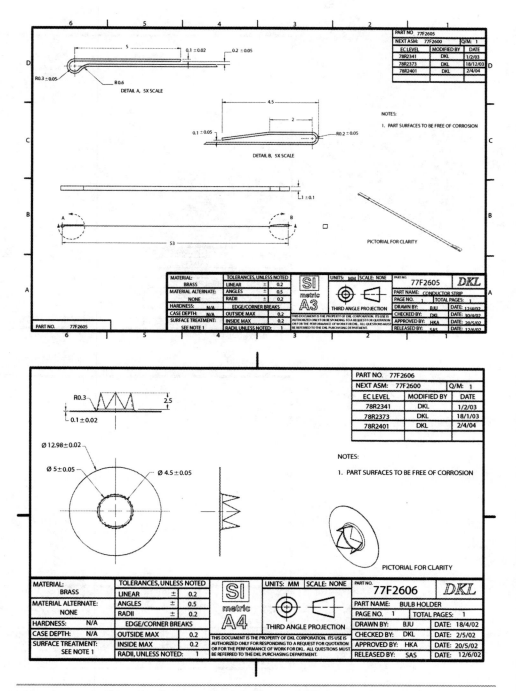

FIGURE 18.25. (CONTINUED) Working drawings for the disposable flashlight.

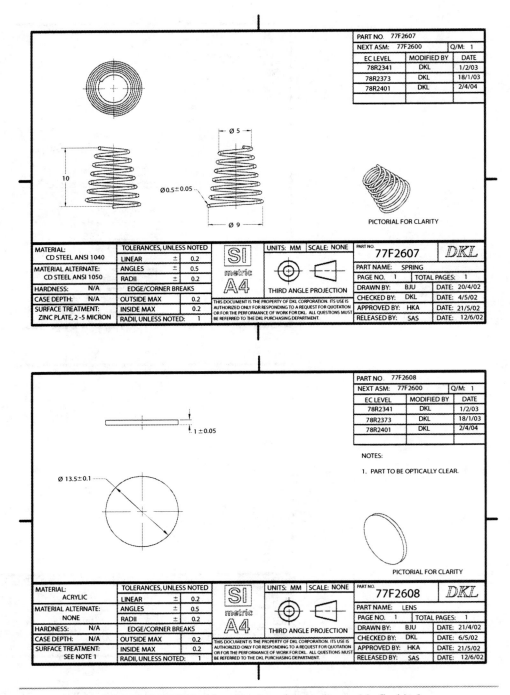

FIGURE 18.25. (CONTINUED) Working drawings for the disposable flashlight.

The 3-D model of a computer disk drive spindle is shown in Figure 18.26. The working drawings for this spindle are shown in Figure 18.27. The anticipated production volume of this product (more than 250,000 per month) is very high; however, performance requirements for its application demand very strict tolerance control on many of its part dimensions. Close attention needs to be paid to fabrication techniques to ensure that the required tolerances can be met with a minimum of manufacturing

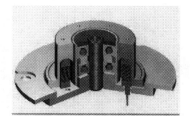

FIGURE 18.26. A 3-D computer-generated model of a computer disk drive spindle.

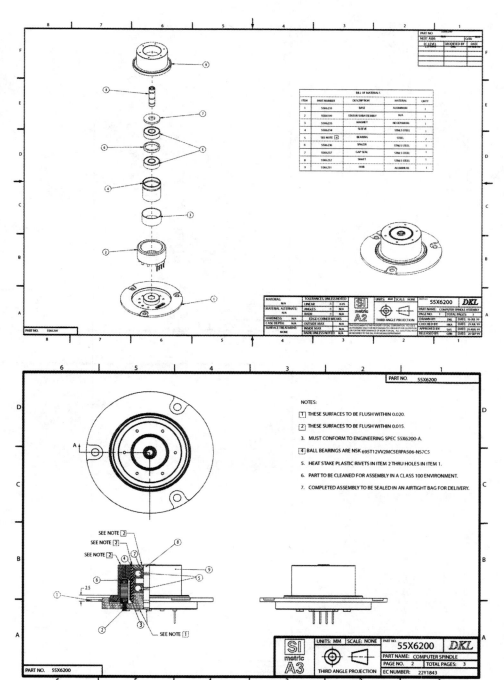

FIGURE 18.27. Working drawings for the computer disk drive spindle.

cost. The computer spindle uses two commercially available ball bearings; detail drawings are not necessary, but they are shown and specified in the assembly drawing and BOM. Note also that one of the parts, the stator, in the main assembly is actually a subassembly. The stator is composed of custom laminations that are stacked, insulated, wound, and insert-molded with connector pins. The part is then delivered as a single piece, ready to be installed into the spindle main assembly.

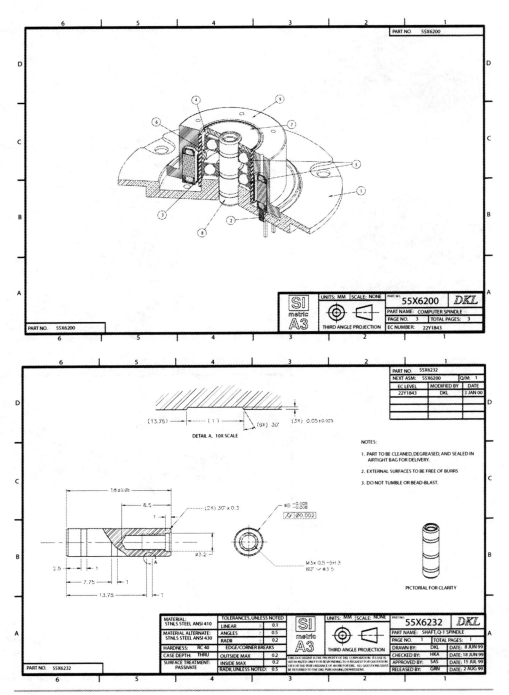

FIGURE 18.27. (CONTINUED) Working drawings for the computer disk drive spindle.

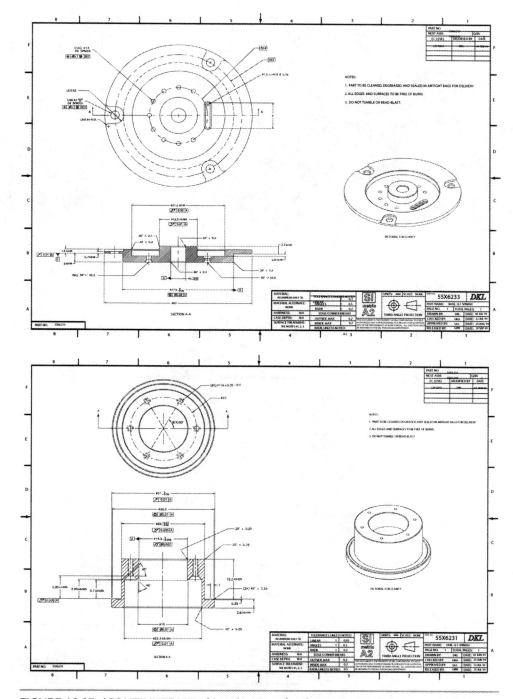

FIGURE 18.27. (CONTINUED) Working drawings for the computer disk drive spindle.

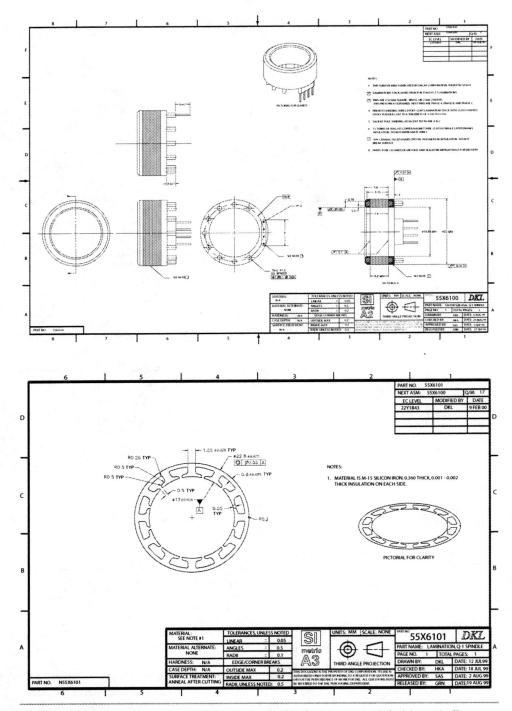

FIGURE 18.27. (CONTINUED) Working drawings for the computer disk drive spindle.

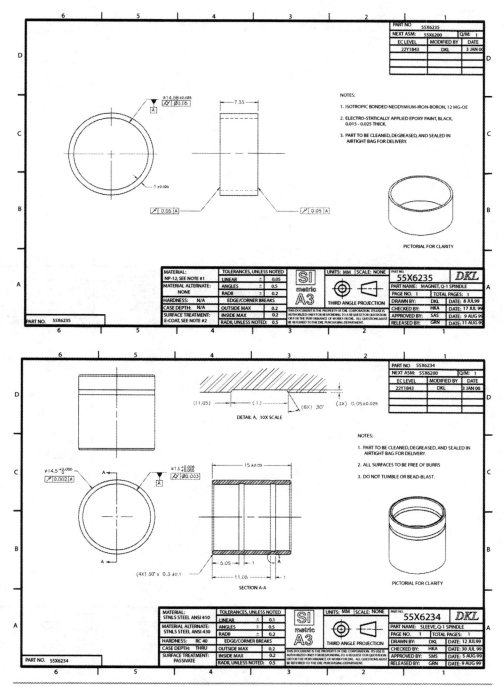

FIGURE 18.27. (CONTINUED) Working drawings for the computer disk drive spindle.

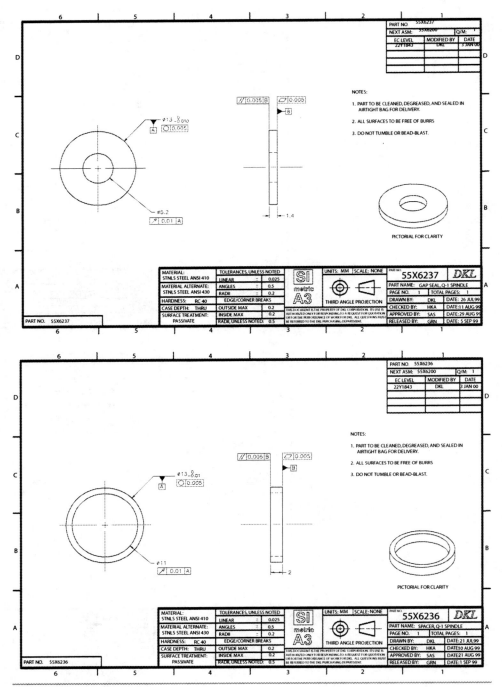

FIGURE 18.27. (CONTINUED) Working drawings for the computer disk drive spindle.

18.07 Construction Drawings

In the previous sections, you learned about working drawings in general and about manufacturing drawings specifically. In the following sections, you will learn about a different type of drawings—those used primarily in the construction of large civil engineering structures. In these sections, the term *structure* refers to any type of large infrastructure project, such as roads, bridges, buildings, and dams.

18.07.01 Why Construction Drawings Are Different from Manufacturing Drawings

Earlier in this chapter you learned that one of the primary differences between manufacturing and construction engineering projects is that mechanical designs are developed for mass production, whereas civil designs represent a single, one-off system. Another significant difference between the two types of engineering projects is that construction projects are typically site-specific and manufacturing projects typically are not. Bridges are constructed at specific locations. Water treatment facilities are located on specific property. Mechanical products are manufactured and shipped to various locations throughout the world—it does not matter where they are manufactured or where they are used.

Another difference between construction and manufacturing projects is their relative size. Construction projects are typically large-scale. Bridges can be several miles in length; buildings can be several stories high; dams can be massively large; sewage treatment plants can cover several acres. Manufactured products are typically shipped from one location to another for eventual use, and their size is relatively small when compared to construction projects.

Yet another difference between construction and manufacturing projects is that in the United States, construction projects are often designed in the English system of units. Although the government has encouraged the construction industry to adopt the metric system of measurement (and in some cases has required that civil designs include metric dimensions), the metric system is generally not used for this type of project. In fact, in many cases where engineers working on infrastructure projects were required to include metric dimensions, they merely converted the dimensions from English to metric and did not actually *design* the system in metric. Thus, a dimension might be given on a construction drawing as 25.4 cm, having been converted from something originally designed to be 10 inches. In contrast, manufacturing projects are often designed from the start in the metric system; so dimensions will appear as whole numbers such as 25 cm or 30 cm.

Infrastructure projects are often designed and constructed for the members of society. In fact, the name *civil engineering* comes from the profession's origins in France where citizens demanded roads, water, and sanitary systems for the *civilians*—these facilities were already in place for the armed forces. Because construction projects are designed for use by the general public, they are usually required to be approved by a registered PE. A PE must pass two tests that assess his or her level of proficiency in solving engineering problems. In addition, an engineer must work for several years under the supervision of a PE before being eligible to attempt the second day-long test. After passing the exam, the new PE is legally and ethically responsible for the integrity of the designs developed under his or her supervision and can be sued if a structure fails. In contrast, manufacturing projects rarely have PEs working on them, although the senior engineer on a project usually has several years of experience and would not have been trusted to verify the integrity of the design without the demonstrated ability to perform this function.

Although 3-D computer modeling predominates in manufactured systems, its use in civil engineering design practice is still fairly limited; this trend will likely continue for the foreseeable future. In some of the larger civil engineering firms, 3-D models of projects are created, but these computer models are typically specialized for civil applications and cannot be used to generate 2-D drawings directly from the models. The 2-D drawings are still created independently from the 3-D models. For manufactured products, drawings are becoming less important, especially as modern software enhances the ability to send 3-D computer models electronically to CNC lathes for production. This is not the case for civil and architectural applications. In civil engineering practice, design and construction are still accomplished primarily through drawings. Construction projects are not built in climate-controlled, clean environments. Projects are constructed outside with exposure to the elements, often far away from electric power sources or network connections. Physical drawings are still far more practical in this environment than are 3-D computer models.

Finally, construction projects are like large-scale assembly projects that are always built from the ground up. With a construction project, the contractor performs the site excavation first; then the foundation is poured. The first floor of a structure must be built before the second floor can be built, and the second floor must be constructed before the third floor can be constructed. All of the floors must be complete before the roof can be added. Also, wiring, plumbing, and ductwork must be in place before the walls and ceilings can be completed. Further, each subsystem on the project, like the wiring and plumbing, is typically put in place by a subcontractor who is hired by the general contractor on the project. Thus, there is a specific order and timing in which the various parts of the project are completed; and significant communication and coordination are required between the client, engineer, contractor, and subcontractors. Scheduling is a significant part of a construction project. Manufacturing projects typically do not require this complex level of communication, scheduling, or coordination and do not typically have a rigid order for assembly. (Although, of course, some subassemblies must be put together before other subassemblies.)

18.07.02 How Construction Drawings Are Different from Manufacturing Drawings

Due to the some of the differences between construction and manufacturing practices described in the previous paragraphs, several differences in the development of working drawings have evolved over time. In the following paragraphs, these differences will be described and illustrated.

Terminology

Drawings used in the design and construction of civil or architectural projects are frequently referred to as **blueprints**. The name *blueprint* is derived from an earlier era when construction drawings were reproduced by a method that resulted in a blue background with white lines. The original drawings were made using ink on large sheets of paper; but there was no such thing as copiers or printers, especially of this size. Special blueprint machines were developed so that multiple copies of the handmade ink drawings could be produced. Although modern-day computer hardware with large printers has enabled the creation of construction drawings with black lines on a white background, they are still often referred to as blueprints. Figure 18.28 shows a blueprint of a hand-drawn sketch of a mixer plate design. Note that the title block shows the date that this blueprint was drawn.

In construction applications, **plan views** are views made from a vantage point above the "object." Thus, plan views can be thought of as top views. You are probably familiar with the term **floor plan**; in fact, you may have seen a floor plan in a newspaper or magazine. A floor plan is a drawing made from a vantage point above a building that shows the layout of all of the rooms on a particular floor. Similarly, a **foundation plan** shows the building foundation from above, the **electrical plan** shows the wiring diagram from above, and the **heating and ventilation plan** shows the location of ducts and equipment from above. **Profile views** show the building or project from the front or the side. In other words, they are views where the top of the structure is seen as an edge. **Elevation views** are drawings that show differences in elevations on a structure. Since changes in elevation can be seen in any view where the top is an edge, elevation views are essentially the same as profile views.

In the design and construction of large infrastructure projects, several drawings are necessary to describe the facility completely so that it can be built. The entire set of drawings is called the **set of construction plans**, or "the plans," even though not all of the drawings represent plan (top) views of the structure. The **specifications**, or **specs**,

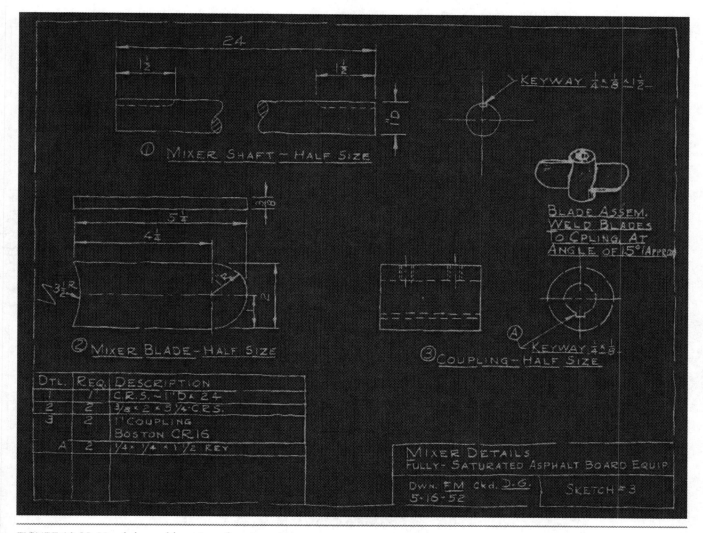

FIGURE 18.28. Hand-drawn blueprint of a mixer plate.

consist of written instructions regarding the construction of the facility. Together the plans and specs make up the entire construction documentation. In this text, you will focus on understanding the drawings—specifications are beyond its scope.

Size Considerations

Construction drawings are almost always created or printed on E size sheets. Recall that E size sheets are 34″ × 44″; however, smaller sheets may be used for drawings that are brought into the field. Large sheets are used for construction drawings due to the relative large size of the projects. For a bridge that is three miles long, it would be difficult to show the entire structure on an 11″ × 17″ sheet of paper (B size) or to show it in sufficient detail for understanding. Construction drawings are always made to scale, with 1 inch sometimes equaling hundreds of feet. It would be impossible (and impractical) to draw a large structure true size—imagine the size of the sheet of paper that would be required.

The relative large size of construction projects also makes strict tolerancing relatively meaningless. When a slab of concrete is specified as 10'-6" × 40'-9", no one expects the slab to be *exactly* that size; plus or minus a few tenths of an inch is probably acceptable. For concrete slabs, making sure that the surface is level is far more important than its overall surface area. Smaller tolerances may be needed when bolt holes are located on a steel structural member; however, once again, the tolerances are nowhere near the precision found in manufacturing projects where tolerances as small as 0.001" are acceptable and routine. A contractor would likely laugh out loud if a tolerance of 0.001" were ever specified on the design drawings for an infrastructure project.

Another difference in the working drawings that results due to the large size of construction projects is that views typically do not project orthogonally from one view to the next. Often the plan view (or top view) is on one sheet with the elevation view (or front view) located several sheets away. Sometimes even the scale used to draw the plan view differs from the scale used to draw the elevation view, meaning you could not separate the sheets and try to line them up if you wanted to see how features projected from one view to the next. In this respect, the need for well-developed 3-D spatial skills may be even more important for engineers working on construction projects. You often must remember what the plan view looks like as you search for the elevation view on a separate sheet.

Site-Specific Considerations

In the construction industry, the orientation and location of a project with respect to its surroundings are extremely important. Imagine the problems that would develop if a building were constructed on someone else's property. Several methods used on drawings help the contractor locate the structure properly. **Bearings** of lines may be shown on a drawing. The bearing of a line is the angle that the line makes with a North-South line, as illustrated in Figure 18.29. Bearings of lines are seen only in plan views (i.e., from above). On the construction site, bearings of lines can be obtained by any of several surveying techniques and the building can then be accurately located on the property. Alternatively, a North line may be placed on the drawing to show the relative orientation of the structure.

Control points are often provided on construction drawings to help locate features of the project accurately. With this method, an "origin" for the construction site is designated and all points are referenced north, south, east, or west from it. Thus, a point on a drawing might have coordinates N13750 and E7895, for example. Similar to bearings, the coordinates of the control points are seen only in plan views. The origin for the coordinate system is usually referred to as a **benchmark**. Benchmarks have been established across the United States by the U.S. Geological Survey (USGS) and typically consist of a concrete cylinder with a brass, circular medal on top imbedded in the earth. The location of each benchmark was determined with a high degree of accuracy. Many times job benchmarks are established on construction sites when a USGS benchmark is not located within the vicinity of the project.

Benchmarks are also used to determine the elevation of points on a construction site. Elevations are used to establish vertical distances between points on a building. For example, the top of a floor slab might be specified as having an elevation of 556 feet. Elevations are seen only in profile views (or elevation views) and are usually referenced to true elevations (i.e., the height of the point above sea level) or to job elevations. With job elevations, a benchmark is established and given an arbitrary elevation of, for example, 100 feet. All other elevations for the project are then specified relative to that point. A benchmark elevation of 0 is usually not specified to ensure that job elevations are never negative.

One of the first steps in the design of a structure is to send a crew out to do a **site survey**. Usually there are existing structures or features that must be noted on the plans before the design can proceed. Modern survey equipment is computerized such that the survey data is automatically stored and later easily converted to a drawing.

FIGURE 18.29. Illustration of the definition of a bearing of a line. Bearings are only seen in the plan views.

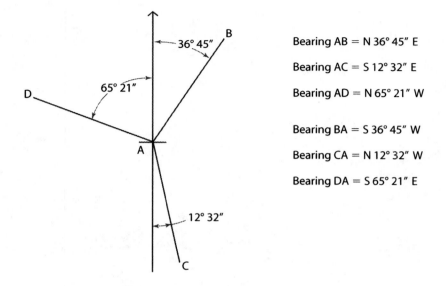

Bearing AB = N 36° 45″ E

Bearing AC = S 12° 32″ E

Bearing AD = N 65° 21″ W

Bearing BA = S 36° 45″ W

Bearing CA = N 12° 32″ W

Bearing DA = S 65° 21″ E

Figure 18.30 shows the survey data for a site taken in the field; Figure 18.31 shows the survey data after it has been converted to a site plan drawing.

One-of-a-Kind Considerations

In manufacturing projects, prototypes of products are created and tested for their integrity and functionality. The prototypes can be virtual or actual physical models. Construction projects are too large and expensive to warrant the building of prototypes; however, sometimes small-scale models are developed to allow clients and others to visualize what a structure will look like when completed. The models built in construction practice have little value in analyzing the structure—they are merely used for display purposes, especially when dealing with a client who may not be able to visualize a project based on the plans. Virtual computer models may also be available for analysis, especially in larger engineering firms. Because large structures are one-offs, unforeseen problems are likely to occur during construction. Ductwork may interfere with

FIGURE 18.30. Data from site survey showing existing structures and other entities.

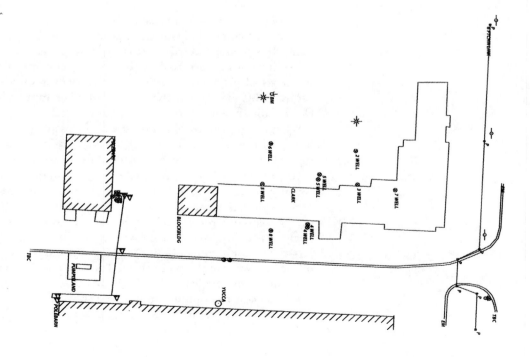

FIGURE 18.31. Survey data converted to site drawing.

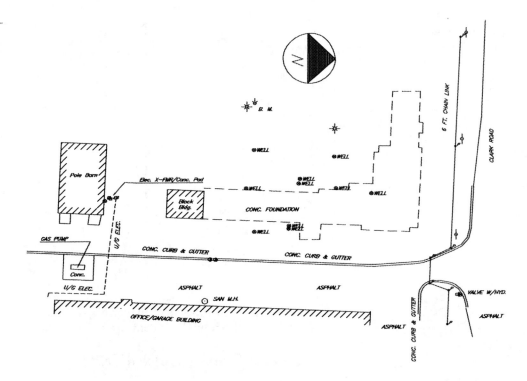

plumbing pipes and need to be rerouted. Dimensions may have inadvertently been left off the drawing. The engineer may discover that walls or doorways need to be moved. Because changes to the original design may need to be made during construction, the contractor keeps track of them on a set of **as-built plans**. As-built drawings graphically show any changes from the original design and are important for future maintenance and operation of the facility.

18.08 Construction Plans

A set of construction plans usually consists of a large number of drawings. The drawings in the plans usually include the cover sheet, site plan, elevation views, foundation plan, floor plans, electrical plans, roofing plans, sections, detail drawings, and any other drawings needed to describe the project completely. The drawings are included in the set of plans in the order in which they are needed for the construction of the project. This means that the foundation plan appears before the first-floor plan, the floor plans appear before the roofing plan, etc.

For a complete set of plans, several sheets are often required for each type of drawing. In addition to the drawings, **schedules of materials**, which list, for example, the types of doors and windows to be used in the construction of the facility, are included on the drawings. In this case, a schedule of materials is much like a BOM for manufacturing projects. Most public projects require the seal and signature of a PE, which often appears on the cover sheet of the drawing set. The PE is legally responsible for the design and construction of the facility even if he or she did not complete all of the analysis for the project. A PE will usually meticulously check the calculations and analysis before signing off on the plans. The name of the PE appears in the title block of each drawing in the set of plans. The title block also typically includes the name of the drafter who made the drawings and others involved with the design; however, title blocks on construction drawings do not typically contain all of the information found on the title block for manufacturing drawings.

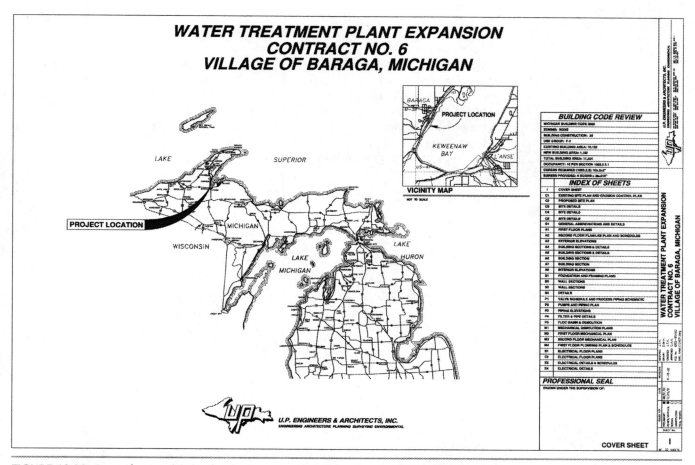

FIGURE 18.32. Cover sheet and index for the Baraga water treatment plant expansion project.

18.08.01 Cover Sheet

The **cover sheet** for the plans typically contains a map of the area surrounding the project site. The map is not overly detailed, but shows the general location of the project. Since the set of drawings for a project usually consists of several sheets, an **index** of all drawings in the set is included on the cover sheet or on the first page following the cover. Figure 18.32 shows the cover sheet from a set of plans drawn for an expansion project for a water treatment plant in the village of Baraga in the state of Michigan. Note the map showing part of the state with the portion of the state near the project site enlarged to show the area in greater detail. Also note the index listing all of the drawings in the set of plans and the area reserved on the cover sheet for the seal of the PE.

18.08.02 Site Plan

One of the first drawings in the set of construction plans is a site map or a **site plan**. Figure 18.33 shows the proposed site plan for the Baraga water treatment facility. Note that this plan shows the highway as well as an arrow indicating north. Since this project constitutes an addition to an existing structure, the outline of that building is shown on the site plan as well. The scale for the drawing is shown in the upper-left corner both graphically and numerically (1 inch = 20 feet). Contour lines showing changes in existing ground elevation are also shown. You will learn more about contour lines and topographic maps in a later chapter.

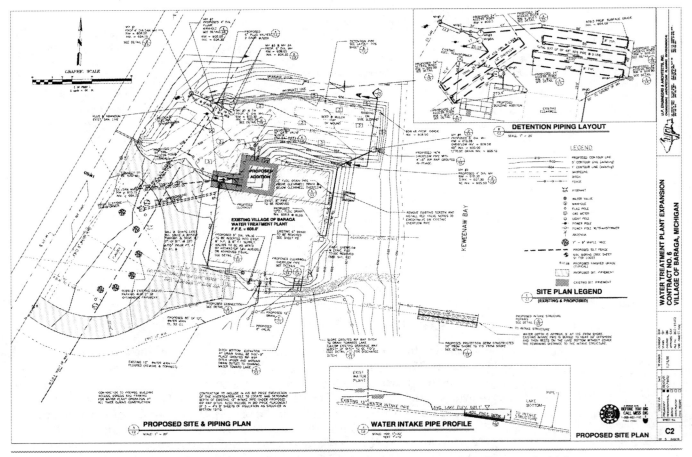

FIGURE 18.33. Site plan for Baraga water treatment facility showing existing structure as well as nearby highway.

18.08.03 Elevation Views

As stated previously, elevation views show the structure from a vantage point where changes in elevation are visible. Elevation views can be thought of as front or side views; but for a large structure, the terms *front* and *side* are fairly meaningless. Elevation views are defined by their orientation with respect to the compass points of North, South, East, and West. A North Elevation shows what the structure would like if you stood to the north of it and looked back, a South Elevation shows what it would look like from the south, etc. Although elevation views do not contain a great deal of detail or many dimensions about the actual construction of the facility, they do help contractors and owners visualize the resulting project. Figure 18.34 shows the South Elevation view for the overflow and drain portion of the lagoon for the Baraga water treatment facility. Note that there are no dimensions on this drawing, but elevations of some features are included—the existing ground profile has an elevation specified of 811.5′ ±, and the proposed ground profile shows an elevation of 814′. The symbol for elevation on the drawing is a circle with a cross through it with the horizontal "crosshair" on the surface whose elevation is being specified.

18.08.04 Foundation and Floor Plans

Because a building is constructed from the foundation up, the foundation plans are among the first drawings in the set of plans. A building foundation is usually constructed out of concrete that has been reinforced with steel bars, or **rebars** (<u>re</u>inforcing <u>bars</u>). Concrete footings support the walls and columns in a building, and the foundation walls are often made of reinforced concrete. Details about the size of the footings and the size and location of rebars are usually included in a wall section drawing. Sometimes a reinforced concrete slab is constructed for the building and included as part of the foundation plan or in a wall section view. Concrete slabs typically contain reinforcing bars or a steel mesh for controlling the thermal expansion and contraction of the slab.

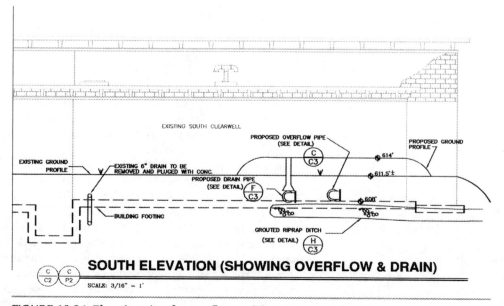

FIGURE 18.34. Elevation view for overflow and drain portion of lagoon.

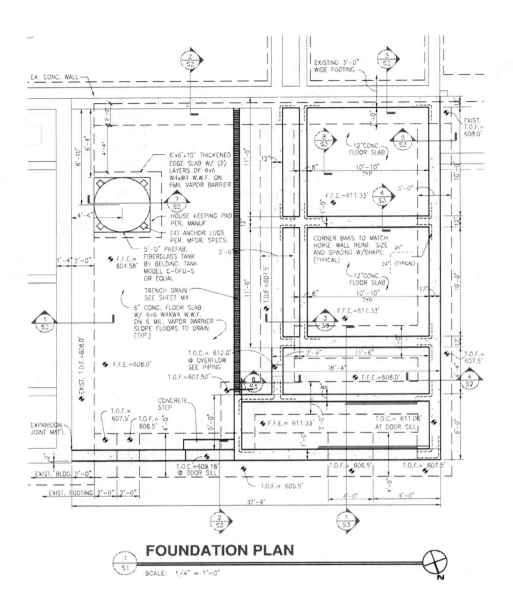

FIGURE 18.35. Foundation plan for portion of the Baraga water treatment facility.

FOUNDATION PLAN

SCALE: 1/4" = 1'-0"

Figure 18.35 shows the foundation plan for a portion of the Baraga water treatment facility. In this drawing, the right portion of the foundation includes a 12″ slab and the left portion includes a 6″ slab. The reinforcing for the 6″ slab is specified on the foundation plan as 6X6 W4XW4 W.W.F. This specification means that the spacing of the bars is 6″ × 6″ and that the diameter of the steel wire is a gage of 4 (approximately two-tenths of an inch). The WWF in this specification refers to welded wire fabric. The dashed lines around both sides of the outer walls of the structure define the footings. Since this project is an addition to an existing structure, the existing footing sizes are given—3′-0″ along one wall and 2′-0″ along another wall. The new footings to be constructed are 4′-0″ and 3′-0″ on each of the remaining two walls, respectively. Note the specification of the elevation of the T.O.F. (top of footing) in various locations on the plan. Also notice the various cutting plane lines for sectional views through the walls. The sectional views will be found on various sheets that are labeled in this view. For example, for the wall located nearest the top of the page, two section lines are shown and both section views will be located on S2 (section sheet 2); they will be drawing 2 and drawing 3, respectively.

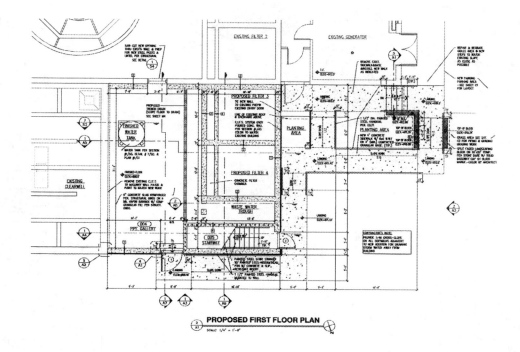

FIGURE 18.36. First floor plan for the Baraga water treatment facility.

PROPOSED FIRST FLOOR PLAN

The type of construction drawing with which you are probably most familiar is the floor plan. A floor plan shows the layout of the rooms in a building. Doors between rooms are shown, as is the location of windows, closets, plumbing fixtures, and any other pertinent information about the drawings. The dimensions of the rooms as well as the thickness of walls are usually shown on the floor plans. Figure 18.36 shows the first-floor plan for the Baraga water treatment facility. Notice how the new construction fits within the existing structures on two sides. For this floor, the new walls will be constructed from concrete. (Dotted cross-hatching is used to show this graphically.) A concrete landing also surrounds the new construction, connecting to the existing generator; and spaces for planting in the landing are included to avoid the "concrete jungle" look. Two doors will be installed in the new construction. (Several are shown on the existing structure.) One of the doors leads to the stairway; the other door leads directly into the pipe gallery. Notice that the way the doors swing is also shown on the plan.

Figure 18.37 shows a different type of floor plan for the first floor—the electrical plan. According to the legend provided with this electrical plan, seven types of electrical devices are to be installed on this floor—duplex convenience receptacles, ground fault interrupt duplex convenience receptacles, single pole wall switches, three-way wall switches, electric control valves, motors, and disconnect switches. Notice that the exact locations of these devices are not shown—just approximations. Their locations are not critical to the integrity of the building, so the electrical subcontractor is free to put them wherever it makes the most sense in the field.

18.08.05 Sections

Sections in construction drawings can be organized into two types: **general sections**, which show room or floor layouts for buildings, or **detail sections**, which show cross sections with enough detail for construction purposes. In fact, a floor plan also can be thought of as a horizontal section through a building. Figure 18.38 shows a vertical section through a house. Note that with this type of general section, not enough detail is included for construction purposes; but the detail that is given is helpful because it provides a general idea about the layout of the rooms and the floors within the house.

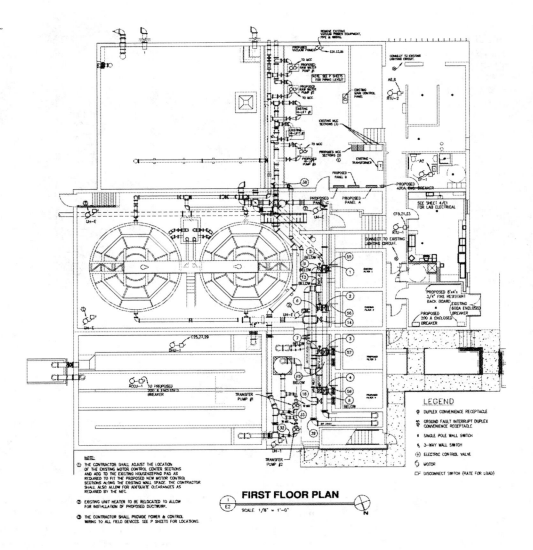

FIGURE 18.37. Electrical plan for the first floor of the Baraga water treatment facility.

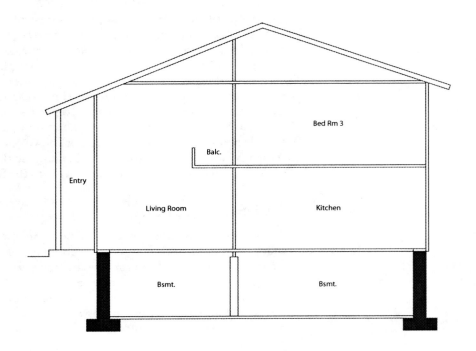

FIGURE 18.38. General section through a house showing room layouts.

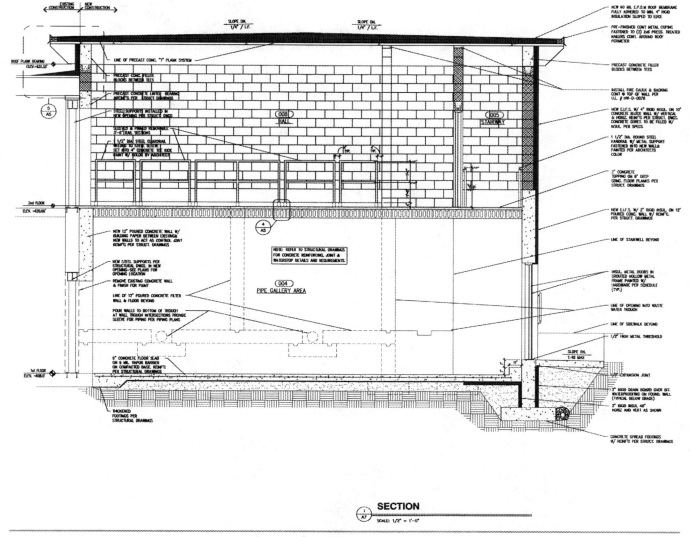

SECTION
SCALE: 1/2" = 1'-0"

FIGURE 18.39. General section for Baraga water treatment facility.

Figure 18.39 shows a general section for the Baraga water treatment facility upgrade. This section shows the general building layout, clearly indicating where the pipe gallery is in relation to the hall above it. Notice that not much detail and very few dimensions are provided in this section; however, the drawing is helpful in understanding the overall design of the facility.

Detail sections provide a great deal of information. They show how the different components in a building system fit together, and they provide information that cannot be shown in large-scale drawings, such as floor plans or elevation views. **Wall sections** are among the most prevalent type of detail sectional drawing in a set of construction plans, although roof framing and foundation sections are also common. Refer to the foundation plan shown for the Baraga project in Figure 18.35. On the wall of the foundation plan toward the top of the drawing, a cutting plane line is shown with an arrow pointing toward the right side of the page. The label for this section line is given as 2/S2. This means that the cross section indicated by the cutting plane line is drawing number 2 found on section sheet 2. Figure 18.40 shows the wall section that corresponds to that cutting plane line. You should note that unlike manufacturing section views, this section did not project orthographically (it was even on another sheet); further, the section view is not

FIGURE 18.40. Detailed wall section for Baraga water treatment facility.

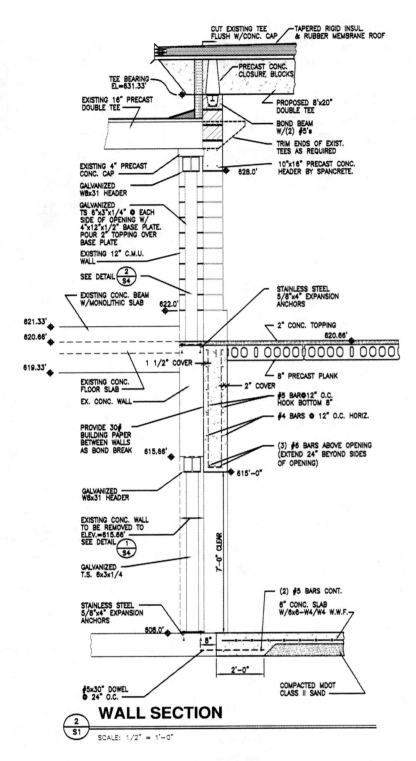

CUT EXISTING TEE
FLUSH W/CONC. CAP

TAPERED RIGID INSUL.
& RUBBER MEMBRANE ROOF

PRECAST CONC.
CLOSURE BLOCKS

TEE BEARING
EL.=831.33'

EXISTING 16" PRECAST
DOUBLE TEE

PROPOSED 8'x20"
DOUBLE TEE

BOND BEAM
W/(2) #5's

TRIM ENDS OF EXIST.
TEES AS REQUIRED

EXISTING 4" PRECAST
CONC. CAP

828.0'

10"x16" PRECAST CONC.
HEADER BY SPANCRETE.

GALVANIZED
W8x31 HEADER

GALVANIZED
TS 6"x3"x1/4" @ EACH
SIDE OF OPENING W/
4"x12"x1/2" BASE PLATE.
POUR 2" TOPPING OVER
BASE PLATE

EXISTING 12" C.M.U.
WALL

SEE DETAIL 2/S4

EXISTING CONC. BEAM
W/MONOLITHIC SLAB

822.0'

STAINLESS STEEL
5/8"x4" EXPANSION
ANCHORS

821.33'
820.66'

2" CONC. TOPPING
820.66'

819.33'

1 1/2" COVER

8" PRECAST PLANK

EXISTING CONC.
FLOOR SLAB

EX. CONC. WALL

2" COVER

#5 BAR@12" O.C.
HOOK BOTTOM 8"

#4 BARS @ 12" O.C. HORIZ.

PROVIDE 30#
BUILDING PAPER
BETWEEN WALLS
AS BOND BREAK

815.66'

(3) #6 BARS ABOVE OPENING
(EXTEND 24" BEYOND SIDES
OF OPENING)

615'-0"

GALVANIZED
W8x31 HEADER

EXISTING CONC. WALL
TO BE REMOVED TO
ELEV.=815.66'
SEE DETAIL 1/S4

7'-0" CLEAR

GALVANIZED
T.S. 6x3x1/4

(2) #5 BARS CONT.

6" CONC. SLAB
W/6x6-W4/W4 W.W.F.

STAINLESS STEEL
5/8"x4" EXPANSION
ANCHORS

808.0'

8"

2'-0"

COMPACTED MDOT
CLASS II SAND

#5x30" DOWEL
@ 24" O.C.

WALL SECTION

2/S1

SCALE: 1/2" = 1'-0"

drawn to the same scale as the top view from which it is projecting. The plan view is drawn at a scale of ¼"=1'-0"; the wall section is drawn at a scale of ½"=1'-0".

The wall section shown in Figure 18.40 includes details about the reinforcing (welded wire fabric, dowels, stainless steel expansion anchors, and #6 bars); it includes information about elevations of various portions of the wall (the top of the foundation slab is at 608.0', the top of the slab for the first floor is at 620.66', and the bottom of the

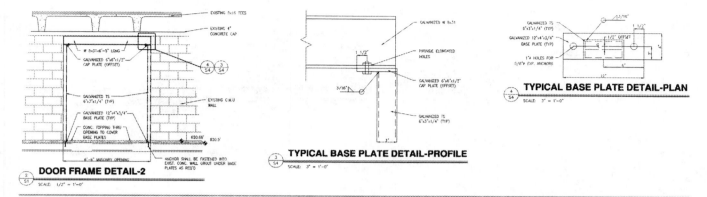

FIGURE 18.41. Detail drawings showing how a door will be installed in the Baraga water treatment facility.

existing precast concrete cap is at 628.0′); it also shows the various components that extend out from the walls (the slabs, the double tee, the existing structure, and the roof).

18.08.06 Detail Construction Drawings

Detail drawings are made to show one or two particular features on the constructed facility so that it can be built. Because constructed facilities are typically large, some of the finer details of the construction cannot be shown adequately on other types of drawings. Thus, detail views show one specific area on a drawing that has been enlarged. Detail views are referenced from existing drawings, and all detail drawings may be shown on one sheet. Figure 18.41 shows the door frame detail for the Baraga project. In the upper-right corner of the detail drawing for the door frame, two new details are referenced—3/S4 and 4/S4, which are also shown in the figure. Detail 3/S4 shows how the cap plate will be bolted to the crossbeam from a profile viewpoint, and Detail 4/S4 shows the connection from a plan viewpoint. You should note that the plan and profile views of the detail do not project orthographically on the sheet. You must mentally line these drawings up in order to understand how the door frame is to be constructed.

18.08.07 Plan and Profile Drawings

Another common type of construction drawing is a **plan and profile drawing**. Recall that plan views show a structure from above and that profile views show the structure from the side or front. In other words, plan views show changes in bearings of lines and profile views show changes in elevations of features. Figure 18.42 shows a plan and profile drawing for a street and a corresponding sewage pipe for a wastewater system in Baraga. Note that in this drawing, things do project orthographically between the plan and the profile views; however, the drawing scales are different between views. For the plan view, the entire view is drawn at a scale of 1″=30′. For the profile view, the scale is 1″=30′ on the horizontal dimension and 1″=10′ on the vertical dimension. The reason for this change in scale is to show the changes in elevation in greater detail.

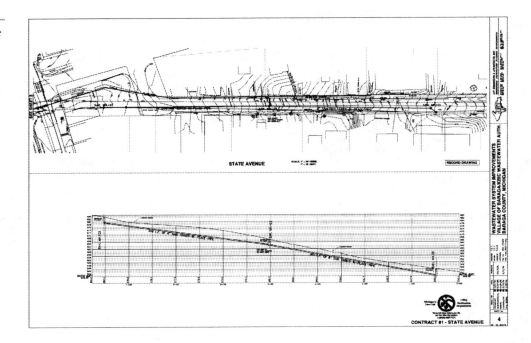

FIGURE 18.42. Plan and profile drawing showing the street and corresponding sewage pipe for wastewater system in Baraga.

18.09 Engineering Scales

As you learned previously, virtually all engineering drawings are made to scale. This is especially true with construction drawings that represent large projects that do not fit on a single sheet of paper. In this age of CAD, engineering designs can be printed to any scale desired. Further, if you decide that you need the drawing at a scale that differs from the one you first chose, you merely adjust the font sizes and reprint the drawing at the new scale. Previously, if you needed the drawing at a new scale, you were required to re-create the entire drawing from the beginning—a tedious task.

It is important to understand that when an object is drawn to scale, its actual size does not change—just its appearance on the paper. Figure 18.43 illustrates the concept of drawing something to scale. Here the objects are the same size; the one on the right just appears to be twice as large as the one on the left. The notation of a 2:1 scale means

FIGURE 18.43. Scaled drawing of object.

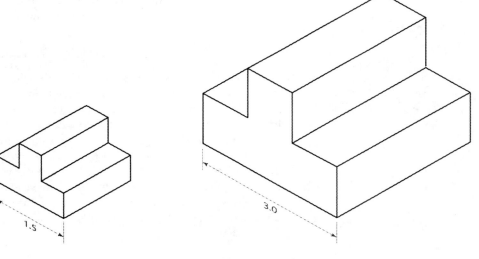

Original Object

Object after Scaling

that 2 inches on paper equals 1 inch on the object. Therefore, the drawing looks larger than the actual object. Conversely, a 1:2 scale would mean that 1 inch on paper represents 2 inches on the physical object; hence, the drawing would look smaller than the actual object.

Another way to think of drawing objects to scale is that the scale indicates how close you are to the object. If you are a substantial distance from the object, it appears very small; whereas if you are very close to the object, it appears large. However, the true object size does not change. Similarly, from an airplane, a house on the ground looks tiny; but if you are standing a few inches from the same house, it appears enormous. It is your perception of the house that changes, not the size of the house.

Scales for drawings are usually reported as ratios. In denoting scales, the first number in the ratio corresponds to the drawing and the second number corresponds to the physical object. However, sometimes drawing scales are denoted with an equal sign rather than a ratio. This is particularly true when scales are given in the English system of units. Thus, a scale may be reported as 1″=50′ or ¼″=1′-0″. The first scale (1″=50′) means that 1 inch on the drawing corresponds to 50 feet on the actual object. These drawing scales can also relate back to their ratio equivalents, i.e., 1″=50′ corresponds to a scale of 1:600 (there are 12 inches in a foot, so 50 feet = 600 inches, resulting in a 1:600 ratio), and a scale of ¼″=1′-0″ corresponds to 1:48.

A scale is a device that was developed over the years to aid in making a drawing to scale; it is usually a triangular prism with six to twelve different drawing scales depicted on one piece of equipment. Figure 18.44 shows three common scales used by engineers—an Engineer's scale, an Architect's scale, and a Metric scale. With modern-day mechanical CAD systems, you typically create a 3-D object in true size and print it out to the scale you need. In civil engineering applications, you create your drawings full-size and print them out to scale. In either case, you must ensure that the text on the drawings is legible when printed to the desired scale.

Due to advances in computer software, physical scales such as those shown in Figure 18.44 are, for the most part, a relic of the past. However, in a few instances, knowledge of scales is helpful—and possibly necessary. Because construction projects

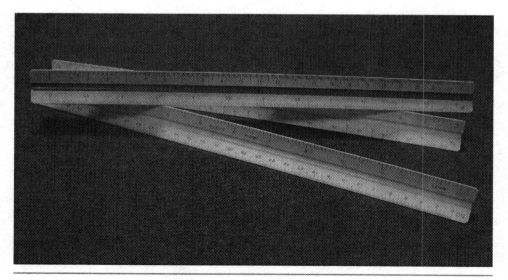

FIGURE 18.44. Three common scales used in creating or measuring dimension on engineering drawings.

are built as one-of-a-kind structures, there may be times when dimensions are inadvertently left off drawings; and despite the diligence of the engineers who check the designs, the lack of a dimension is not known until the project is under construction. In this case, scales can be used in the field to quickly determine the dimension and construction can continue. Since tolerances in civil engineering projects are typically large (or nonexistent), reading a dimension using a scale is often "close enough." Further, in civil engineering projects, scales can be used in the field to measure a dimension on a given sheet rather than looking through a large set of drawings to find the specific sheet where the dimension is "officially" located. In manufacturing applications, scales can be used to quickly estimate dimensions as needed.

In determining a dimension from a drawing that has been drawn to scale, many novices use a calculator. For example, if a drawing has been made at a scale of 1"=40' and you measured a line that is ⅝" long, you could calculate that the line represents 25' on the actual object (⅝ of 40 is 25). Using a calculator to figure out dimension is extremely tedious and would likely result in error. Fortunately, this tedium can be avoided with the use of an appropriate scale. In the following sections, you will learn about the three primary types of scales used in engineering.

18.09.01 Engineer's Scale

An **Engineer's scale** (sometimes called a Civil Engineer's scale) usually consists of 10, 20, 30, 40, 50, and 60 scales. These scales are based on the English system of units, with the inch as the basis for measurement. The divisions on the scales are in increments of tenths of an inch, not eighths of an inch as on ordinary rulers. Engineer's scales can be used to measure a line in any multiple of ten of the basic unit. For example, the 30 scale can be used for reading the following scales from drawings: 1"=3', 1"=300', or 1"=30 mi. Similarly, the 50 scale can be used for drawings with scales of 1"=50', 1"=5 yds, or 1"= 500 mi.

Figure 18.45 shows a line being measured with a 20 scale. The actual length of the line on paper is 3.5"; but since it is drawn at a scale of 1"=200', this line represents a length of 700' on the actual object. By reading the scale in this figure, what is the length of the actual line to point A? (The actual line to point A is 580' long.)

Figure 18.46 shows lines drawn at a scale of 1"=40' and a corresponding 40 Engineer's scale. What is the length of each line segment (OA, OB, OC)? These values can be read directly from the scale, making proper adjustments for decimal places. The line is drawn at a scale of 1"=40'; therefore, the first 2 on the scale represents 20', the 4 represents 40', the 6 represents 60', etc. The unlabeled long tic marks represent 10', 30', 50', etc. The intermediate-length tic marks occur at 5' intervals, and the smaller tic marks represent 1' intervals. Therefore, the length of line OA on this scale can be read as 67'. The line OB is read as 103'. Many times novice scale readers will incorrectly interpret the length of OB as 130'. When the scale is read, care should be taken to put the

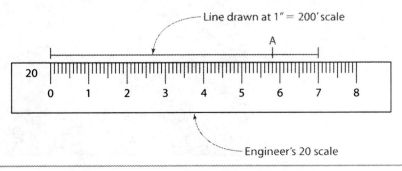

FIGURE 18.45. Line to be measured at a scale of 1"=200' and a 20 Engineer's scale.

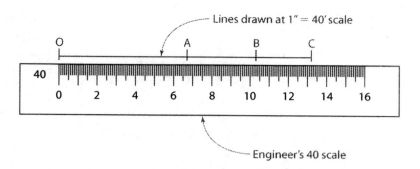

FIGURE 18.46. Lines drawn at a scale of 1"=40' and a 40 Engineer's scale.

decimal in the correct place. The distance OB is read directly as 10.3; but since the scale is 1"=40', the decimal is moved to the right one unit and the correct scale reading becomes 103'. The length of the line OC can be read from the scale as 132'.

In Figure 18.46, what are the lengths of the lines if they are drawn at a scale of 1"=4000'? Note that you still use the same Engineer's scale (the 40 scale) to make this reading but you add more zeros to the number that you read on the scale. Thus, the line OA has a length of 6700', OB has a length of 10,300', and OC has a length of 13,400' at a scale of 1"=4000'. What if the lines are drawn at a scale of 1"=4 yds? At that scale, the line OA has a length of 6.7 yds, OB has a length of 10.3 yds, and OC has a length of 13.4 yds.

18.09.02 Metric Scale

Metric scales are similar to Engineer's scales except that they are based on the metric system of units. Because metric units are based on decimals, unlike the English system of units (12" per foot, 3' per yard, 1,760 yds per mile, etc.), Metric scales are reported as ratios. Thus, typical Metric scales are reported as 1:1, 1:2, 1:5, and 1:10, for example. The same principal used to measure distances with an Engineer's scale is used for Metric scales. Like an Engineer's scale, the Metric scales can be used for multiples of ten of the basic unit. Thus, a 1:5 scale can also be used to measure 1:50, 1:500, and 1:5000 scales. Figure 18.47 shows a line drawn at a 1:2000 scale and a 1:20 Metric scale. On a Metric scale, the numbers (0.5, 1.0, 1.5, etc.) generally represent meters; and you adjust the decimal according to the specific scale at which you are measuring. If you read the scale directly, the length of the line is 1.84 m. But since the scale depicts a drawing scale of 1:20 and the line was drawn at a scale of 1:2000, you must move the decimal two units to the right to account for the difference. Thus, the length of the line is equal to 184 m. Similarly, if the line was drawn at a 1:200 scale, the length of the line would be 18.4 m.

Figure 18.48 shows a Metric scale of 1:100 and a set of lines drawn at a 1:1 scale. What are the lengths of each line? If you read the length of OA directly from the scale, you see that it is 7.7 m. Since the scale is 1:100 and the line is drawn at 1:1, you move the decimal place two units to the left; therefore, the length of the line is 0.077 m. Alternatively, you could report the length of the line as 7.7 cm or 77 mm. What is the length of OB? The value read from the scale is 10.7 m. If you move the decimal place two units to the left, the length is determined as 0.107 m (or 10.7 cm or 107 mm). Similarly, the length of line OC is 0.124 m (12.4 cm).

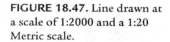

FIGURE 18.47. Line drawn at a scale of 1:2000 and a 1:20 Metric scale.

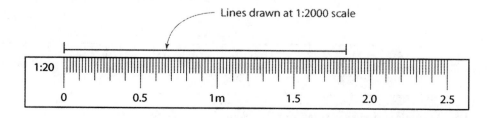

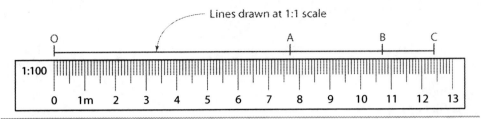

FIGURE 18.48. Lines drawn at 1:1 scale and a 1:100 Metric scale.

18.09.03 Architect's Scale

An **Architect's scale** is similar to an Engineer's scale in that it is based on the English system of units. One of the differences between the two scales is that the Architect's scale is based on fractions of an inch. (Recall that the Engineer's scale is based on tenths.) Another significant difference is that with an Architect's scale, drawing scales are always reported as something=1'-0". Thus, a scale might be reported as ¼"=1'-0" or as ⅜"=1'-0". Some of the more common scales depicted on an Architect's scale are as follows:

12"=1'0" (full size)	6"=1'-0" (half size)	3"=1'-0" (quarter size)
1½"=1'-0" (⅛ size)	1"=1'-0" (1/12 size)	¾"=1'-0" (1/16 size)
½"=1'-0" (1/24 size)	⅜"=1'-0" (1/32 size)	¼"=1'-0" (1/48 size)
3/16"=1'-0" (1/64 size)	⅛"=1'-0" (1/96 size)	3/32"=1'-0" (1/128 size)

Architect's scales usually look significantly different than Engineer's or Metric scales. The biggest difference is that each edge of the Architect's scale typically depicts two scales—one reading from left to right and the other reading from right to left. Thus, twice as many scales (twelve versus six) are depicted on an Architect's scale when compared to an Engineer's or Metric scale. The other difference is that fractional gradations are shown only at the ends of the scale. Thus, when you are measuring a distance with an Architect's scale, you must place one end of the line at the nearest whole number foot on the scale and read the fractional foot at the end with the gradation. Figure 18.49 shows an Architect's ¼ scale (this means the ¼"=1'-0") and line to be measured with this scale. In this figure, the ¼ scale is read from right to left on the scale and the ⅛ scale is read from left to right. To read the length of this line, you place one end of the line on the nearest even foot mark of the scale. In this case, it is 11'. (Remember that you are reading from right to left for the ¼ scale.) Notice that the closest foot mark is not labeled for you. For the ¼ scale, the even foot markers are labeled but the odd ones are not. The smaller tic marks for this scale represent one-half foot divisions. Be careful not to line up the end of the line with the half-foot marks instead of the foot markers. The fractional feet are shown in the last foot of the scale (past the 0). This last foot is divided into twelve gradations, so each tic mark on the scale represents 1" because there are 12 inches in a foot. Thus, the length of this line is 11'-7".

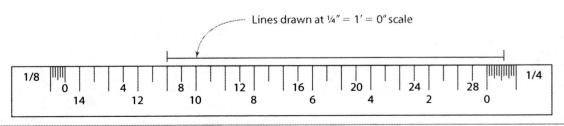

FIGURE 18.49. Line drawn at a scale of ¼"=1'-0" and a ¼" Architect's scale.

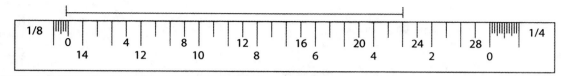

FIGURE 18.50. Line drawn at a scale of ⅛"=1'-0" and a ⅛" Architect's scale.

What happens if you read the length of this line using the ⅛ scale? Figure 18.50 shows the same line being measured with the ⅛ scale. The same procedure is followed to read the length of the line at this scale. In this case, the nearest even foot mark is 23'. Notice that on this scale, only every fourth (4, 8, 12, etc.) foot marker is labeled and that the long tic marks from left to right represent the odd foot marks. The short tic marks from left to right represent the intermediate even foot markers. The final foot of this scale is divided into six increments compared to twelve for the ¼ scale. Thus, each division in the final foot represents 2″. As shown in this figure, the length of the line at a ⅛ scale is 23'-2″. (Note that this makes sense because $2 \times 11'-7'' = 22'-14''$, or 23'-2″). The Architect's scale usually requires a great deal of practice on your part to be able to read it with confidence.

As you may have realized from the previous discussion of drawing scales (Engineer's, Architect's, and Metric), these devices are time-saving and relatively easy to use. Unfortunately, many students have a tendency to use calculators when working with scaled drawings for the first time. It is important that you learn to use a scale for working with engineering drawings.

CAUTION

The guidelines for creating working drawings are structured to minimize the number of errors and amount of missing information. New engineers who are not familiar with these guidelines (or choose to ignore them) sometimes create errors. Errors in working drawings are likely to cause mild embarrassment for the originator at best. When errors are more serious, they can slow the process of the drawing being interpreted or cause confusion in the cataloging or organizing of the part. The following sections are a compilation of the most common beginner errors and ways to avoid them.

No Drawing Border

The absence of a border on a formal drawing is usually the result of an inexperienced attempt to create a custom drawing header. A well-defined border defines the limits of a drawing. Without a border, as shown in Figure 18.51, it is sometime unclear, especially when copying the drawing and especially when the drawing's full size is unknown, to know what should be included. When additional views, details, comments, or corrections are added, this information may become lost. Including a border clearly shows what is part of the drawing and what is not.

No Title Block or Poor Title Block

A poor or missing title block, as shown in Figure 18.52, is also a sign of an inexperienced attempt to create a formal drawing header. Although drawing headers vary between organizations, title blocks are always expected along with a minimum amount of information. When creating a custom title block, a good place to start is with the ANSI blocks shown in Figure 18.14. Spaces can then be added for the information required for the specific needs of your company. For example, products that carry high financial or safety risks may consistently require additional levels of engineering or management approval for the release of a drawing to fabricators. Some companies require that their material specialists approve all drawings to ensure that hazardous materials are not used and that all parts are recyclable at their end of life.

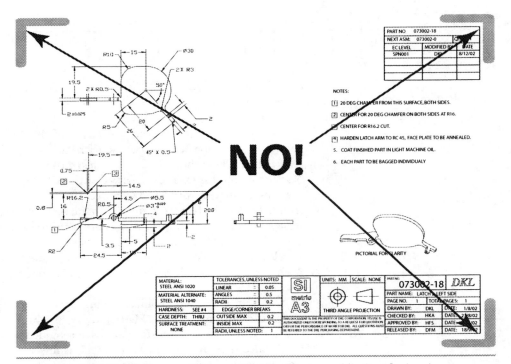

FIGURE 18.51. A common error. Without a border, the size and limits of a drawing are uncertain.

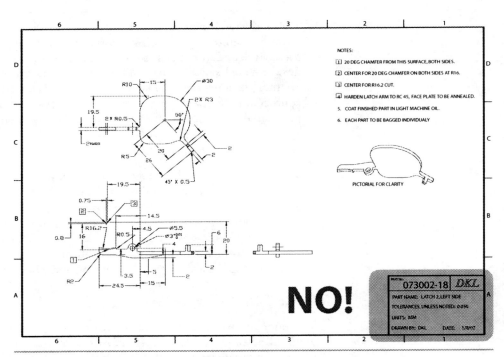

FIGURE 18.52. A common error. A poor header makes it too easy to omit important information.

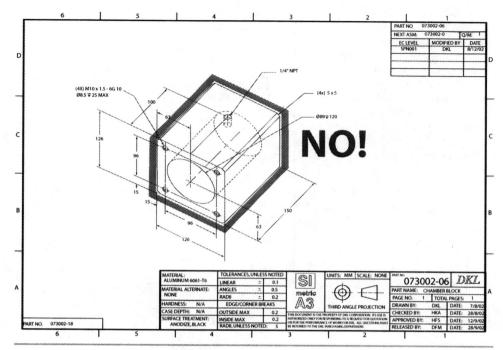

FIGURE 18.53. A common error. Applying dimensions to a pictorial is considered incorrect practice for formal working drawings.

No Multiview Presentation

The use of multiple orthogonal views to present an object, showing as many of its edges in true length or true shapes as possible, is considered the standard for manufacturing drawings; however, recall that doing so usually is not standard practice in the construction industry. The use of pictorials for manufacturing drawings is to provide additional clarity only; pictorial drawings are rarely included with construction plans due to the complexity of the designed systems. Showing dimensions on a pictorial, as in Figure 18.53, may seem reasonable but is generally not accepted as being correct because true shapes on the object are distorted and some features may be partially or completely hidden.

Poor Multiview Presentation

When a multiview presentation is used for manufacturing drawings, the object should be oriented to show as many of its edges as visible, rather than hidden, edges for defining dimensions. In the example shown in Figure 18.54, the object is oriented such that its edges can be seen in their true shape in at least one view. However, hidden lines define the edges of the bore and groove. It would be much better to turn the object so that the opening of the bore faces the right side; that view would show the edges as visible. An alternative solution would be to add a left side view to the object and show the dimension of the bore in that view.

FIGURE 18.54. A common error. Poor orientation of the object in a multiview presentation produces hidden lines instead of solid edges on the face containing the bore opening and four tapped holes. The opening of the bore should have been placed facing the reader in the front view.

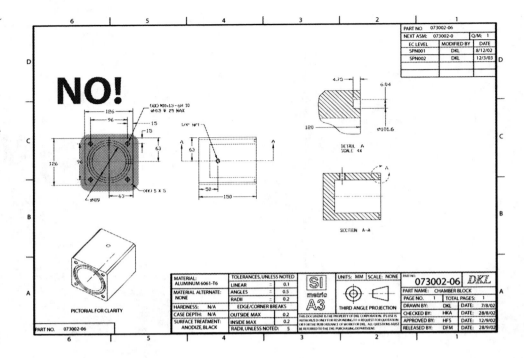

Crowding or Poor Dimension Placement

The dimensions on a drawing should be placed so that they are easy to see and interpret. When the dimensions are crowded, placed inside the object, or placed such that many dimension lines and extension lines cross, as in Figure 18.55, the presentation appears unorganized and is confusing.

FIGURE 18.55. A common error. Poorly placed and/or crowded dimensions make the drawing difficult and time-consuming to read.

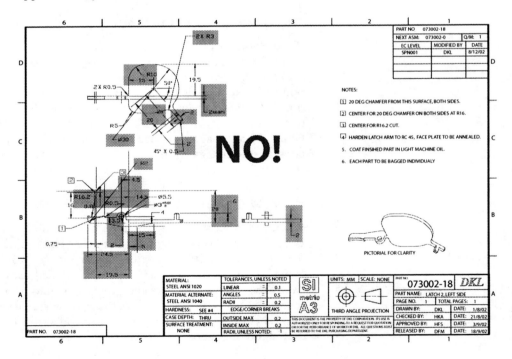

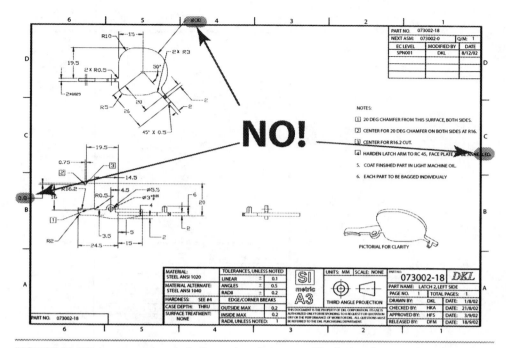

FIGURE 18.56. A common error. Information that overspills the border must be contained within the border to be a part of the drawing.

Content That Is Outside the Border

Everything that is of importance to a drawing must be contained entirely within its border. In Figure 18.56, some dimension text and notes overspill the border. This is considered sloppy work and should be avoided. When there is not enough room on the sheet to contain all of the information within the border, a larger sheet must be used.

Bad Choice for Sheet Size

Objects that are of a simple geometry, with few features that need to be defined and dimensioned, can be drawn on smaller sheets. Objects with more complicated geometries that have many features must be drawn on larger sheets. The choice of a proper sheet size is subjective, but the cases in Figure 18.57 show sheet size that is either too small or too large. Too small a sheet results in crowding of information on the drawing. Too large a sheet is a waste of paper and results in a drawing that is more difficult to handle than is necessary.

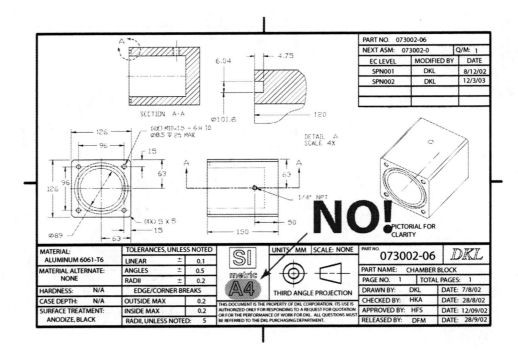

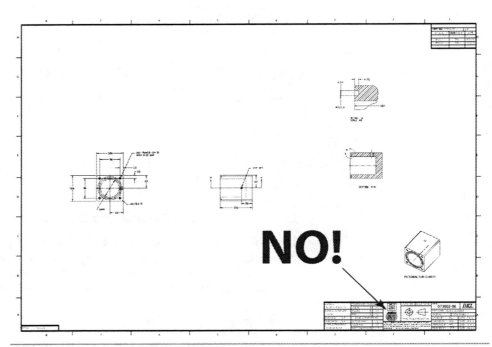

FIGURE 18.57. A common error. Poor choice of sheet size: too small (above) and too large (below).

Bad Choice for Drawing Scale

Objects that are of a simple geometry, with few large features that need to be defined and dimensioned, can be drawn to a smaller scale. Objects with more complicated geometries that have many features must be drawn to a larger scale so that the geometries can be seen and defined. As with the selection of sheet size, the choice of a proper drawing scale is subjective; but the cases in Figure 18.58 provide examples of drawing scales that are too small and too big. Too small a scale results in crowding of information and indiscernible object features on the drawing. Too large a scale results in an unnecessarily large sheet size and text that is unnecessarily small when the entire object is presented.

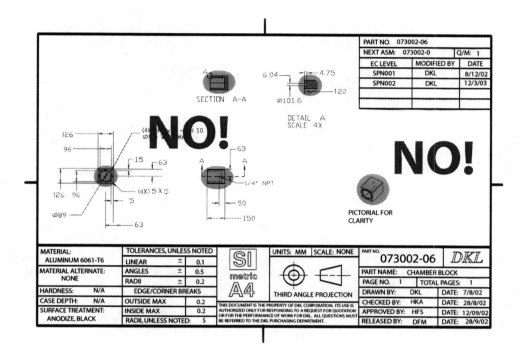

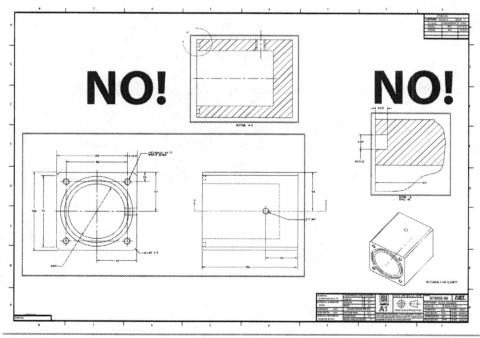

FIGURE 18.58. A common error. Poor choice of drawing scale: too small (above) and too large (below).

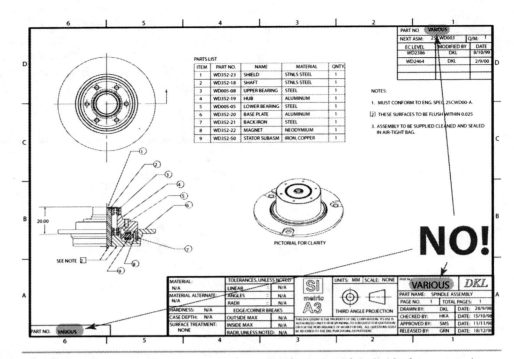

FIGURE 18.59. A common error. Omitted part numbers. As with individual parts, a unique part number is required for each subassembly and assembly.

No Part Number

Every piece in a device or manufactured system must have its own unique part number within the company that designed it. Part numbers are often neglected for assemblies and subassemblies, as shown in Figure 18.59. One reason for this common error is the misconception that part numbers are for parts only. Part numbers are required to identify assemblies and subassemblies as well.

Same Part Number for Different Parts

Occasionally, due to carelessness or poor record keeping, different parts within the same company or organization end up having the same part number, as shown in Figure 18.60. This error will undoubtedly cause much confusion when the time comes to fabricate the correct part.

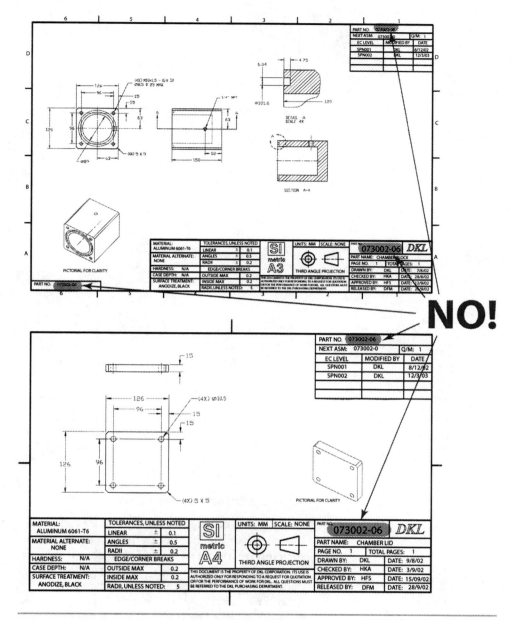

NO!

FIGURE 18.60. A common error. These two drawings claim to have the same part number.

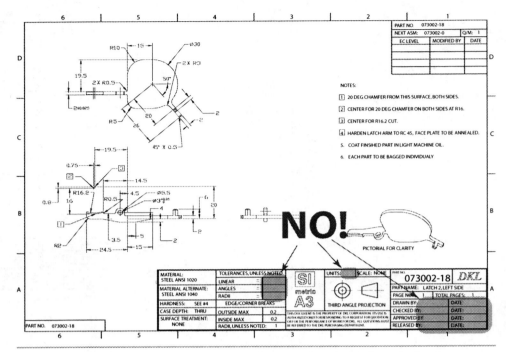

FIGURE 18.61. A common error. Important information is missing from the header.

Missing Information in the Title Block

One purpose of using a drawing header with a comprehensive title block is to prompt the creator of the drawing to include information that may otherwise be neglected. If such information is not included, as shown in Figure 18.61, there is little point in using the drawing header. All of the information requested in the title block should be supplied. If the information has no relevance for a particular drawing (for example, the default tolerances on an assembly drawing with no assembly dimensions), that space should be marked with N/A or a similar notation.

Portrait Instead of Landscape Orientation

Although portrait orientation, shown in Figure 18.62, is permitted in formal engineering drawings, landscape orientation is preferred. New engineers unfamiliar with formal drawing sometimes use portrait orientation (especially for size A or A4 drawings) because it is the same orientation used to create text documents, with which they are familiar from school. Although some companies use portrait orientation for drawings, the majority of drawings are done in landscape orientation.

Nonstandard Sheet Size

In the strictest sense, it is not incorrect to create a drawing in portrait orientation, where the height of the sheet is larger than the width (shown in Figure 18.63). However, engineering drawings are almost exclusively created using landscape orientation, where the width is larger than the height. To maintain a more professional appearance, landscape orientation should be used for drawings.

FIGURE 18.62. A common error. A portrait sheet orientation is not preferred in engineering drawings; landscape orientation is.

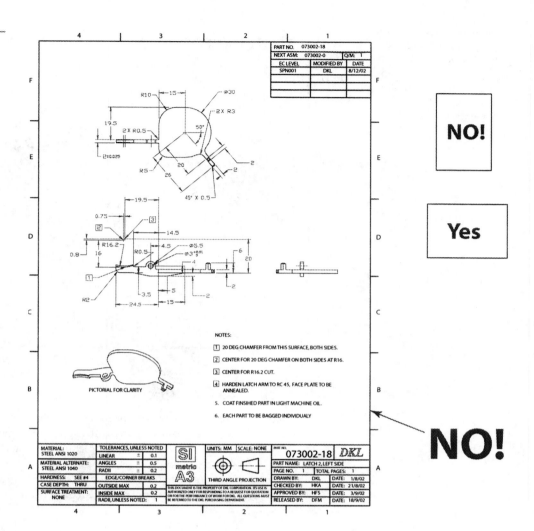

FIGURE 18.63. A common error. Nonstandard sheet sizes. Landscape orientation is used almost exclusively for drawings.

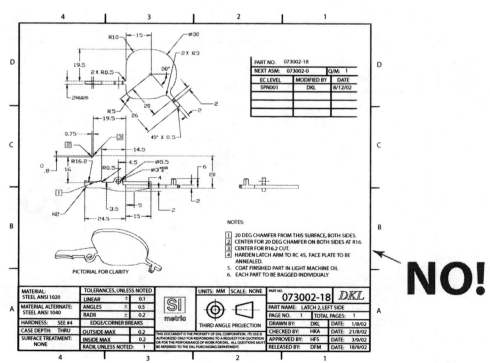

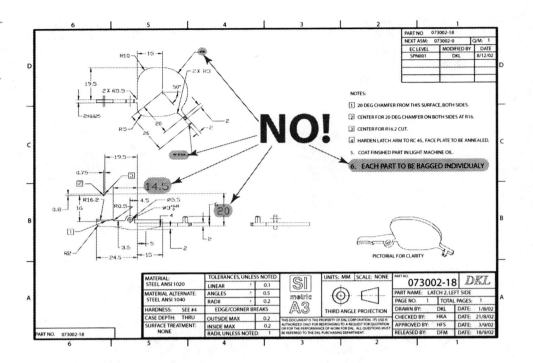

FIGURE 18.64. A common error. Lettering that is too large, too small, or inconsistent in size. Font sizes should be appropriate and used consistently on a drawing.

Poor or Inconsistent Fonts

The lettering size for the text and numbers on a drawing should be in the range of 3–6 mm in height when the drawing is printed to its specified sheet size. Of course, when the drawing is reduced in size (for example, for the convenience of printing on a letter-sized sheet from a desktop printer), the fonts will appear smaller. Lettering that is too large, too small, or inconsistent in size on a drawing implies that not enough thought was given to a professional appearance. Incorrect font sizes are shown in Figure 18.64.

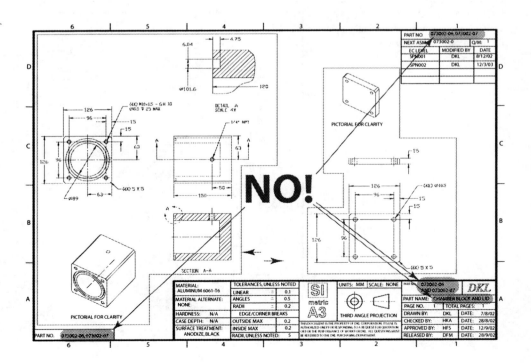

FIGURE 18.65. A common error. Detail drawings showing multiple parts. Each drawing should contain only one part.

Multiple Parts on a Single Detail Drawing

It is sometimes tempting to save time, effort, and paper by putting more than one part on a single detail drawing, as shown in Figure 18.65. Each part must have its own detail drawing. The practice of putting multiple parts on a single drawing is considered incorrect for manufacturing drawings; however, construction drawings often show several details or sections on a single sheet, as shown in Figure 18.66. In the case of construction drawings, one drawing per sheet is considered poor practice. The reason for this difference between manufacturing and construction drawings is that in

FIGURE 18.66. Drawing showing multiple details from a set of construction plans.

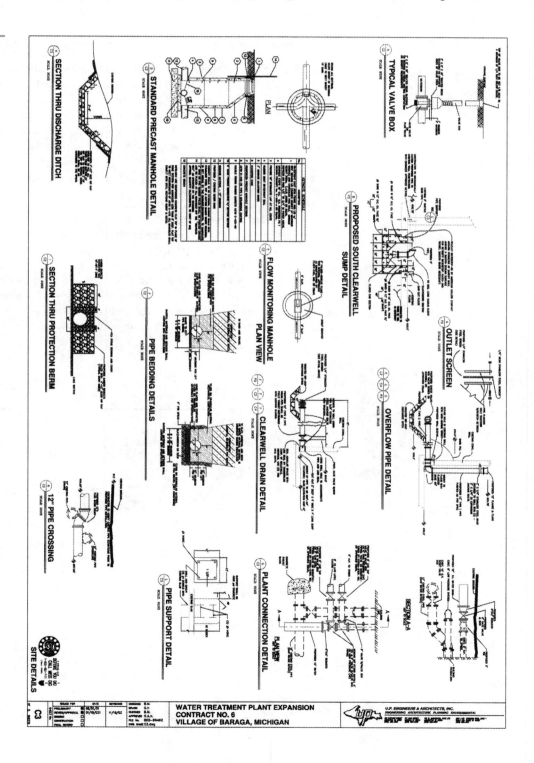

manufacturing, it is common to have different parts made by different fabricators. For construction projects, the same contractor is working on the entire project and needs to be able to see all of the details and the way they fit in the overall project. Further, the set of construction drawings is typically so large—as is the sheet size (size E)—that having one detail per sheet would make a thick set of plans even thicker. Having multiple manufactured parts on the same sheet creates confusion about which part is to be made and which drawing details belong to which part. The exception in manufacturing drawings is in the case of a family of parts with the same general appearance and function that differ in a few dimensions only. Such parts are generally intended to be made at the same fabricator.

Detail Dimensions on an Assembly Drawing

Putting part dimensions on an assembly drawing for a manufactured system, as shown in Figure 18.67, is incorrect. Part dimensions belong on the detail drawing for that part. It is quite common for dimensions and tolerances to be modified on a part. If these dimensions or tolerances change, it is easier and less confusing when the changes are made to the detail drawing only. Adding part dimensions to assembly drawings is redundant information, which should be unnecessary for assembly drawings.

Handwritten Notes on an Electronic Drawing

When an electronic (CAD) drawing is modified, its data file must be changed. Although it seems easy to modify the drawing by hand, as shown in Figure 18.68, handwritten notes are not reflected in the drawing's electronic file. When a manufacturing drawing is submitted for approval or is provided to a fabricator, it should contain no handwriting. If errors or corrections are noted on a submitted drawing, these errors must be corrected in the original electronic file and a new drawing issued. The exception to this general rule is in construction projects where a contractor applies handwritten notes to a drawing in the creation of the as-built drawings. These notes should be transferred to the electronic files at a later date.

FIGURE 18.67. A common error. Dimensions for individual parts shown on assembly drawings. The dimensions belong on the detail drawings.

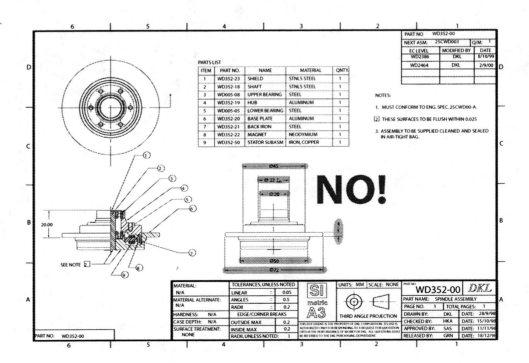

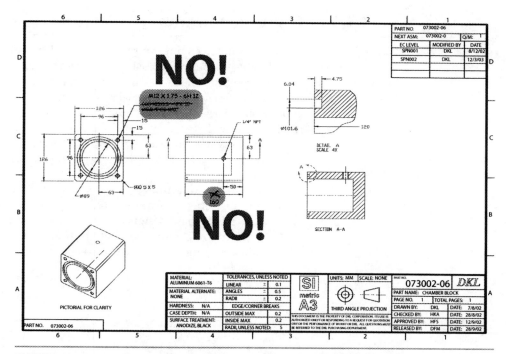

FIGURE 18.68. A common error. Amending or editing by hand an electronically generated drawing. Doing so does not alter the original data file; it needs to be updated.

18.10 Considerations for 3-D Modeling

The development of 3-D computer modeling has greatly reduced the time and effort required to produce a manufacturing drawing; however, as stated previously, 3-D modeling is not predominant in the construction industry and is not likely to be so for several years. In the following paragraphs, the considerations for 3-D modeling are given for projects in the realm of manufacturing.

There are provisions on most 3-D modeling software to easily generate different views of an object or assembly, including multiviews, section and detail views, auxiliary views, and pictorials. Dimensions can also be made to appear on any of the views. Because of the ease with which these graphics are generated, there is no excuse not to include as many different views as needed to communicate the geometry of the part or device. Formal drawing headers also are easily created, usually recalled from a library of premade headers with different complexities as demanded by the application of the device to be made.

Three-dimensional modeling software, however, cannot fully interpret the functional requirements of the device that is to be built. That knowledge resides with the designer or engineer. For example, depending on the functional requirements of a part, only the engineer or designer can know what dimension tolerances are acceptable for the part to work properly. Since most numerically controlled machine tools (described in the chapter on fabrication processes) can easily hold tolerances to within 25 microns for most small parts, it is sometimes tempting to use this number as a default tolerance for every dimension. However, if tighter tolerances are required by the engineer, special manufacturing processes may be required. An example is in the computer disk drive spindle detailed in Figure 18.27; it shows that tolerances in the range of 5 microns are required for some dimensions. Only the engineer or designer can know those requirements. The software can present only what the engineer or designer wants.

18.11 Chapter Summary

With any type of engineering drawing, the key word is *communication*. The drawing must be able to communicate to the reader the desires of the engineer or designer for a part or assembly. When working drawings are created, this communication must occur even in the absence of the drawing's originator. Use of the formal drawing format—with proper views, sheet sizes, headers, and drawing organization—serves to maximize the probability that the device will be built correctly. Almost as important is the fact that the quality of a working drawing is a reflection of the person, company, or organization that produced it. A high-quality and professional presentation must be maintained.

A formal working drawing succeeds not because it looks good, but because it clearly and unambiguously tells a fabricator or contractor how to produce a desired product. What you have designed may well be beautiful once it is produced, but that is irrelevant initially. The only goal at the start is to produce a working drawing that allows your conception to be made into reality.

18.12 glossary of key terms

approval signatures: The dated signatures or initials of the people responsible for certain aspects of a formal drawing, such as the people who did the drafting or the engineer responsible for the function of the part.

Architect's scale: A device used to measure or draw lines in the English system of units with a base unit of inches and fractions of an inch.

as-built plans: Drawings that show exactly how buildings were constructed, especially when variations exist between the final building and the plans created during the design phase.

assembly: A collection of parts and/or subassemblies that have been put together to make a device or structure that performs a specific function.

assembly dimensions: Dimensions that show where parts must be placed relative to other parts when the device is being put together.

balloons: Closed geometric shapes, usually circles, containing identification numbers and placed beside parts on a layout or assembly drawing to help identify those parts.

bearing: The angle that a line makes with a North-South line as seen in a plan view.

benchmarks: Points established by the U.S. Geological Survey that can be used to accurately locate control points on a construction site.

bill of materials (BOM): A drawing or table in a drawing that lists all of the parts needed to build a device by (at least) the part number, part name, type of material used, and number of times the part is used in the device.

blueprints: The name sometimes given to construction drawings based on historical blue-on-white drawings that were produced from ink drawings.

border: A thick line that defines the perimeter of a drawing.

construction drawings: Working drawings, often created by civil engineers, that are used to build large-scale, one-of-a-kind structures.

continuation blocks: Header blocks used on the second and subsequent pages of multipage drawings.

control points: Points at a construction site that are referenced to an origin by north, south, east, or west coordinates.

cover sheet: The first page in a set of construction drawings showing a map of the location of the project and possibly an index.

default tolerances: Usually appearing in the drawing header, the tolerances to be assumed for any dimension show on a part when that dimension does not specify any tolerances.

detail drawing: A formal drawing that shows the geometry, dimensions, tolerances, materials, and any processes needed to fabricate a part.

detail sections: Drawings included in a set of construction plans that show how the various components are assembled.

EC Level: A number included in the title block of a drawing indicating that the part has undergone a revision.

electrical plan: A plan view showing the layout of electrical devices on a floor in a building.

elevation views: Views of a structure that show changes in elevation (side or front views).

Engineer's scale: A device used to measure or draw lines in the English system of units with a base unit of inches and tenths of an inch.

engineering change (EC) number: A dated number that defines the degree to which the specifications of a part have been updated.

exploded assembly drawing: A formal drawing, usually in pictorial form, that shows the orientation and sequence in which parts are put together to make a device.

floor plan: A plan view of a single floor in a building that shows the layout of the rooms.

foundation plan: A plan view of the foundation of a building showing footings and other support structures.

general sections: Sections through entire structures that show the layout of rooms but provide little detail.

header: A premade outline on which working drawings are created to ensure that all information required for fabrication and record keeping is entered.

heating and ventilation plan: A plan view of the ventilation systems on a specific floor of a building, including ductwork and devices such as air conditioning units.

index: A list of all sheets of drawings contained in a set of construction plans.

item number: A number used to identify a part on a layout or assembly drawing.

international sheet sizes: The internationally accepted paper dimensions used when drawings are created or printed to their full intended size.

landscape: The drawing orientation in which the horizontal size is larger than the vertical size.

layout drawing: A formal drawing that shows a device in its assembled state with all of its parts identified.

location grid: An imaginary alphanumeric grid, similar to that of a street map, on a drawing that is used to specify area locations on the drawing.

main assembly: A completed device usually composed of multiple smaller parts and/or subassemblies.

main title block: A bordered area of a drawing (and part of the drawing header) that contains important information about the identification, fabrication, history, and ownership of the item shown on the drawing.

manufacturing drawings: Working drawings, often created by mechanical engineers, that are used to mass-produce products for consumers.

Metric scale: A device used to measure or draw lines in the metric system of units with drawings scales reported as ratios.

notes: Additional information or instructions placed on a drawing that are not contained on the dimensions, tolerances, or header.

one-off: A one-of-a-kind engineering project for which no physical prototypes are created.

outline assembly drawing: *See* layout drawing.

part: An object expected to be delivered from a fabricator as a single unit with only its external dimensions and functional requirements specified.

part name: A very short descriptive title given to a part, subassembly, or device.

part number: Within a company, a string of alphanumeric characters used to identify a part, a subassembly, an assembly, or a device.

parts list: *See* bill of materials.

plan and profile drawings: Construction drawings typically used for roads or other linear entities that show the road from above as well as from the side, with the profile view usually drawn with an exaggerated vertical scale.

plan views: Drawings created from a viewpoint above the structure (top view).

portrait: The drawing orientation in which the vertical size is larger than the horizontal size.

professional engineer (PE): An individual who has received an engineering degree, who has worked under the supervision of a PE for a number of years, and who has passed two examinations certifying knowledge of engineering practice.

profile views: Views of a structure that show horizontal surfaces in edge view (side or front views).

quantity per machine (Q/M): The number of times a part is required to build its next highest assembly.

rebars: Steel bars added to concrete for reinforcement or for temperature control.

reference dimensions: Unneeded dimensions shown for the convenience of the reader used to show overall dimensions that could be extracted from other dimensions on the part or from other drawings.

schedule of materials: A list of the materials, such as doors and windows, necessary for a construction project.

secondary title block: An additional bordered area of a drawing (and part of the drawing header) that contains important information about the identification, fabrication, and history of the item shown on the drawing.

sectioned assembly drawing: A formal drawing, usually in pictorial form, that shows the device in its assembled form but with sections removed from obscuring parts to reveal formerly hidden parts.

18.12 glossary of key terms (continued)

set of construction plans: A collection of drawings, not necessarily all of them plan views, needed to construct a building or infrastructure project.

site plan: A plan view showing the construction site for an infrastructure project.

site survey: Data regarding the existing topography and structures gathered during the preliminary design stages by trained surveying crews.

specifications (specs): The written instructions that accompany a set of construction plans used to build an infrastructure project.

subassemblies: Collections of parts that have been put together for the purpose of installing the collections as single units into larger assemblies.

title block: Usually the main title block, which is a bordered area of the drawing (and part of the drawing header) that contains important information about the identification, fabrication, history, and ownership of the item shown on the drawing.

trail: Dashed lines on an assembly drawing that show how various parts or subassemblies are inserted to create a larger assembly.

US sheet sizes: The accepted paper dimensions used in the United States when drawings are created or printed to their intended size.

wall sections: Sectional views of walls from foundation to roof for a construction project.

working drawings: A collection of all drawings needed to fabricate and put together a device or structure.

18.13 questions for review

1. What is the purpose of a header on a formal engineering drawing?

2. What type of information is typically included on a drawing header?

3. What signatures (or initials) typically appear in a drawing header?

4. Why is it important that dates be included on a drawing?

5. Why is it important that part numbers be unique to each part?

6. When should the part number for a particular part be changed?

7. What considerations need to be made in the selection of a sheet size for a drawing?

8. What considerations need to be made in the selection of a scale for a drawing?

9. What are the three different types of assembly drawings? How do they differ?

10. What is a revision (or engineering change) to a drawing?

11. How is a subassembly different from a main assembly?

12. What sort of information is typically included in a bill of materials?

13. What types of dimensions are permitted on an assembly drawing?

14. List three ways that manufacturing drawings differ from construction drawings.

15. Construction projects are site-specific. What does that mean?

16. What is the bearing of a line? In which view is it seen?

17. What does the term *professional engineer* mean?

18. What are plan, profile, and elevation views?

19. What is meant by the term *one-off*?

20. For construction drawings, what is a general section?

21. What are the three types of scales used in engineering?

22. Which scales are based on the English system of units?

18.14 problems

1. The parts shown in Figure P18.1 are to be assembled into a screw clamp. Create a complete set of working drawings for the device, including an outline assembly drawing, an exploded assembly drawing, a bill of materials, and all detailed part drawings. Specify appropriate tolerances for all dimensions. All parts are made of steel. You may use metric dimensions or convert the metric dimensions to their nearest inch equivalents.

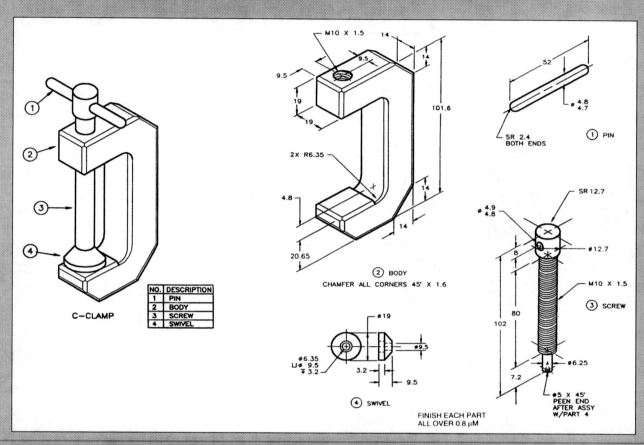

FIGURE P18.1.

18.14 problems (continued)

2. The parts shown in Figure P18.2 are to be assembled into a tool holder. Create a complete set of working drawings for the device, including an outline assembly drawing, an exploded assembly drawing, a sectioned assembly drawing, a bill of materials, and all detailed part drawings. Specify appropriate tolerances for all dimensions. All parts are made of steel. You may use metric dimensions or convert the metric dimensions to their nearest inch equivalents.

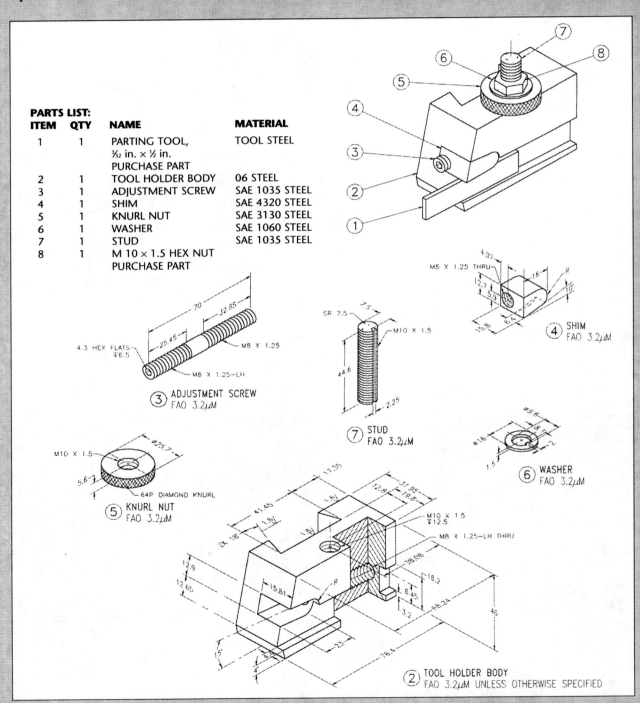

PARTS LIST:

ITEM	QTY	NAME	MATERIAL
1	1	PARTING TOOL, ³⁄₃₂ in. × ½ in. PURCHASE PART	TOOL STEEL
2	1	TOOL HOLDER BODY	06 STEEL
3	1	ADJUSTMENT SCREW	SAE 1035 STEEL
4	1	SHIM	SAE 4320 STEEL
5	1	KNURL NUT	SAE 3130 STEEL
6	1	WASHER	SAE 1060 STEEL
7	1	STUD	SAE 1035 STEEL
8	1	M 10 × 1.5 HEX NUT PURCHASE PART	

FIGURE P18.2.

18.14 problems (continued)

3. A conceptual layout of a wood clamp is shown in Figure P18.3. Detail the design by specifying appropriate dimensions and tolerances for each part. Create a complete set of working drawings for the device, including an outline assembly drawing, an exploded assembly drawing, a bill of materials, and all detailed part drawings. All parts are made of steel. You may use the given inch dimensions or their nearest metric equivalents.

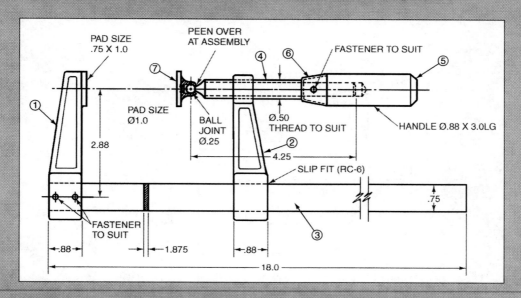

FIGURE P18.3.

4. A conceptual layout of an adjustable drawing compass is shown in Figure P18.4. Detail the design by specifying appropriate dimensions and tolerances for each part. Create a complete set of working drawings for the device, including an outline assembly drawing, an exploded assembly drawing, a bill of materials, and all detailed part drawings. All parts are made of steel. It is not necessary to create a drawing of the LEAD. You may use the given inch dimensions or their nearest metric equivalents.

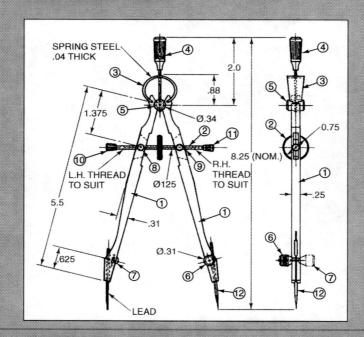

FIGURE P18.4.

18.14 problems (continued)

5. A conceptual sketch of a general duty clamp is shown in Figure P18.5. Detail the design by specifying appropriate dimensions and tolerances for each part. Create a complete set of working drawings for the device, including an outline assembly drawing, an exploded assembly drawing, a bill of materials, and all detailed part drawings. All parts are made of steel. You may use metric dimensions or convert the metric dimensions to their nearest inch equivalents.

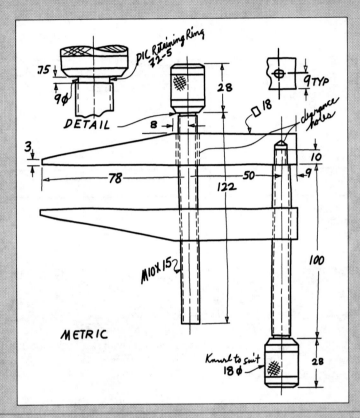

FIGURE P18.5.

18.14 problems (continued)

6. A conceptual sketch of a toggle clamp is shown in Figure P18.6. Detail the design by specifying appropriate dimensions and tolerances for each part. Create a complete set of working drawings for the device, including an outline assembly drawing, an exploded assembly drawing, a bill of materials, and all detailed part drawings. All parts are made of steel. You may use the given inch dimensions or their nearest metric equivalents.

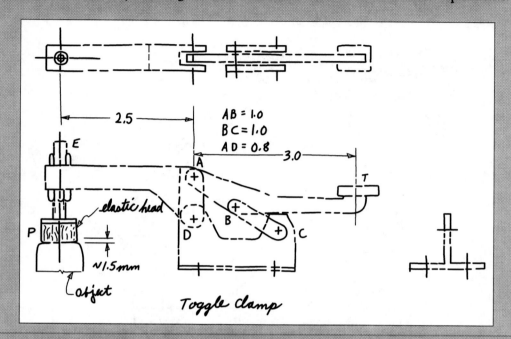

FIGURE P18.6.

18.14 problems (continued)

7. A conceptual layout of an adjustable lifting clamp is shown in Figure P18.7. Detail the design by specifying appropriate dimensions and tolerances for each part. Create a complete set of working drawings for the device, including an outline assembly drawing, an exploded assembly drawing, a bill of materials, and all detailed part drawings. All parts are made of steel. You may use the given inch dimensions or their nearest metric equivalents.

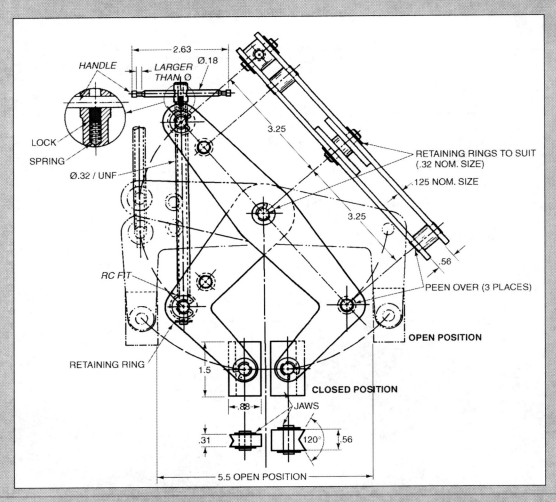

FIGURE P18.7.

18.14 problems (continued)

8. A conceptual model for a pen-type eraser is shown in whole and in cutaway view in Figure P18.8. Using reasonable materials and dimensions of your choice, expand the concept to create a complete set of working drawings for the device, including an outline assembly drawing, an exploded assembly drawing, a sectioned assembly drawing, a bill of materials, and all detailed part drawings. Specify appropriate tolerances for all dimensions.

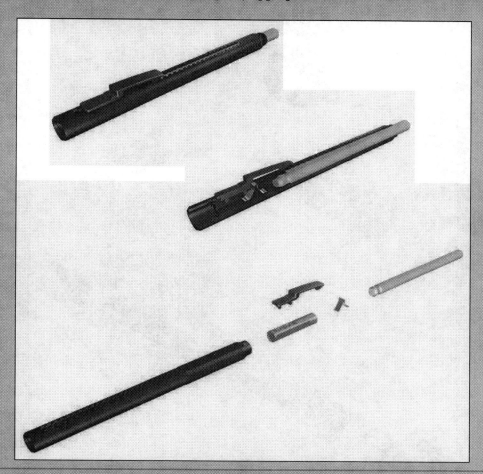

FIGURE P18.8.

18.14 problems (continued)

9. A conceptual model for a garden hose nozzle is shown in whole, cutaway, and exploded views in Figure P18.9. Using reasonable materials and dimensions of your choice, expand the concept to create a complete set of working drawings for the device, including an outline assembly drawing, an exploded assembly drawing, a sectioned assembly drawing, a bill of materials, and all detailed part drawings. Specify appropriate tolerances for all dimensions.

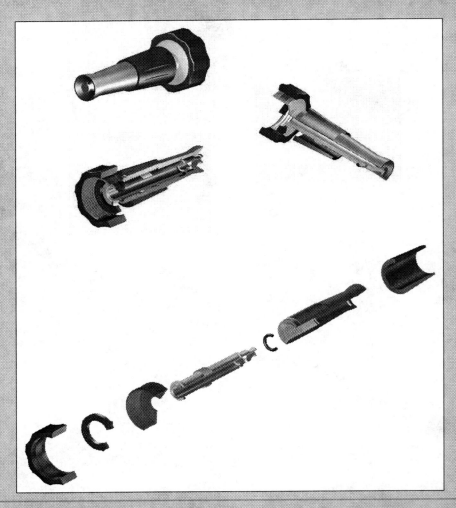

FIGURE P18.9.

18.14 problems (continued)

10. Conceptual sketches for a wheelbarrow are shown in Figure P18.10. Using reasonable materials and dimensions of your choice, expand the concept to create a complete set of working drawings for the device, including an outline assembly drawing, an exploded assembly drawing, a sectioned assembly drawing, a bill of materials, and all detailed part drawings. You may use either inch or metric dimensions. Specify appropriate tolerances for all dimensions.

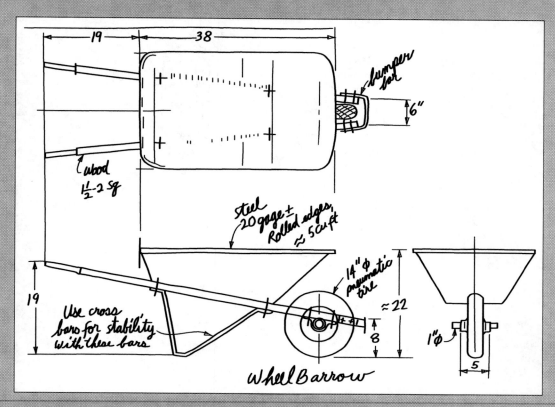

FIGURE P18.10.

18.14 problems (continued)

11. Conceptual sketches for a caster are shown in Figure P18.11. Using reasonable materials and dimensions of your choice, expand the concept to create a complete set of working drawings for the device, including an outline assembly drawing, an exploded assembly drawing, a sectioned assembly drawing, a bill of materials, and all detailed part drawings. You may use either inch or metric dimensions. Specify appropriate tolerances for all dimensions.

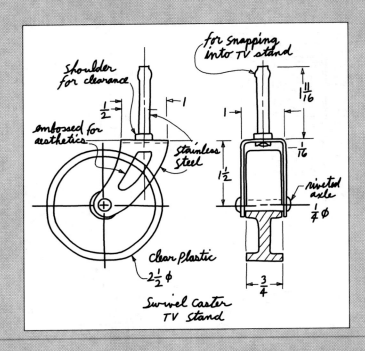

FIGURE P18.11.

18.14 problems (continued)

12. Find the errors and poor practices in these drawings.

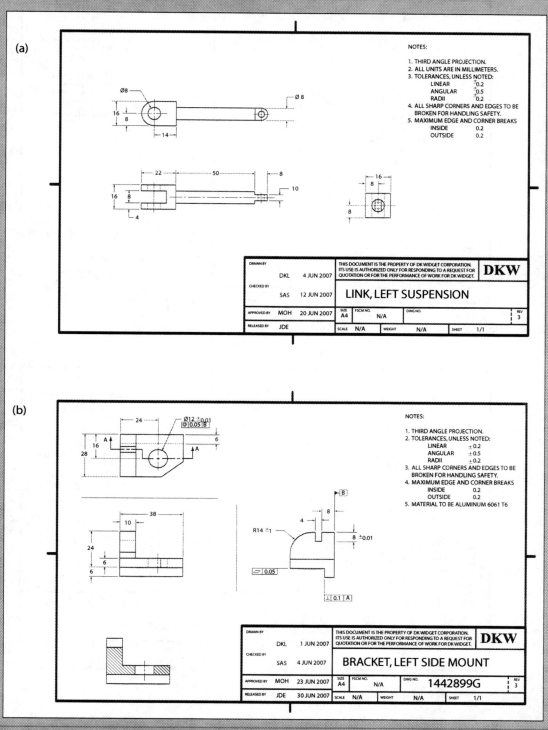

FIGURES P18.12.

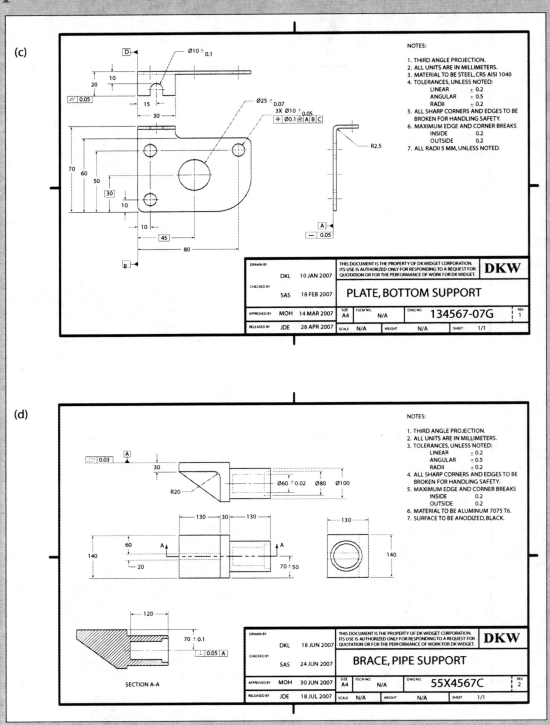

(c)

NOTES:

1. THIRD ANGLE PROJECTION.
2. ALL UNITS ARE IN MILLIMETERS.
3. MATERIAL TO BE STEEL, CRS AISI 1040
4. TOLERANCES, UNLESS NOTED:
   LINEAR   ± 0.2
   ANGULAR   ± 0.5
   RADII   ± 0.2
5. ALL SHARP CORNERS AND EDGES TO BE
   BROKEN FOR HANDLING SAFETY.
6. MAXIMUM EDGE AND CORNER BREAKS
   INSIDE   0.2
   OUTSIDE   0.2
7. ALL RADII 5 MM, UNLESS NOTED.

DRAWN BY	DKL	10 JAN 2007	THIS DOCUMENT IS THE PROPERTY OF DK WIDGET CORPORATION. ITS USE IS AUTHORIZED ONLY FOR RESPONDING TO A REQUEST FOR QUOTATION OR FOR THE PERFORMANCE OF WORK FOR DK WIDGET.		**DKW**
CHECKED BY	SAS	18 FEB 2007	PLATE, BOTTOM SUPPORT		
APPROVED BY	MOH	14 MAR 2007	SIZE A4	FSCM NO. N/A	DWG NO. 134567-07G	REV 1
RELEASED BY	JDE	28 APR 2007	SCALE N/A	WEIGHT N/A	SHEET 1/1	

(d)

NOTES:

1. THIRD ANGLE PROJECTION.
2. ALL UNITS ARE IN MILLIMETERS.
3. TOLERANCES, UNLESS NOTED:
   LINEAR   ± 0.2
   ANGULAR   ± 0.5
   RADII   ± 0.2
4. ALL SHARP CORNERS AND EDGES TO BE
   BROKEN FOR HANDLING SAFETY.
5. MAXIMUM EDGE AND CORNER BREAKS
   INSIDE   0.2
   OUTSIDE   0.2
6. MATERIAL TO BE ALUMINUM 7075 T6.
7. SURFACE TO BE ANODIZED, BLACK.

SECTION A-A

DRAWN BY	DKL	18 JUN 2007	THIS DOCUMENT IS THE PROPERTY OF DK WIDGET CORPORATION. ITS USE IS AUTHORIZED ONLY FOR RESPONDING TO A REQUEST FOR QUOTATION OR FOR THE PERFORMANCE OF WORK FOR DK WIDGET.		**DKW**
CHECKED BY	SAS	24 JUN 2007	BRACE, PIPE SUPPORT		
APPROVED BY	MOH	30 JUN 2007	SIZE A4	FSCM NO. N/A	DWG NO. 55X4567C	REV 2
RELEASED BY	JDE	18 JUL 2007	SCALE N/A	WEIGHT N/A	SHEET 1/1	

FIGURES P18.12. (CONTINUED)

18.14 problems (continued)

13. Answer the following questions regarding the site plan for the water main extension project in the village of Baraga shown here.

    a. What are the names of the four streets bordering the area under consideration?

    b. How many existing fire hydrants are shown on the plan?

    c. How many proposed fire hydrants are shown on the plan?

    d. Counting all houses and separate garages, how many buildings are in the area?

    e. What is the diameter of the supply main to be abandoned?

    f. What is the diameter of the new water main? How many total linear feet of it is required?

    g. For the houses and garages shown on the plan, how many have gravel driveways and how many have bituminous driveways?

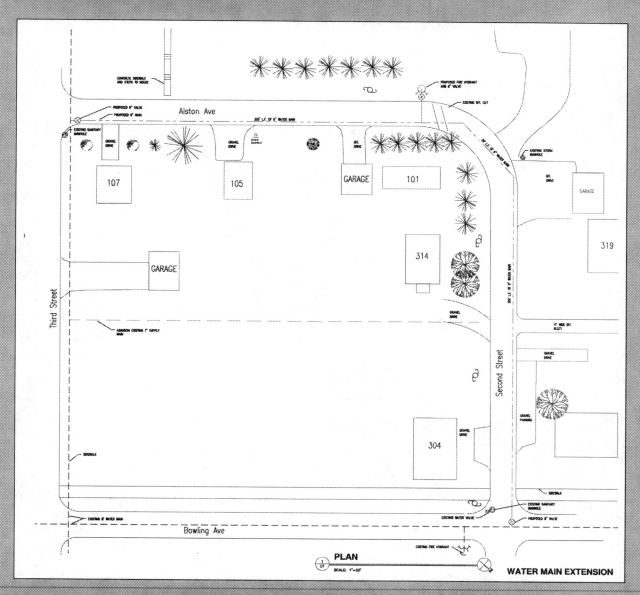

18.14 problems (continued)

14. Answer the following questions regarding the trench detail for the water main extension project in the village of Baraga shown here.

  a. What is the trench width for an 8" pipe? for a 12" pipe?

  b. What is the minimum depth from the ground to the top of the pipe? Who can approve a smaller minimum depth?

  c. What is the slope of the sides of the trench?

  d. Where will the contractor find the specifications for the bedding requirements?

  e. What is the minimum distance between the bottom of the pipe and the bottom of the trench?

  f. What type of compacted material surrounds the pipe?

  g. This drawing is made N.T.S. (meaning "not to scale"). Why do you suppose this is an acceptable practice?

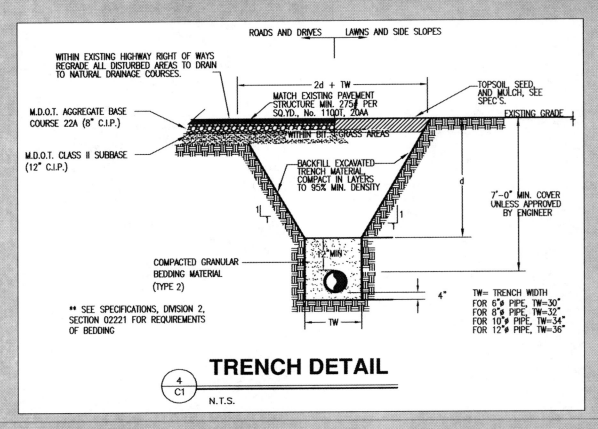

FIGURE P18.14.

18.14 problems (continued)

15. Answer the following questions regarding the wall section for the water treatment plant expansion project in the village of Baraga shown here.

    a. What is the elevation of the top of the footing?

    b. What is the elevation of the top of the concrete slab?

    c. What is the elevation of the top of the concrete sidewalk?

    d. What is the elevation of the bottom of the proposed double tee?

    e. What is the depth of the concrete topping that covers the 8" precast plank?

    f. What is the size and type of insulation for the upper portion of the wall?

    g. What is the minimum concrete cover for the steel rebars in the wall?

    h. How many rebars are required at the top of the door opening? What is the size of the bars there?

    i. What is the width of the footing?

    j. #4 and #5 rebars are used as reinforcement throughout the wall and footing. What size is used in the footing? What size is used for horizontal reinforcement? What size is used for vertical reinforcement?

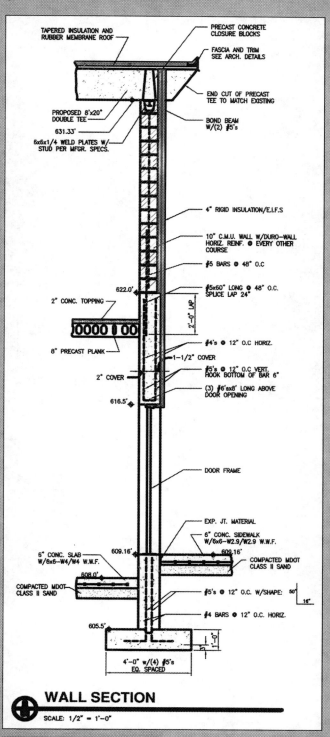

FIGURE P18.15.

18.14 problems (continued)

16. For the figure shown here, measure the lengths of the lines at the indicated scales. (Do not use a calculator for this exercise.) What are the lengths of lines A through F if they are drawn at the indicated scales?

   a. 1"=4000'
   b. 1"=5 yds
   c. 1"=60'
   d. 1"=2'
   e. ¼"=1'-0"
   f. ¾"=1'-0"
   g. ¼"=1'-0"
   h. ½"=1'-0"
   i. 1:2 (use Metric scale)
   j. 1:500 (use Metric scale)
   k. 1:75 (use Metric scale)

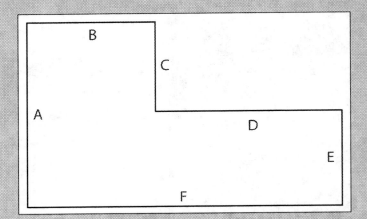

FIGURE P18.16.

Fasteners

objectives

After completing this chapter, you should be able to

- Explain various methods to attach parts such that the parts can be disassembled

- Identify and specify common threaded fasteners

- Explain the processes used to manufacture threads

- Create CAD models of threaded fasteners using exact geometry and simplified representations

- Prepare drawings for fastening devices, including correct notes for threaded fasteners, threaded holes, and other fasteners

- Recognize other types of non-threaded fasteners, including pins, rivets, keys, and snap-fit systems

17.01

introduction

Everyone is familiar with various methods used to join multiple sheets of paper. If only a few sheets need to be held together temporarily, you could use a paper clip. For more security, you might want to staple the sheets. If there are many sheets, they could be punched and placed in a binder, bound into a book using adhesive, or even sewn together. The method used to fasten the papers together depends on many factors, such as how many sheets there are and whether the fastening is to be temporary or permanent. Similarly, assemblies of manufactured parts that need to be held together can be joined using many different methods.

Very few products consist of a single part; most products are assemblies of many components. As a new product is developed, determining how to fasten the pieces of it together is a major consideration. Some products are designed to be taken apart easily; others are designed to be assembled permanently. The product typically must be assembled quickly and securely. A mechanical **fastener** is a manufactured part whose primary function is to join two or more parts. Mechanical fasteners are often used in assemblies as they are readily available and low in cost. Many considerations are required as to what kind, type, and material of fastener should be used. In this chapter, you will learn about the different types of fasteners, standards in the fastener industry, ways to model fasteners and document fasteners on drawings, and considerations for the selection of fasteners for your designs.

Fastening systems play a critical role in most product design. They often do more than position and secure components. In many cases, fastening systems have a direct effect on the product's durability, reliability, size, and weight. They affect the speed with which the product may be assembled and disassembled both during manufacturing and later in field service. Fastening systems also affect cost not only for the fasteners but also for the machining and assembly operations they require. Unless a designer has had a great deal of experience using different fastening devices and techniques, it is often difficult to choose a fastener that combines optimum function with maximum economy. A fastening system that is best for one product may not be desirable for another. Thus, it is important for you to know about all types of fasteners so that you will be able to select appropriate fasteners for your designs.

There are two major classifications of fasteners: permanent and temporary. Permanent fasteners are used when parts will not be disassembled. Permanent fastening methods include welding, brazing, stapling, nailing, gluing, and riveting. Temporary fasteners are used when the parts will be disassembled at some future time. Temporary fasteners, including screws, bolts, keys, and pins, are discussed in this chapter. Snap fasteners, which are integrated into the design of parts, are widely used to reduce the number of parts in an assembly and will be covered in this chapter.

17.02 Screw Threads

There are many types and sizes of fasteners, each designed for a particular function. Many temporary fasteners include threads in their design. **Screw threads** are a helix or conical spiral formed on the external surface of a shaft or on the internal surface of a cylindrical hole. Figure 17.01 shows a typical screw thread on a standard bolt. Screw threads are used for a variety of purposes, including the following:

- For fastening parts together, such as a nut and a bolt

FIGURE 17.01. A hexagonal head bolt.

For leveling or fine adjustment between parts in relation to each other, such as the fine adjusting screw on a surveyor's transit

For fine measurement, such as a micrometer

For transmitting motion or power, such as an automatic screw threading attachment on a lathe or a house jack

Although screw threads have many important uses, only their use as fasteners and only the most-used kinds of fasteners are discussed in this chapter.

17.02.01 Thread Terminology

This section will describe the shape, or **form**, of some common threads. Figure 17.02 shows an external thread, such as what you would find on a common bolt. **External threads** are located on the outside of a part. The following terms describe thread geometry:

- **Axis**—A longitudinal center line of the thread.
- **Root**—The bottom of the cut on external threads.
- **Crest**—The top of the external threads.
- **Major diameter**—The largest diameter of a screw thread. The distance is measured from crest to crest through the axis on an external thread.
- **Minor diameter**—The smallest diameter of a screw thread. The dimension is measured from root to root through the axis on an external thread.
- **Pitch diameter**—An imaginary diameter measured from a point halfway between the major and minor diameters through the axis to a corresponding point on the opposite side.
- **Pitch**—The distance from a point on a screw thread to a corresponding point on the next thread as measured parallel to the axis.
- **Depth of thread**—The distance between the crest and the root of a thread as measured perpendicular to the axis.
- **Angle of thread**—The included angle between the sides of the thread.
- Body—That portion of a screw shaft that is left unthreaded.
- Chamfer—An angular relief at the last thread to help the thread engage more easily with a mating part. Chamfers are commonly applied to the first thread to help start a thread in its mating part.

Figure 17.03 shows an internal thread, such as what would be found on the inside of a hole or in a nut. Note that the major diameter is measured from root to root and the minor diameter is measured across the crests.

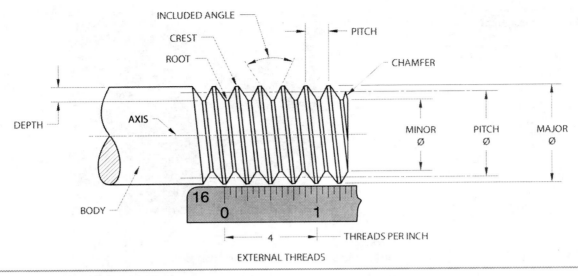

FIGURE 17.02. External screw thread components.

Other terminology used in the designation of screw threads is as follows:

- Classes of threads—A designation of the amount of tolerance and allowance specified for a thread.
- Fit—Identifies a range of thread tightness or looseness.
- **Thread series**—Groups of common major diameter and pitch characteristics determined by the number of threads per inch.
- **Lead**—The distance a screw thread advances axially in one full turn.

17.02.02 Single and Multiple Threads

Most threads are single threads. A **single thread** is composed of one continuous ridge. The lead of a single thread is equal to the pitch. **Multiple threads** are made up of two or more continuous ridges following side by side. The lead of a double thread is

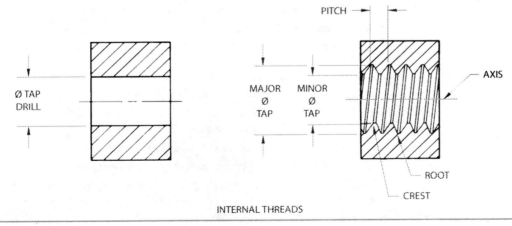

FIGURE 17.03. Internal screw thread components.

FIGURE 17.04. Single and multiple threads.

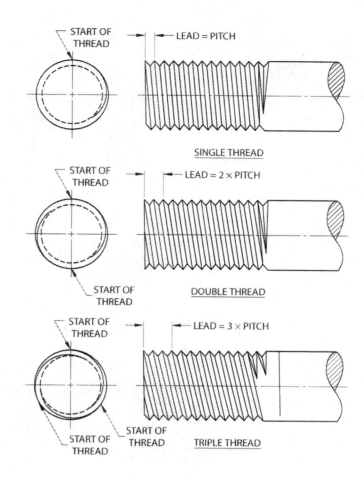

equal to twice the pitch. The lead of a triple thread is equal to three times the pitch, as shown in Figure 17.04. Multiple threads are used when the installation speed or travel distance is an important design factor. A good example of a double or triple thread is found in an inexpensive ballpoint pen. Take a ballpoint pen apart and study the end of the external threads. You will probably see two or three ridges starting at the end of the threads. Notice how fast the parts screw together. The speed of assembly, not power, is the characteristic of multiple threads.

17.02.03 Right-Hand and Left-Hand Threads

Threads can be either right-handed or left-handed. A right-handed thread engages with a mating thread by rotating clockwise, or with a turn to the right when viewed toward the mating thread. Using the right-hand rule, if you curl the fingers of your right hand in the direction of rotation, your thumb will point in the direction of axial travel. A left-handed thread engages with a mating thread by rotating it counterclockwise, or with a turn to the left when viewed toward the mating thread. To distinguish between a right-hand and a left-hand thread, you can use the simple trick illustrated in Figure 17.05. A right-hand thread winding tends to lean toward the left. If the thread leans toward the left, the right-hand thumb points in the same direction. If the thread leans to the right, the left-hand thumb leans in that direction, indicating that it is a left-hand thread.

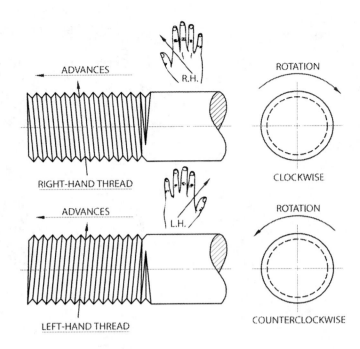

FIGURE 17.05. Right-hand and left-hand threads.

ADVANCES

R.H.

RIGHT-HAND THREAD

ROTATION

CLOCKWISE

ADVANCES

L.H.

LEFT-HAND THREAD

ROTATION

COUNTERCLOCKWISE

17.02.04 Thread Standards

In earlier days, nuts and bolts from one company would not fit nuts and bolts from another company. In 1841, Sir Joseph Whitworth worked toward some kind of standardization throughout England. His efforts were finally accepted, and England came up with a standard thread form called Whitworth threads. The shape of the Whitworth thread will be shown in the next section along with other standard thread shapes.

In 1864, the United States tried to develop its own thread standard; but because these threads were not compatible with English Whitworth threads, the proposed standard was not adopted. It was not until 1935 that the United States adopted the American Standard thread, which was a 60° V-thread form originally proposed in 1864. The lack of standardization between countries caused many problems, but nothing was done until World War II forced the issue of interchangeability on the Western Allies. As a result of problems experienced by the Allies, in 1948, the United States, Canada, and Great Britain developed the Unified Screw thread, which was a compromise between the American Standard thread and the Whitworth threads.

With the recent standardization about the metric system, the International Organization for Standardization (ISO) has developed a single international system using metric screw threads. This new ISO standard will be united with the American National Standards Institute (ANSI) standards. The present is a time of transition, with a combination of both systems still being used.

17.02.05 Thread Forms

The form of a screw thread is its profile shape. There are many kinds of screw thread forms. Several thread forms commonly used in fasteners and adjustments are shown for comparison in Figure 17.06. Unified threads are the most common threads used on threaded fasteners. American National threads are similar to the Unified thread, but have a flat root. The American National thread has been the standard thread used in the United States, Canada, and the United Kingdom since 1948. The sharp-V thread, although not commonly used, is a thread that fits and seals tightly. It is difficult to manufacture since the sharp crests and roots of the threads are easily damaged. The sharp-V thread was the original U.S. standard thread form. The ISO metric thread form

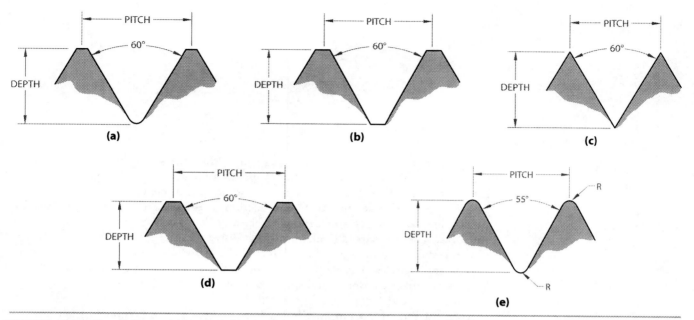

FIGURE 17.06. Thread forms: (a) Unified, (b) American National, (c) sharp-V, (d) ISO metric, and (e) Whitworth.

is the new standard to be used throughout the world. Its form or profile is very similar to that of the Unified National thread except that the thread depth is slightly less. The Whitworth thread forms, sometimes referred to as parallel screw threads, are being used primarily for replacement parts.

Transmitting power through screw threads requires different thread forms. Some typical thread forms used for power transmission are shown in Figure 17.07. The square thread profile is exactly as its name implies, that is, square. The faces of the teeth are at right angles to the axis; and theoretically, this is the best thread for transmitting power. Square thread forms have a longer pitch than Unified threads. Because the square thread is difficult to manufacture, it has been replaced by the Acme thread. The Acme

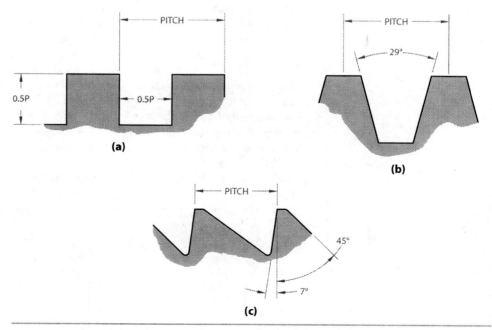

FIGURE 17.07. Power thread forms: (a) square, (b) Acme, and (c) buttress.

FIGURE 17.08. A rolled thread form.

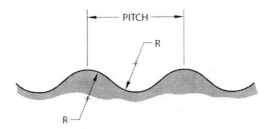

thread is easier to manufacture and is stronger than the square thread. Acme thread forms are commonly used when rapid traverse movement is a design requirement. Acme threads are popular on designs such as screw jacks, vice screws, and other equipment and machinery that require rapid screw action or the transmittal of power. Buttress threads are designed for applications where high stress occurs in one direction along the thread axis. The thread flank or side that distributes the thrust or force is within 7° of perpendicular to the axis. This small angle helps reduce the radial reaction force to the thrust. Examples of applications for buttress threads are in the breech assemblies of large guns, airplane propeller hubs, and columns for hydraulic presses.

Rolled thread forms, sometimes called knuckle threads, are usually rolled from sheet metal and are used in light bulbs, light sockets, and sometimes bottle tops. The knuckle thread is also sometimes cast. An example is shown Figure 17.08.

17.03   Thread Cutting

Various methods are used to produce inside and outside threads. The simplest method uses thread-cutting tools called taps and dies. A **tap** cuts **internal threads**; a **die** cuts **external threads**.

In making an internal threaded hole, the hole must be drilled first. This hole is approximately the same diameter as the minor diameter of the threads. There are two major kinds of interior holes: **through holes** and **blind holes**. A through hole, as its name implies, goes completely through an object. A blind hole is a hole that does not go completely through an object. When an internal screw thread does not go through the part, it is a common practice to drill deeper than the depth of the required thread. This process saves time and reduces the chance of breaking a tap when it hits the bottom of the hole. The thread may extend to the bottom of a hole, but producing such a thread requires an extra process using a special shaped "bottom" tap.

A tap set is made up of a taper tap, a plug tap, and a bottom tap, as shown in Figure 17.09. The taper tap is generally used to start a thread. The threads are tapered to within ten threads from the end. The tap is tapered so the tool more evenly distributes the cutting edges through the depth of the hole. The plug tap has the threads tapered to within five threads from the end. The plug tap can be used to thread completely through material or to thread a blind hole if full threads are not required all the way to the bottom. The bottom tap is used when threads are needed at the bottom of a blind hole.

Thread cutting dies, as shown in Figure 17.10, are available for most standard thread sizes. External and internal threads also may be cut on a lathe. Figure 17.11 shows how a cutting tool can make an external thread.

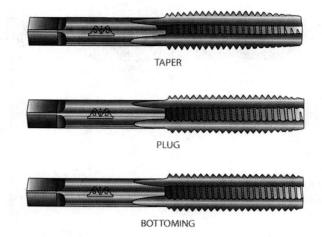

TAPER

PLUG

BOTTOMING

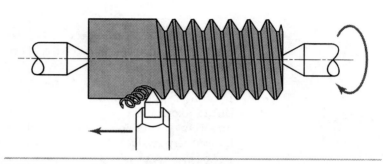

FIGURE 17.11. Thread cutting on a lathe.

17.04 Modeling Screw Threads

CAD models and drawings should conform to proper ANSI standards for representing screw threads. For most purposes, it is not necessary to model the complex helical thread form. Because thread forms have been standardized, it is necessary only to indicate the shape of the thread with a note, instead of modeling the exact shape. These thread notes will be explained in the next section of this chapter. In this section, you will learn about simplified threads and exact geometric representations.

17.04.01 Thread Representations for Drawings

Drawing a thread exactly as it looks is unnecessary. Engineers have developed two systems for representing screw threads. These representations are illustrated in Figure 17.12. The classic schematic representation shows the threads as a series of lines that are perpendicular to the thread axis. The crest of the thread is shown as a line across the full diameter of the shaft or hole and the root as a slightly shorter line that does not reach the full diameter. The simplified system of representing threads is quicker and in greater use today.

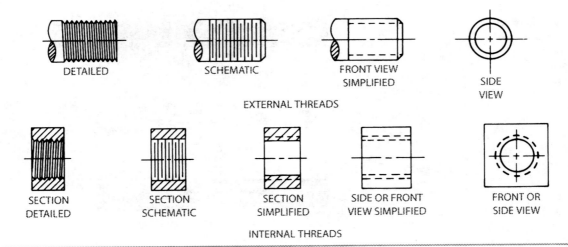

EXTERNAL THREADS

INTERNAL THREADS

FIGURE 17.12. Schematic and simplified thread representations.

This representation shows the major diameter of the shaft or hole and the threads as a dashed, or hidden, line parallel to the thread axis. In Figure 17.12, note how section views are illustrated using schematic and simplified systems.

To illustrate a blind hole, the drafter illustrates the pilot hole and the threaded portion as shown in Figure 17.13. The hidden lines representing the major and minor thread diameters are spaced far enough apart to be clearly separate. The spacing is important because on threads, the difference between the major and minor diameters is often very small; and if drawn to actual size, the lines would run together. The hidden line dashes are usually drawn staggered for clarity.

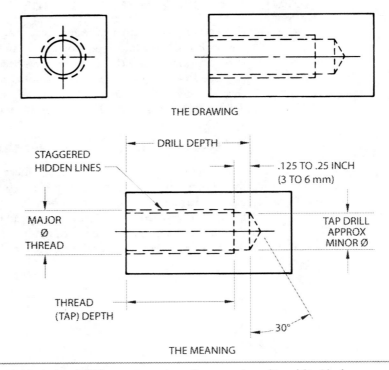

FIGURE 17.13. A simplified representation of a screw thread in a blind hole.

FIGURE 17.14. Fasteners in
section drawings.

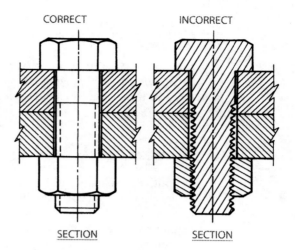

CORRECT   INCORRECT

SECTION   SECTION

Figure 17.14 shows a bolt fastener as it would appear drawn in a sectioned assembly drawing of two mating parts using simplified thread representation. If the cutting plane passes through the axis of any fastener, the fastener is not sectioned. The illustration at the left is drawn correctly. The figure at the right is drawn incorrectly.

17.04.02 Thread Representation in Solid Models

Many CAD models of threaded fasteners show only the cylindrical shaft (or hole) and then represent the threads by using a simplified display and/or a note on the model. These simplified representations are sometimes called cosmetic features. In the case of a thread, the cylindrical outline of the thread's major and minor diameters may be superposed on the shaft of the bolt (or inside the hole), as shown in Figure 17.15.

When necessary, it is usually simple to create an accurate representation of screw threads using solid models. Most solid modeling software includes a helical sweep feature. The profile of the thread is specified as are the axis of rotation, the pitch, and the length of the threaded feature. The sweep can be either a protrusion or a cut. Figure 17.16 shows a bolt with a thread feature. Note the highlighted profile (thread form) and axis.

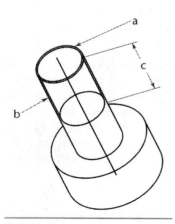

FIGURE 17.15. A simplified or
cosmetic thread feature on a
solid model, displayed in
wireframe mode.

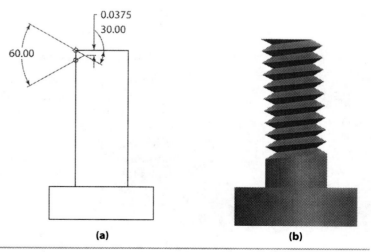

0.0375
30.00
60.00

(a)   (b)

FIGURE 17.16. A solid model of a bolt with exact representation using
the helical sweep feature to create a screw threads (a) profile and a
trajectory of sweep (b) solid model.

Helical sweep thread features are quite accurate visually; but to render or display on the computer screen, they require larger computational resources than simplified representations. It usually is not necessary to display the precise geometry of the screw threads except in situations that require a pictorial display of threads (such as in a sales catalog or a display drawing). It also may be necessary to create an accurate model of a screw or bolt when you are designing the fastener itself and want to study its strength or tolerances.

17.05 Thread Notes

Simplified, schematic, and detailed thread representations clearly show where threads are located on a part or assembly drawing or in a CAD model. However, the representations alone do not give the full information about the thread. The entities are not meant to be exact, but they are meant to describe the location of the thread. The information that clearly and completely identifies the thread is the **thread note**.

17.05.01 Metric Threads

The following metric thread notes are the recommended standard as specified by the ISO. The thread note components are as follows:

M A x B – C D E

- M is the symbol for ISO metric threads.
- A is the nominal major diameter in millimeters, followed by the symbol x.
- B is the thread pitch in millimeters, followed by a dash (–).
- C is a number that identifies the grade of tolerance, from fine to coarse, on the diameter. The number may be 3, 4, 5, 6, 7, 8, or 9. The larger the number, the larger the tolerance. Grades 3 through 5 are fine, and 7 through 9 are coarse. Grade 6 is the most commonly used and is the medium tolerance metric thread.
- D is a letter placed after the number that gives the tolerance class of the pitch of the thread. The term *allowance* refers to the tightness of fit between the mating parts. Internal threads are designated by uppercase letters such as E (good), G (better), or H (best); external threads are defined with lowercase letters such as e, g, or h.
- A blank space after the tolerance class denotes a right-hand thread, a thread that engages when turned to the right. A right-hand thread is assumed unless an LH is written in this space. LH, which indicates a left-hand thread, must be specified for a thread that engages when rotated to the left.
- Provided at the end of the note, E is the depth of internal threads or the length of external threads in millimeters. When the thread goes through the part, this space is left blank, although some companies prefer to add the description THRU.

An example of a metric thread specification is M 10 x 1.5 – 6g. This note would appear on an external metric thread with a major diameter of 10 mm and a pitch of 1.5 mm. A medium tolerance is specified by the designation 6g. An example of a left-hand metric thread is M 12 x 1.25 – 4H – LH 15. This note would appear on a hole with a major diameter of 12 mm and a pitch of 1.25 mm. This is a fine thread with no allowance (4H). The thread depth is 15 mm. More detailed information on tolerance classes for fasteners may be found in the ISO standards or *Machinery Handbook*.

17.05.02 Unified National Threads

Unified threads also may be specified using standard notation, as prescribed by ANSI standards. The thread note is always written in the order shown. The components of the note are described as follows:

$$A - B\,C - D\,E$$

- *A* is the major diameter of the thread in inches followed by a dash (–). The major diameter is generally given as a fractional value, although some smaller diameters are denoted with a number designation.

- *B* is the number of threads per inch.

- *C* is the series of threads, such as coarse or fine threads. UNC means Unified National Coarse. Other series are UNF for Unified National Fine, UNEF for Unified National Extra Fine, and UNS for Unified National Special.

- *D*, class of fit, indicates the amount of tolerance. 1 means a large tolerance, 2 is a general purpose moderate tolerance, and 3 is for applications requiring a close tolerance.

- *E* designates internal or external threads. The letter *A* means an external thread, while *B* means an internal thread. The *A* or *B* may be omitted if the thread is clearly external or internal, as shown on the drawing.

- Additional information may be appended to the end of the note in the following order. Unless otherwise specified, a right-hand thread with a single lead is assumed. LH identifies a left-hand thread. If a double or triple lead is required, the word DOUBLE or TRIPLE must be inserted here. Finally, the internal thread depth or external thread length in inches may be added. When the drawing clearly shows that the thread goes through, this space is left blank. If clarification is needed, the word THRU may be inserted here.

An example of a unified thread note is 3/8 – 16 UNC – 2A LH. This is an external thread with a major diameter of 3/8 inch and 16 threads per inch. The thread form is Unified National Coarse, with a general purpose tolerance (2). It is a left-hand thread. For sizes less than 1/4 inch, the major diameter is indicated by a number. For example, 8 – 36 UNF – 2B .5 indicates a No. 8 thread with a major diameter of 0.164 inches, 36 threads per inch. (UNF series are fine threads.) The threads are cut to a depth of 0.5 inches in the hole. (An internal thread is indicated by the letter *B*.)

17.05.03 Other Thread Forms

Other thread forms, such as Acme, are noted on a drawing using the same format. For example, 5.8 – 8 ACME – 2G describes an Acme thread with a 5.8-inch major diameter, 8 threads per inch, and a general purpose (G) class 2 thread fit. More complete analysis of threads and thread forms can be found in a machinery or machinists' handbook.

17.05.04 Thread Notes on a Drawing

The thread note is usually applied to a drawing with a leader in the view where the thread appears as a circle for internal threads, as shown in Figure 17.17. The leader points to the circle; and the note describes the hole diameter, pitch, thread series, and depth of threads. External threads may be labeled with a leader, as shown in 17.18,

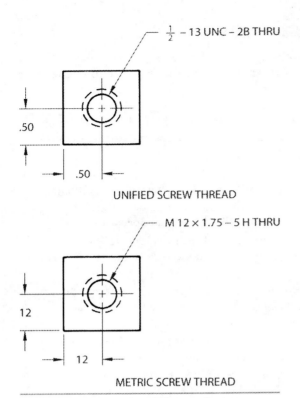

UNIFIED SCREW THREAD

METRIC SCREW THREAD

FIGURE 17.17. Noting internal screw threads (simplified representation).

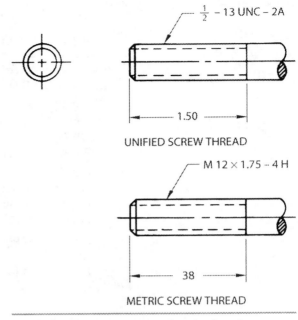

UNIFIED SCREW THREAD

METRIC SCREW THREAD

FIGURE 17.18. Noting external screw threads (simplified representation).

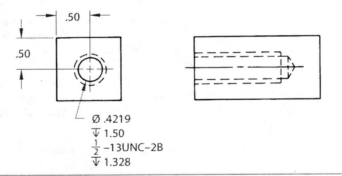

Ø .4219
▽ 1.50
½ –13UNC–2B
▽ 1.328

FIGURE 17.19. A drawing note showing tap manufacturing information.

with the thread length given as a dimension or at the end of the note. The leader points to the threaded portion of the shaft in the profile view.

Many companies require only the thread note and depth. The complete drilling and tapping process is determined in manufacturing. However, some companies may require the designer to indicate the complete process needed to machine a threaded hole, including noting the **tap drill** (used to create the pilot hole) size, tap drill depth if it is not through, thread note, and thread depth if it is not through (as shown in Figure 17.19). In this example, the diameter of the tap hole is 0.4219 inches, with a depth of 1.5 inches. The thread has a major diameter of 1/2 inch with a coarse thread and a pitch of 13 threads per inch. The threads are cut to a depth of 1.328 inches. Notice that the tap drill is smaller than the major diameter of the threads and the tap drill depth is deeper than the thread cut depth.

FIGURE 17.20. Assorted fasteners.

17.06 Threaded Fasteners

There are many different types of threaded fasteners, as shown in Figure 17.20. The type of fasteners used in an assembly must accommodate the available tools, space limitations, required joint strength, and other considerations. In this section, you will learn how to identify the most common types of threaded fasteners.

17.06.01 Bolts and Nuts

A **bolt** is a threaded fastener that passes completely through the parts and uses a **nut** to tighten or hold the parts together. Bolts can be tightened or released by torque applied to the head or to the nut. Bolts are identified by a thread note, length, and head type; for example, 5/8 – 11 UNC – 2 × 1-1/2 LONG HEXAGON HEAD BOLT. This is a 5/8 inch diameter bolt with 11 threads per inch (coarse pitch), class 2 (general purpose) with a length of 1-1/2 inches and a hexagonal head. The length of the bolt is measured from the bottom of the head and does not include the thickness of the head. The thread lengths are standardized and are somewhat shorter than the overall length but are sufficient for engagement with the mating nut over a useful working range for assembly. Figure 17.21 shows various types of bolt heads.

Nuts are used in combination with bolts to hold two or more pieces of material together. The nut thread must match the bolt thread. For clearance and ease of assembly, the hole in the parts is usually drilled slightly larger than the bolt. Figure 17.22 shows common types of nuts. Nuts are available in hexagonal or square shapes and may be slotted to allow them to be secured with a pin or key. Acorn nuts are capped for appearance. Self-locking nuts are available with neoprene gaskets that help keep the nut tight when movement or vibration is a problem. Nuts are classified by thread specifications and type and are available with a flat base or a washer face.

17.06.02 Machine Screws and Cap Screws

Machine screws are threaded fasteners used for general assembly of machine parts and are specified by thread, length, and head type. Machine screws are commonly available in coarse (UNC) and fine (UNF) threads and in sizes that range from 0.060 to 0.50 inches in diameter and lengths of 1/8 to 3 inches. Several types of heads are available, as

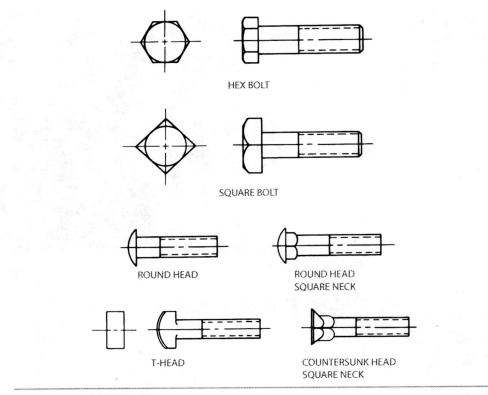

HEX BOLT

SQUARE BOLT

ROUND HEAD

ROUND HEAD
SQUARE NECK

T-HEAD

COUNTERSUNK HEAD
SQUARE NECK

FIGURE 17.21. Bolt head types.

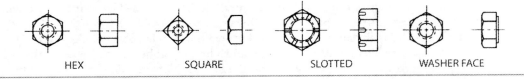

HEX

SQUARE

SLOTTED

WASHER FACE

FIGURE 17.22. Types of nuts.

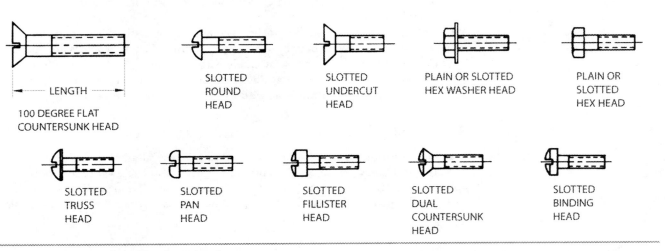

LENGTH

100 DEGREE FLAT
COUNTERSUNK HEAD

SLOTTED
ROUND
HEAD

SLOTTED
UNDERCUT
HEAD

PLAIN OR SLOTTED
HEX WASHER HEAD

PLAIN OR
SLOTTED
HEX HEAD

SLOTTED
TRUSS
HEAD

SLOTTED
PAN
HEAD

SLOTTED
FILLISTER
HEAD

SLOTTED
DUAL
COUNTERSUNK
HEAD

SLOTTED
BINDING
HEAD

FIGURE 17.23. Types of machine screw heads.

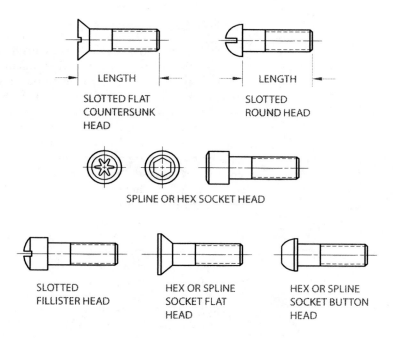

FIGURE 17.24. Cap screw head types.

LENGTH
SLOTTED FLAT
COUNTERSUNK
HEAD

LENGTH
SLOTTED
ROUND HEAD

SPLINE OR HEX SOCKET HEAD

SLOTTED
FILLISTER HEAD

HEX OR SPLINE
SOCKET FLAT
HEAD

HEX OR SPLINE
SOCKET BUTTON
HEAD

illustrated in Figure 17.23. Heads may be selected for recess in countersunk or counter-bored holes and/or for features such as tool sockets to facilitate assembly. Most machine screws are threaded within a thread or two to the head.

A **cap screw** is fine-finished machine screw that is typically used without a nut (i.e., it passes through a clearance hole in one part and screws into a threaded hole in the mating part). Cap screws have a variety of head types and range in diameter from 0.060 inches and up, with a large range of lengths. A chamfer to the depth of the first thread is present to facilitate installation. Various standard head forms are shown in Figure 17.24. Detailed dimensions of standard machine screws and cap screws are given in the Appendix.

17.06.03 Studs

A **stud** is a fastener with different threads at each end. It is screwed into a threaded hole and holds other parts with a nut on its free end. A stud typically has fine threads at one end and coarse threads at the other end or Class 3-fit threads at one end and Class 2-fit threads at the other end. Fit classes are explained later in this chapter. Some typical stud fasteners are shown in Figure 17.25.

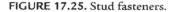

FIGURE 17.25. Stud fasteners.

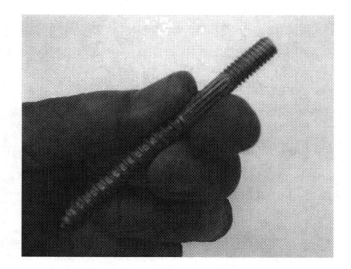

17.06.04 Design Considerations for Threaded Fasteners

Several design guidelines should be considered when choosing fasteners for assemblies. The function of the joint and the available assembly methods must be considered. Forces may be present that tend to pull the joint apart; therefore, it is important to select fasteners that have sufficient strength so that the threads will not fail. More ductile materials require more thread engagement. Typically, the minimum full thread length for a screw or stud is at least the bolt diameter in steel; at least 1.5 times the diameter in cast iron, brass, or bronze; and at least 2 times the diameter in aluminum, zinc, or plastic. In addition, there must be a slight allowance for incomplete threads due to **tool runout**. Tool runout is the distance a tool may go beyond the required full thread length, as shown in Figure 17.26. Standard thread forming tools generally have lead-in chamfers that produce two or more incomplete threads on the leading edge of the tool, as shown in Figure 17.09. Generally, an allowance of three pitch lengths minimum should be used to accommodate tool runout.

Where mating parts must be held tightly against a supporting shoulder on a threaded fastener, the last one or two threads must be removed, or relieved. When a threaded joint with a shoulder is designed, a counterbore is provided on the internal thread feature (hole) or a relief is provided on the external threaded feature (bolt or screw). The relief is done no deeper than to the root of the threads, as shown in Figure 17.27, so the fastener in not weakened.

Holes threaded to receive a fastener are produced as either a through hole or a blind hole. Through holes are preferred over blind holes from a manufacturing standpoint. This eliminates consideration of incomplete threads, facilitates chip disposal, and allows use of the most effective production methods. Unless the thickness of the material to be threaded is considerably greater than the required thread length, the tap drill for the thread should be drilled through the part.

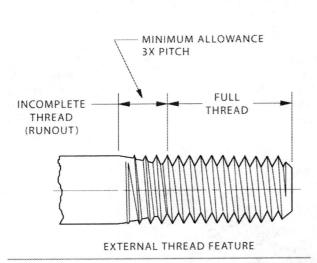

FIGURE 17.26. Tool runout is the incomplete threads that a tool may go beyond the required full thread length.

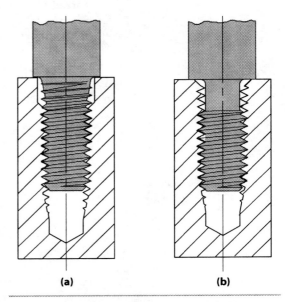

FIGURE 17.27. When designing a threaded joint with a shoulder, provide (a) a counterbore on the internal threaded feature (hole) or (b) a relief on the external threaded feature (bolt).

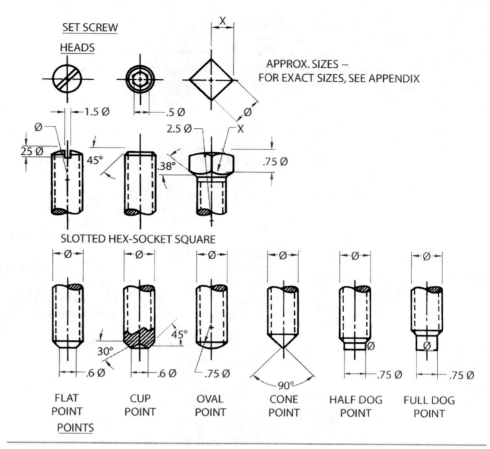

FIGURE 17.28. Set screws.

17.06.05 Set Screws

A **set screw** is used to prevent motion between mating parts, such as the hub of a pulley on a shaft. The set screw is screwed into and through one part so that it applies a force against another part. Set screws are usually made of steel and are hardened to make them stronger than the average fastener. Set screws have various kinds of heads and points, as shown in Figure 17.28. Set screws are ordered by specifying the thread and length, type of head, and type of point. Headless set screws are available with slotted or hex sockets. Detailed sizes and lengths can be found in the Appendix.

17.06.06 Self-Tapping Screws

The mating threads for **self-tapping screws** are created by the fasteners themselves. These screws are used to hold two or more mating parts when one of the parts becomes a fastening device. A clearance hole is required through the first part(s) while the last part receives a pilot hole similar to a tap drill for unified threads. The self-tapping screw then forms its own threads by cutting or displacing material as it enters the pilot hole. There are several different types of self-tapping screws, with head variations similar to cap screws. The specific function of the screw is important as these screws may be designed for applications ranging from sheet metal to hard metal fastening.

17.07 Rivets

Rivets are permanent fasteners that take the form of cylindrical pins with various shaped heads, as shown in Figure 17.29. Most rivets are made of wrought iron or soft steel for general applications (such as pressure vessels, structures, and machine members) and copper, aluminum, alloy, or other exotic metals for special applications (such as in aerospace). During installation, holes are punched or drilled in the parts to be fastened, the rivet is inserted through the holes, and the end of the rivet opposite its head is deformed using a special hammer or press. *Shop rivets* are installed in the factory, whereas *field rivets* are installed on the job at a construction site.

17.07.01 Kinds of Rivets

There are five major kinds of rivets: truss head, button head, pan head, countersunk head, and flat head. Small solid rivets are shown in their approximate standard proportions in Figure 17.30.

The two kinds of basic rivet joints are the **lap joint** and the **butt joint**, shown in Figure 17.31. In the lap joint, the parts overlap each other and are held together by one or more rows of rivets. In the butt joint, the parts are butted and are held together by a cover plate or butt strap that is riveted to both parts.

Some factors considered in the design of riveted joints are the type of joint, type and diameter of rivet, rivet material, distance between rivets (pitch), and size of clearance holes. Rivet holes can be punched, punched and reamed, or drilled. As a general rule, holes are usually made slightly larger in diameter than the nominal rivet shank diameter to facilitate assembly. The countersunk-head rivet is not as strong as the other kinds of rivets; therefore, more countersunk-head rivets must be used to produce the same joint.

Rivets are represented on drawings according to a standard convention using symbols such as those illustrated in Figure 17.32. The assembly drawing must identify what size and kind of rivet to use, to which side of the joint the rivet is applied, and whether the rivet is to be countersunk.

FIGURE 17.29. Rivet head styles.

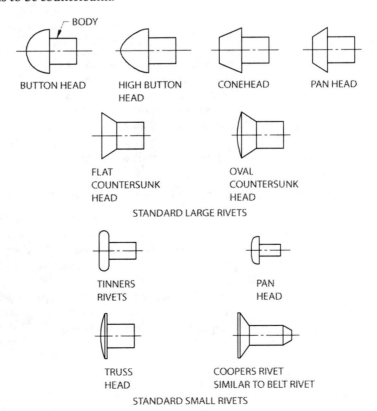

BODY

BUTTON HEAD   HIGH BUTTON HEAD   CONEHEAD   PAN HEAD

FLAT COUNTERSUNK HEAD   OVAL COUNTERSUNK HEAD

STANDARD LARGE RIVETS

TINNERS RIVETS   PAN HEAD

TRUSS HEAD   COOPERS RIVET SIMILAR TO BELT RIVET

STANDARD SMALL RIVETS

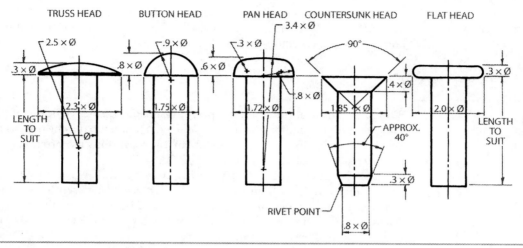

FIGURE 17.30. Dimensions of standard rivets.

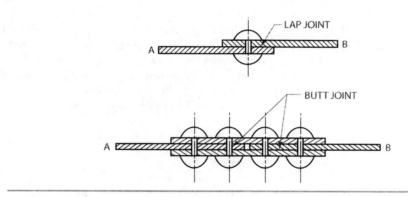

FIGURE 17.31. Rivet joint configurations.

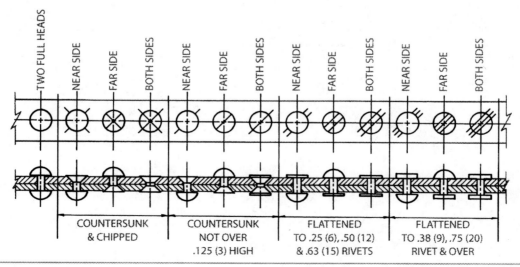

FIGURE 17.32. Illustrated rivet code.

17.08 Washers

A **washer** is a flat disk with a center hole to allow a fastener to pass through it, as shown in Figure 17.33. Washers are typically used under nuts or bolt heads or at machinery wear points to serve as cushions or bearing surfaces, to prevent leakage, or to relieve friction.

17.09 Pins

Pins are cylindrical (or slightly tapered) fasteners that are typically used to maintain some desired position or orientation between parts. A pin may be used as an axis, allowing the two mating parts to rotate about the joint. Pins are often used to accurately align two parts relative to each other.

Dowel pins are used to keep parts in a fixed position. Dowel pins must generally be pressed into a hole with an interference tolerance of between 0.0002 to 0.001 inches (.005 to .025 mm) depending on the material and the function of the parts. Figure 17.34 shows a cross section of two parts held with a dowel pin. Figure 17.35 shows a table of some standard dowel pins from a catalog.

For applications that require more precise alignment of accurately constructed parts, tapered dowel pins may be better than straight dowel pins. Taper pins also are used for parts that must be disassembled frequently or for cases where removal of straight dowel pins may cause excess hole wear. Figure 17.36 shows an example of a taper pin assembly. Taper pins sizes, shown in Figure 17.37, range in diameter, D, from 0.0625 inches to 0.875 inches; lengths, L, vary from 0.375 inches to 8 inches.

Grooved fasteners are used to solve metal-to-metal pinning needs with shear application, as shown in Figure 17.38. Grooved fasteners have great holding power and are resistant to shock, vibration, and fatigue. They are available in a wide range of types, sizes, and materials. A grooved fastener often has a better appearance than most other methods of fastening. This can be important to the overall design when the fastener is visible.

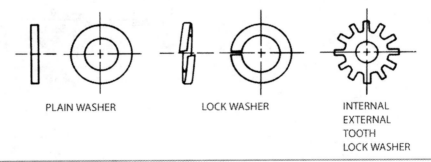

PLAIN WASHER   LOCK WASHER   INTERNAL
                                           EXTERNAL
                                           TOOTH
                                           LOCK WASHER

FIGURE 17.33. Types of washers.

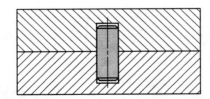

FIGURE 17.34. A sectional view of a dowel pin in place.

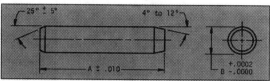

DOWEL PINS

Hardened-Press Fit

Diameters: 1/16 – 3/8
Lengths: 3/16 – 1-1/2

Material: 416 Stainless Steel
Hardened to: 36-42 Rockwell C

ORDER BY CATALOG NUMBER

A	1/16 DIA. PIN B=.0626	3/32 DIA. PIN B=.0939	1/8 DIA. PIN B=.1251	5/32 DIA. PIN B=.1563
	Catalog Number	Catalog Number	Catalog Number	Catalog Number
3/16	EPS-D1-1	EPS-D2-1	EPS-D3-1	–
1/4	EPS-D1-2	EPS-D2-2	EPS-D3-2	–
5/16	EPS-D1-3	EPS-D2-3	EPS-D3-3	–
3/8	EPS-D1-4	EPS-D2-4	EPS-D3-4	EPS-D4-4
7/16	EPS-D1-5	EPS-D2-5	EPS-D3-5	EPS-D4-5
1/2	EPS-D1-6	EPS-D2-6	EPS-D3-6	EPS-D4-6

NORDEX   800-243-0986   In CT: 203-775-4877 fax 203-775-6552   info@nordex.com   24E

FIGURE 17.35. A standard dowel pin chart. *Courtesy of Nordex, Inc.*

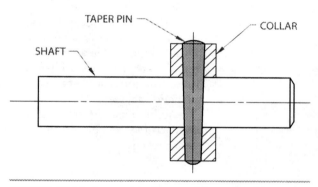

FIGURE 17.36. A taper pin in assembly section view.

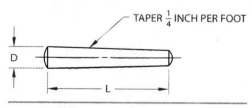

FIGURE 17.37. A taper pin.

FIGURE 17.38. A grooved fastener.

FIGURE 17.39. A sectioned view of a grooved fastener (a) before and (b) after insertion.

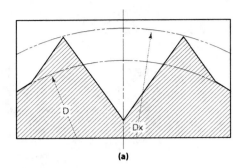

(a)

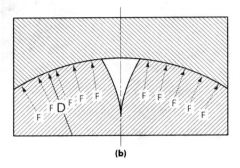

(b)

Grooved fasteners have three equally spaced parallel grooves pressed longitudinally on their exterior surface. The grooves are made by a special tool that displaces the pin material to one side. A raised portion, or flute, extends along each side of the groove, as shown in Figure 17.39a. The grooved fastener is installed by forcing it into a hole that is slightly larger than the undeformed diameter of the pin, as shown in Figure 17.39b. The installation cost of grooved pins is usually less than that of other pins because of the larger allowable hole tolerances.

Another type of fastener is the **spring pin**, shown in Figure 17.40. Spring pins are manufactured by cold-forming strip metal in a progressive roll-forming operation. After forming, the pins are broken off, deburred, and heat-treated to produce the desired

FIGURE 17.40. A spring pin.

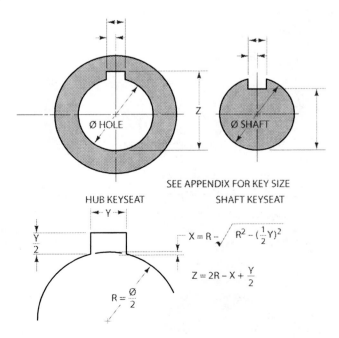

FIGURE 17.41. Spring pin applications.

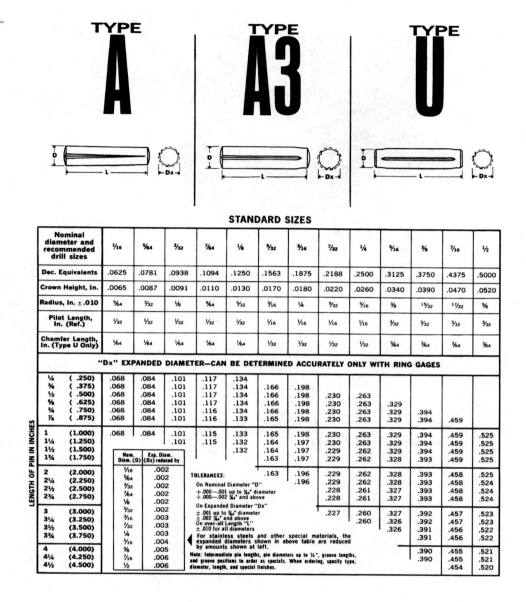

hardness. Before installation, the pins are slightly larger in diameter than the hole into which they are to be inserted. The pins are radially compressed as they are driven into the hole. Spring pins are typically made from high-carbon steel, stainless steel, brass, or beryllium copper. Some sizing guidelines for spring pins are shown in Figure 17.41.

17.10 Retaining Rings

Retaining rings provide removable shoulders for positioning or limiting the movement of parts in an assembly, as shown in Figure 17.42. Typical ring applications are shown in Figure 17.43 and Figure 17.44.

Retaining rings are made of materials that have good spring properties. This permits the rings to be deformed substantially, and then spring back to their original shape during assembly and disassembly. Most retaining rings are intended for installation in grooves; however, they are sometimes placed on parts in their deformed condition so they grip the parts by friction.

Internal axial rings are compressed for insertion or removal into a bore, using special pliers that grasp the rings securely, as shown in Figure 17.45. External axial rings are

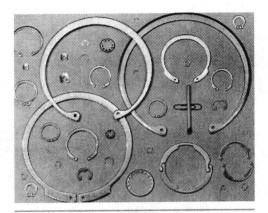

FIGURE 17.42. Retaining rings.
Courtesy of Koh-I-Noor Rapidograph

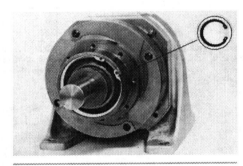

FIGURE 17.44. An internal retaining ring used in an electromagnetic clutch brake.
Courtesy of Koh-I-Noor Rapidograph

FIGURE 17.46. Internal ring pliers; when the pliers are squeezed, the lugs are spread apart.
Courtesy of Koh-I-Noor Rapidograph

FIGURE 17.43. An external retaining ring used in a precision differential gearset.
Courtesy of Koh-I-Noor Rapidograph

FIGURE 17.45. Internal ring pliers; when the pliers are squeezed, the lugs are compressed toward each other.
Courtesy of Koh-I-Noor Rapidograph

FIGURE 17.47. Special fixture and tool used to dispense and assemble external retaining rings.
Courtesy of Koh-I-Noor Rapidograph

expanded with special pliers, as shown in Figure 17.46, so the rings can be slipped over the end of a shaft, stud, or similar part. Radial external rings have a large gap and, through the use of a special tool, are pushed into the shaft directly in the plane of the groove, as shown in Figure 17.47. In addition to the tools shown here, retaining rings can be installed with equipment designed specifically for high-speed automatic assembly lines.

Retaining ring grooves serve to assure precise seating of the ring in the assembly and to permit the ring to withstand heavy thrust loads. The grooves must be located accurately and are precut in the housing or shaft before the rings are installed. Self-locking rings are held in place by friction and do not require grooves. They are used mainly as positioning or locking devices where the ring will be subjected only to moderate or light loads.

17.11 Keys

A **key** is a removable part that provides a means of transferring torque and preventing slippage between rotating parts where they are joined along a shaft. Figure 17.48 shows a typical application where a gear is mounted to a shaft. A **keyseat** is a rectangular groove machined into the shaft, and a **keyway** is a rectangular groove machined into the hub to receive the key.

The five major kinds of keys used in industry today are illustrated in Figure 17.49: square key, flat key, gib head key, Pratt & Whitney key, and Woodruff key. For transmission of large torques, double keys and keyseat can be used.

There are three classifications of fit for keys:

▨ **CLASS 1**—A clearance fit obtained by using bar stock key and keyseat tolerances. This is a relatively free fit.

▨ **CLASS 2**—A possible interference or clearance fit obtained by using bar stock key and keyseat tolerances. This is a relatively tight fit.

▨ **CLASS 3**—An interference fit obtained by interference fit tolerances. This is a very tight fit and has not been generally standardized.

As a general rule, the key width is about one-fourth the nominal diameter of the shaft. More detail on recommended key sizes can be found in a machinery handbook.

Guidelines for dimensioning keyways and keyseats for a standard key are shown in Figure 17.50, with more detail provided in the Appendix. For a Woodruff keyseat, the key number must be included in a note, as shown in Figure 17.51. Guidelines for dimensioning a Pratt & Whitney keyseat are shown in Figure 17.52.

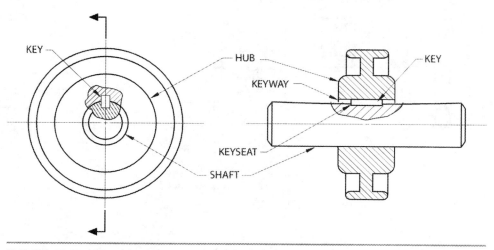

FIGURE 17.48. The relationship between key, keyway, keyseat, hub, and shaft.

KEYS

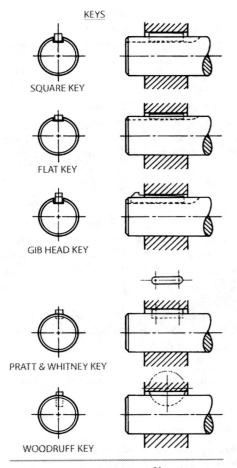

SQUARE KEY

FLAT KEY

GIB HEAD KEY

PRATT & WHITNEY KEY

WOODRUFF KEY

FIGURE 17.49. Five types of keys.

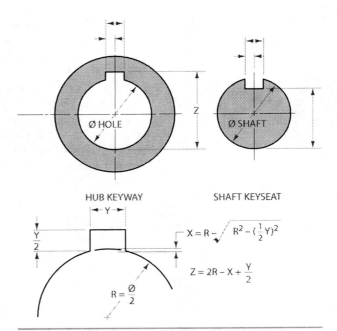

Ø HOLE

Ø SHAFT

HUB KEYWAY   SHAFT KEYSEAT

$$X = R - \sqrt{R^2 - \left(\tfrac{1}{2}Y\right)^2}$$

$$Z = 2R - X + \frac{Y}{2}$$

$$R = \frac{\emptyset}{2}$$

FIGURE 17.50. Dimensioning keyways and keyseats. Note that diametral dimensions are measured from the opposite side of the hole or shaft; the actual depth of the cut is not measured.

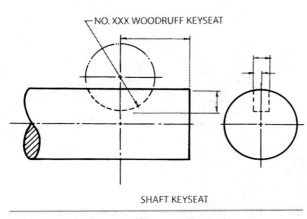

NO. XXX WOODRUFF KEYSEAT

SHAFT KEYSEAT

FIGURE 17.51. Woodruff keyseat dimensions.

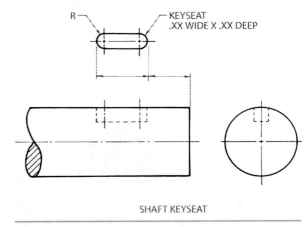

R

KEYSEAT
.XX WIDE X .XX DEEP

SHAFT KEYSEAT

FIGURE 17.52. Pratt & Whitney keyseat dimensions.

17.12 Snap-Fit Fasteners

Snap-fit attachments are a system of features on mating parts that consist of compatible locators and locking geometries that form a mechanical attachment between the two components. The use of snap-fit methods can reduce the number of parts in an assembly. Snap-fits are commonly used on plastic parts; but they also may be used with parts made of other materials, such as sheet metal. Compared to conventional fasteners, snap-fits are quick and easy to assemble and thus reduce assembly costs as well as inventory costs. Snap-fit assembly is easily automated, and snap-fit joints can be designed to be easily disassembled or to be permanent. However, snap-fits generally increase the complexity of the individual parts. Also, because snap-fit features protrude from the part, they are subject to damage during handling. Nonetheless, snap-fits are widely used by designers because of their many advantages.

Snap-fit joints generally fall into two categories: cantilever (snap legs) and cylindrical joints. Cantilever designs are commonly used on plastic housings for consumer products and latches for cabinets. Cylindrical snap-fit joints are found on childproof medicine bottles, for example. A cantilever snap-fit joint, as shown in Figure 17.53, consists of a protruding beam or leg on one part and a ledge on the mating part. The beam must be flexible enough to deflect or bend as it passes over the ledge during assembly. The design should allow the leg to return nearly to its original shape in the assembled position so that the beam experiences little bending force after it is assembled. Other features of the snap leg, as shown in Figure 17.54, include the foot, which engages the ledge, and a fillet, which reduces stresses at the base. The lead angle, α, and return angle, β, also are important features of the design.

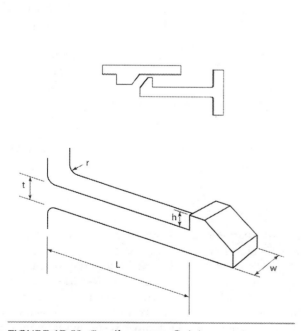

FIGURE 17.53. Cantilever snap-fit joint.

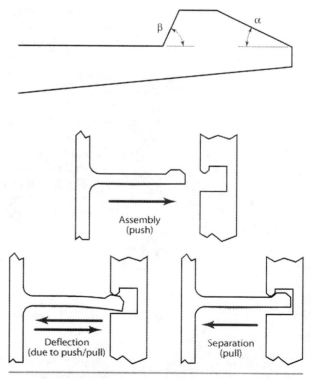

FIGURE 17.54. The function of features on a snap-fit joint.

U-Shaped Cantilever

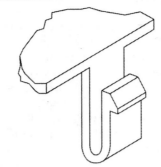

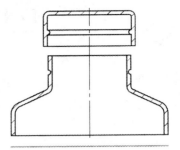

FIGURE 17.56. A cylindrical snap-fit.

L-Shaped Cantilever

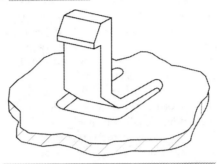

FIGURE 17.55. Other cantilever snap-fit designs.

Other configurations of the basic snap beam include the snap loop, the L-shaped leg, and the U-shaped leg, which are shown in Figure 17.55. Another configuration is the use of a slot in the mating part instead of the ledge. In this case, the foot of the beam is retained in the slot when the joint is assembled. These variations are used on designs that have space limitations or that require special retention characteristics to reduce the risk of unintentional disassembly.

Cylindrical or annular snap joints consist of a part with an external lip and a mating part with an internal lip or groove, as shown in Figure 17.56. Usually the outer part expands or stretches to fit over the inner part, then returns to its original shape after assembly. The diameters of the lip and groove, assembly and disassembly angles, and material properties determine the assembly and disassembly forces.

The details of snap-fit design are complicated due to the large deflections, nonlinear materials properties, and frictional effects. Further information can usually be found in design guides from plastics manufacturers.

17.13 Chapter Summary

Fasteners are used in many applications to attach parts in an assembly, which may be disassembled later or may be permanent. Many common fasteners feature screw threads. Standardization of screw threads has led to the development of the commonly used Unified National, ISO metric, and Acme screw thread forms, as well as others. In CAD models, it usually is not necessary to model the exact thread geometry; standard fasteners can be modeled using simplified representations. Threads can be shown on drawings using *schematic* or *simplified* representations. For a more accurate representation, threads are modeled using a helical sweep feature. When specifying a threaded fastener or threaded hole feature in a drawing, it is important to include in the thread note all of the information about the threads. Standardized notation makes it easy to understand the thread notes and to avoid confusion regarding the exact specification of the fastener and mating hole. Non-threaded fasteners, including various types of rivets, pins, retaining rings, keys, and integrated snap-fit fasteners, also may be used in certain applications.

17.14 glossary of key terms

angle of thread: The angle between the side of a thread and a line perpendicular to the axis of the thread.

axis: The longitudinal centerline that passes through a screw.

blind hole: A hole that does not pass completely through a part.

bolt: A threaded fastener that passes completely through parts and holds them together using a nut.

butt joint: A joint between two parts wherein the parts are butted, or placed next to each other.

cap screw: A small threaded fastener that mates with a threaded hole.

crest: The top surface or point joining the sides of a thread.

depth of thread: The distance between the crest and the root of a thread, measured normal to the axis.

die: A machine tool used for cutting external threads.

external thread: Threads that are formed on the outside of a cylindrical feature, such as on a bolt or stud.

fastener: A manufactured part whose primary function is to join two or more parts.

form: The shape of the thread cross section when cut through the axis of the thread cylinder.

internal thread: Threads that are formed on the inside of a hole.

key: A small removable part similar to a wedge that provides a positive means of transferring torque between a shaft and a hub.

keyseat: A rectangular groove cut in a shaft to position a key.

keyway: A rectangular groove cut in a hub to position a key.

lap joint: A joint between two parts wherein the parts are overlapped.

lead: The distance a screw thread advances axially in one full turn.

machine screw: A threaded fastener wherein the threads are cut along the entire length of the cylindrical shaft. Machine screws can mate with a threaded hole or nut.

major diameter: The largest diameter on an internal or external thread.

minor diameter: The smallest diameter on an internal or external thread.

multiple thread: A thread made up of two or more continuous ridges side by side.

nut: The threaded mate to a bolt used to hold two or more pieces of material together.

pin: A cylindrical (or slightly tapered) fastener typically used to maintain a desired position or orientation between parts.

pitch: The distance from one point on a thread to the corresponding point on the adjacent thread as measured parallel to its axis.

pitch diameter: The diameter of an imaginary cylinder that is halfway between the major and minor diameters of the screw thread.

retaining rings: Precision-engineered fasteners that provide removable shoulders for positioning or limiting movement in an assembly.

rivet: A cylindrical pin with heads at both ends, one head being formed during the assembly process, forming a permanent fastener often used to hold sheet metal together.

root: The bottom surface or point of a screw thread.

screw thread: A helix or conical spiral formed on the external surface of a shaft or on the internal surface of a cylindrical hole.

self-tapping screw: A fastener that creates its own mating thread.

set screw: A small screw used to prevent parts from moving due to vibration or rotation, such as to hold a hub on a shaft.

single thread: A thread that is formed as one continuous ridge.

spring pin: A hollow pin that is manufactured by cold-forming strip metal in a progressive roll-forming operation. Spring pins are slightly larger in diameter than the hole into which they are inserted and must be radially compressed for assembly.

stud: A fastener that is a steel rod with threads at both ends.

tap: The machine tool used to form an interior thread. Tapping is the process of making an internal thread.

17.14 glossary of key terms (continued)

tap drill: A drill used to make a hole in material before the internal threads are cut.

thread note: Information on a drawing that clearly and completely identifies a thread.

thread series: The number of threads per inch on a standard thread.

through hole: A hole that passes completely through a part.

tool runout: The distance a tool may go beyond the required full thread length.

washer: A flat disk with a center hole to allow a fastener to pass through it.

17.15 questions for review

1. What types of fasteners can be used to join parts that will permit disassembly later?
2. What information is included in a standard metric thread note? in what order?
3. What information is included in a standard U.S. thread note? In what order?
4. What tools and methods are used to manufacture external threads?
5. Describe the process and tools used to manufacture internal threads.
6. Describe how schematic and simplified thread representations appear on a drawing.
7. What type of solid modeling feature is used to create an exact representation of a screw thread?
8. When would you use an exact model of a threaded feature as opposed to a simplified model?
9. What are other uses for threads besides fastening things together?
10. If you have a 1/4 – 20 UNC threaded screw and rotate it ten full turns, what will be the axial travel of the screw?
11. What is the purpose of using a retaining ring? What applications use a key and keyseat?
12. What are some advantages and disadvantages of snap-fit systems?

17.16 problems

1. Create a proper thread note that can be used on a drawing for the following thread specifications.

    a. ISO Basic Metric thread, 12 mm major diameter, moderate tolerances on diameter and pitch, external thread, right-handed

    b. Unified National Coarse thread, 1/4 in. major diameter, moderate tolerances, internal thread, right-handed

    c. Unified National Fine thread, 5/16 in. major diameter, fine tolerances, external thread, right-handed

    d. Unified National Extra Fine thread, 5/8 in. major diameter, fine tolerances, internal thread, right-handed

    e. ISO Basic Metric thread, 10 mm major diameter, coarse tolerances on diameter and pitch, internal thread, right-handed

    f. Unified National Coarse thread, 3/4 in. major diameter, moderate tolerances, internal thread, right-handed

    g. Unified National Fine thread, 0.190 in. major diameter, fine tolerances, external thread, right-handed

    h. Unified National Coarse thread, 3/4 in. major diameter, moderate tolerances, external thread, left-handed

    i. ISO Basic Metric thread, 6 mm major diameter, fine tolerances on diameter and pitch, external thread, right-handed

    j. ISO Basic Metric thread, 20 mm major diameter, moderate tolerances on diameter and pitch, external thread, right-handed

    k. Unified National Coarse thread, 0.125 in. major diameter, fine tolerances, internal thread, right-handed

    l. Unified National Fine thread, 1.375 in. major diameter, fine tolerances, external thread, left-handed

17.16 problems (continued)

2. For the following thread notes, describe in detail the specification of the desired thread.

    a. M12 X 1.75 – 6g

    b. 10-24 UNC – 3A

    c. 5/8-24 UNEF – 3B LH

    d. M16 x 2 – 3H

    e. 1/4-28 UNF – 2B

    f. M24 x 3 – 8e LH

    g. 10-32 UNF – 1A RH

    h. M6 x 1 – 6G

    i. 8-36 UNF – 2A

    j. 1¼-5 UNC – 1B RH

3. For the object shown in Figure P17.3, create a fully dimensioned multiview drawing in which the two 0.50 in. diameter holes are replaced with holes that are tapped with a right-handed Unified Coarse thread, 1/2 in. major diameter, with moderate tolerances.

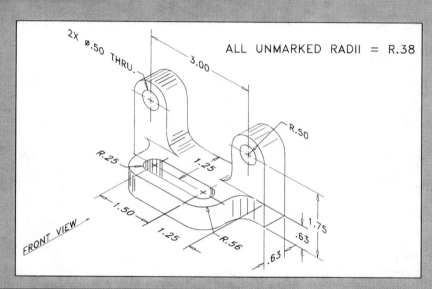

FIGURE P17.3.

4. For the object shown in Figure P17.4, create a fully dimensioned multiview drawing in which the two 0.56 in. diameter holes are replaced with holes that are tapped with a right-handed Unified Fine thread, 5/16 in. major diameter, with fine tolerances.

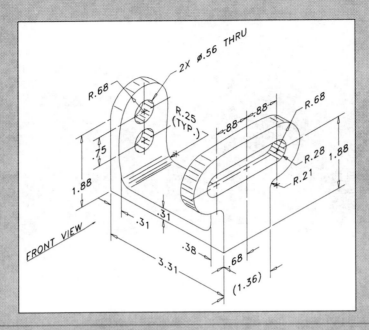

FIGURE P17.4.

5. For the object shown in Figure P17.5, create a fully dimensioned multiview drawing in which the slotted part of the 1.5 in. diameter shaft is replaced with a right-handed Unified Fine thread, 1 in. major diameter, with fine tolerances. A relief of 0.25 in. is required at the base of the thread.

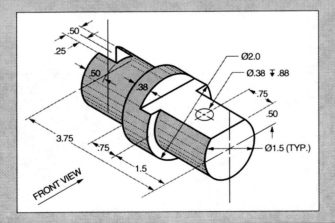

FIGURE P17.5.

17.16 problems (continued)

6. For the object shown in Figure P17.6, create a fully dimensioned multiview drawing in which the 12 mm diameter slotted shaft is replaced with a right-handed Basic Metric thread, 12 mm major diameter, with fine tolerances. A relief of 5 mm is required at the base of the thread.

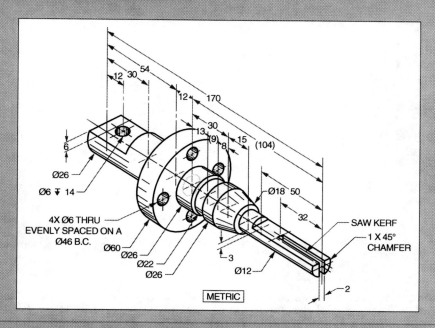

FIGURE P17.6.

7. For the object shown in Figure P17.7, create a fully dimensioned multiview drawing in which the six 0.28 in. diameter holes are replaced with holes that are tapped with a right-handed Unified Coarse thread, 1/4 in. major diameter, with coarse tolerances.

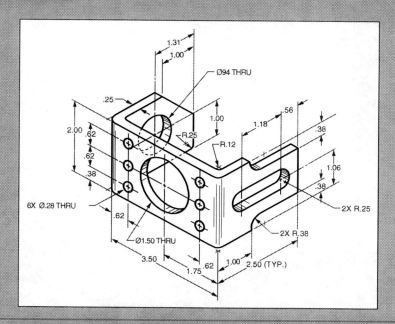

FIGURE P17.7.

17.16 problems (continued)

8. For the object shown in Figure P17.8, create a fully dimensioned multiview drawing in which the three 0.50 in. diameter holes are replaced with holes that are tapped with a right-handed Unified Extra Fine thread, 1/2 in. major diameter, with fine tolerances. Include a half-section view that shows one of the threaded holes in cross section.

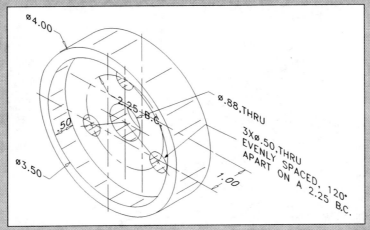

FIGURE P17.8.

9. For the object shown in Figure P17.9, create a fully dimensioned multiview drawing in which the eight 5 mm diameter holes are replaced with holes that are tapped with a right-handed Basic Metric thread, 6 mm major diameter, with fine tolerances. The pilot hole is to be 10 mm deep, and there must be at least five full threads in the hole. Include a half-section view that shows one of the threaded holes in cross section.

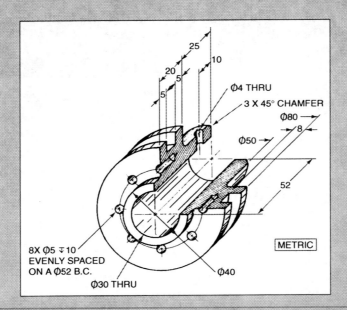

FIGURE P17.9.